Creative Problem Solving
in School Mathematics

George Lenchner

About the Author

Dr. George Lenchner was formerly the Director of Mathematics for the Valley Stream High School District, and Consultant to the three associated Elementary School Districts in Long Island, NY. He was the founder of the Nassau County Interscholastic Mathematics League (Mathletes) in 1955. He also organized the Mathematical Olympiads for Elementary and   Middle Schools (MOEMS) in 1979 and served as its Executive Director until his retirement in 1996. He currently continues to serve MOEMS as its Executive Director Emeritus.

Dr. Lenchner is the author of many mathematics textbooks and articles appearing in national publications. He brings to this book over 40 years of experience as a mathematics teacher, supervisor, teacher-trainer, and creator of problems. Harvard University has honored him for Outstanding and Distinguished Secondary School Teaching.

Publisher

Glenwood Publications Inc., East Meadow, NY

Printer

Tobay Printing Company, Inc., Copiague, NY

ISBN: 0-9626662-2-X

Contents

Preface

Creative Problem Solving in School Mathematics is a problem solving handbook for teachers of mathematics. Although it was written especially for elementary and middle school teachers, much of the material in the book is also appropriate at the secondary level.

The writing of this book was inspired by an inservice course designed for elementary and middle school teachers. The purpose of the course was to acquaint the participating teachers with rich and exciting problem solving experiences related to the core mathematics of the school curriculum. The teachers found that solving interesting and significant mathematical problems enhanced their interest and curiosity in mathematics, and they learned that by approaching problem solving creatively in the mathematics classroom they could similarly arouse the interest and curiosity of their students.

The basic text of Creative Problem Solving in School Mathematics consists of three parts. Part A is a brief discussion of teaching techniques that have been found to be especially effective in the teaching of problem solving. Part B highlights some strategies that are commonly used in school mathematics and provides a few practice problems for each strategy. In Part C, problem solving is examined in relation to many standard topics of the school mathematics curriculum, and the discussion of each topic is followed by a comprehensive set of related practice problems. At the end of the book, the special section entitled Resource Problems contains a collection of one hundred additional problems that cumulatively encompass all the strategies and mathematical topics that were discussed in the basic text. Part B, Part C, and the Resource Problems each conclude with a complete set of solutions to the problems presented within the section.

The purpose of Creative Problem Solving in School Mathematics is to help teachers improve each student's ability to solve problems. However, it is a well-known saying that we learn by doing. Therefore, this book affords teachers an opportunity to learn more about problem solving by trying out some new approaches and new techniques themselves. Through these experiences it is hoped that teachers will be able to bring to their classrooms some fresh insights and ideas.

I would like to express my appreciation to Morris Panem, coach of my high school mathematics team, who made each practice session an exciting and thrilling mathematical experience for me; and to Harry Sitomer, my first mathematics mentor, who encouraged me to teach mathematics creatively and who suggested some problems for this book.

George Lenchner

Part A

Teaching Problem Solving

What Is Problem Solving?

It seems that everyone concerned with mathematics education today is talking about problem solving. Professional organizations are recommending that problem solving become the focus of school mathematics, curriculum guides are listing problem solving skills as key objectives at all levels, and it is difficult to find a meeting of educators that doesn't have at least one problem solving session on its agenda. However, we should be careful not to think of this interest in problem solving as just another "bandwagon." The ultimate goal of school mathematics at *all* times is to develop in our students the ability to solve problems.

Some teachers believe that the ability to solve problems develops automatically from mastery of computational skills. This is not necessarily true. Problem solving is itself a skill that needs to be taught, and mathematics teachers must make a special effort to do so.

Since we will be using the word "problem" repeatedly, let's begin by agreeing on its meaning. Any mathematical task can be classified as either an exercise or a problem. An *exercise* is a task for which a procedure for solving is already known; frequently an exercise can be solved by the direct application of one or more computational algorithms. A *problem* is more complex because the strategy for solving is not immediately apparent; solving a problem requires some degree of creativity or originality on the part of the problem solver.

Let's look at an example. Suppose you are talking with your class about a collection of coins that consists of three nickels, two dimes, and one quarter. Pause to jot down some questions you might ask. Did you list any of these?

- How many coins are in the collection?
- What is the total value of the collection in cents? in dollars?
- Which of the sets of different types of coins has the greatest value? the least value?
- How many different amounts of money can be made using one or more coins from this collection?
- How many different combinations of one or more coins can be made using the coins in this collection?
- How many other combinations of nickels, dimes, and quarters have the same value as the given collection?

Notice that the first three questions listed have a quality different from the last three in that they can be solved by simple inspection or by using a computational algorithm. We consider these to be exercises. For the last three questions, no routine process of solving is applicable; the person faced with these questions must determine an appropriate strategy for solving before actually proceeding with the solving. We classify these questions as problems.

Using a Four-Step Method

Problems can be solved in a variety of ways, and no one of these ways is appropriate to the solution of all problems. However, children often find it helpful to have at least a general framework within which they can organize their efforts. In his classic book *How to Solve It,* George Polya outlined the following four steps as a guideline for successful problem solving.

1. Understanding the problem
2. Planning how to solve the problem
3. Carrying out the plan
4. Looking back

Originally proposed in the 1940s, this four-step method has withstood the test of time. Let's examine it step-by-step, considering how each step might be implemented in the mathematics classroom today.

Understanding the Problem

Before your students ever set pencil to paper, encourage them to *think* about the problem at hand. Allow them to ask you questions as long as their questions concern the problem itself. At this point, you should decline to answer any questions related to the process of solving the problem.

If your students seem to have no questions, you may wish to be the one who queries. Your questions may prompt their questions. Here are some examples.

- Does the problem give you enough information? too much information?
- What is the question you are being asked?
- What will your answer look like?

Some of the difficulties that children experience in understanding a problem are related to the language of the problem. If you think that language may be a barrier to their understanding, ask your students questions that will pinpoint the source of the difficulty. You may also find it an effective technique to ask a student to restate the problem in her or his own words. Either process helps to identify vocabulary that is unfamiliar and to reveal any areas of ambiguity in the statement of the problem.

Even when you feel sure that your students understand the problem at the outset, you will find that an ambiguity occasionally surfaces after they have begun solving. For example, if a problem refers to a person's work for one week, your students may not realize until they have started solving the problem that the number of workdays in a week is unclear. If this type of difficulty arises, it should be discussed and clarified before your students continue solving.

Planning How to Solve the Problem

Once students understand the problem situation that they are facing, it is time for them to decide on a plan of action to follow in solving the problem. That is, they must choose a reasonable problem solving *strategy*. The strategies appropriate to solving mathematical problems are many and varied, but the following are some of the most commonly used.

- Drawing a picture or diagram
- Finding a pattern
- Making an organized list
- Making a table
- Solving a simpler problem
- Trial and error
- Experimenting
- Acting out the problem
- Working backwards
- Writing an equation
- Using deduction

For any given problem, strategies such as these may be used singly or in combination. Also, you will find that different problem solvers use different strategies in solving the same problem.

It is important to realize that we cannot expect children to use strategies that are unfamiliar to them. Just like other skills, problem solving skills are learned. Therefore, students need to be exposed to a wide variety of problems so that they can try out new strategies and practice using them. In Part B of this book we will take a closer look at the strategies listed above and at some suggested practice problems for each strategy.

Carrying Out the Plan

Carrying out the problem solving plan is often confused with the plan itself. The difference, though, is that in carrying out the plan the problem solver finally sets pencil to paper, implementing the planned strategy to arrive at the answer to the problem.

Although children often are able to work on their own at this point, the teacher remains essential to the problem solving process. Since carrying out the plan frequently involves arithmetic calculations, be ready to provide help and guidance if your students are having computational difficulties. If solving the problem involves two or more steps, remind students to check their work at the end of each step before proceeding. Should students find that their planned strategy is not effective, suggest that they consider changing their point of view.

There is a tendency to emphasize carrying out the plan almost to the exclusion of the other three steps of the problem solving process. Remember that the careful consideration of *each* step develops the student's perception of problem solving and helps the student realize that computation is just a part of a broad and powerful process.

Looking Back

Children often believe that they are "done" with a problem when they have an answer—any answer—and that looking back on what they have done is unnecessary. The result is that they omit an important part of the problem solving process.

Encourage your students always to look back and consider the *reasonableness* of their answers. A simple and effective way to achieve this is to require your students to write an answer in the form of a complete sentence. This should result in their review of the statement of the problem and of the question being asked. It should also help in the detection of a possible error. If the answer *does* make sense, encourage students to make one final check for computational accuracy.

Children should be taught to pause and reflect not only on the answer to a problem, but also on how they arrived at the answer. Whenever possible, take time to discuss the strategy or strategies that were used in solving a given problem. If different students used different strategies, compare and contrast the strategies in regard to their relative efficiency and simplicity. This focus on strategies may lead some students to relate the problem at hand to similar problems solved in the past, thereby strengthening their accumulated body of experiences in solving problems.

One worthwhile way to look back on a problem is to consider how it might be extended. This usually entails changing the question asked, the numerical information given, or a condition of the problem. Let's look at an example.

A wooden cube that measures 3 cm along each edge is painted red. The painted cube is then cut into 1-cm cubes as shown below. How many of the 1-cm cubes do not have red paint on any face?

Before you read on, pause first to solve the problem. Did you observe that there is only one 1-cm cube in the middle that does not touch the surface of the original 3-cm cube? Therefore, there is only one 1-cm cube that does not have red paint on any surface.

Now look back on your work in solving this problem. Do you have any ideas for extending the problem? If so, jot them down. Did you list any of these?

- How many 1-cm cubes have red paint on just 1 face?
- How many 1-cm cubes have red paint on just 2 faces?
- How many 1-cm cubes have red paint on just 3 faces?
- Do any 1-cm cubes have red paint on 4 or more faces?
- How many 1-cm cubes would not have red paint on any face if the original cube measured 4 cm along each edge?
- How many 1-cm cubes would not have red paint on any face if the original cube measured 5 cm along each edge?
- Are there any patterns among the results for the 3-, 4-, and 5-cm cubes?

There are of course other questions that could be asked in extending just this one problem, and perhaps you had some of these on your list. How do you know how far to carry these extensions with a class? The answer is to let your students' interest and enthusiasm be your guide. You may not wish to extend every problem, but by all means do so when a problem has captured the curiosity and imagination of your students. Be aware that ideas for appropriate extensions often come from the children themselves in the form of "What if . . . " or "Suppose . . . " questions. However, always be sure that all students understand the original problem and its solution before proceeding to an extension with your class.

Choosing Problems

Equally as important as knowing *how* to teach problem solving is knowing *what* problems to use with your students. Many sources are available to you. Start with your textbook, which probably contains a fairly sound collection of routine word problems related to the topic you are currently teaching. Use these problems as they occur, but also consider how you might adapt or extend them to meet your classroom needs and your students' interests. Also look for related *nonroutine* problems; such problems may be found in special sections of your textbook or teacher's guide, in professional publications, and in puzzle books.

Children themselves can be a valuable resource when you encourage them to create their own problems. Although this activity usually is highly motivational in itself, you might add to your students' enthusiasm by using their problems as a bulletin board display. Also invite your students to share in the fun of solving each other's problems. You will probably find that problem *creating* helps to sharpen children's problem *solving* skills.

As you go through this book, consider how you might use the problems contained in it with your students. You probably will find that some problems are appropriate for your classroom just as presented. For other problems, you may think of changing one or more conditions to make them simpler or more complex, whichever is needed to meet the abilities of your students. Perhaps some problems will inspire you to invent other, similar problems. Remember throughout that one of the best sources of problems is you, the creative and imaginative teacher.

Evaluating Problems

Especially when choosing a problem from a source other than your textbook or teacher's guide, it is important that you evaluate the problem to determine if it is a *good* problem for your students. Sometimes a problem that seems appropriate at first glance reveals itself to be inappropriate upon closer inspection: it may be too easy or too difficult, too routine or too involved, too simple or too time-consuming, and so on. How can you determine if a problem is a good problem? You may find the following set of guidelines to be helpful.

A good problem is sufficiently interesting and challenging to make the reader want to solve it. If children are not interested in a problem, they usually are not interested in its solution. Many children are motivated to solve problems that deal with their everyday experiences or that in some way spark their curiosity. Many children are also attracted to problems of the nature of puzzles or brainteasers.

A good problem can be approached through a variety of strategies. Although each of these strategies is effective in carrying out the task of solving the problem, children generally benefit from the opportunity to consider several approaches from the viewpoint of relative directness and efficiency. It also is worthwhile for children to realize that, for any given problem, different approaches may be more effective for different people.

A good problem can be extended or related to other problems. After solving a problem, it is a valuable experience for children to consider new problems or to recall past problems that require a similar approach. Problem solving skills are strengthened when children can generalize as a result of their accumulated problem solving experiences.

A good problem should be at the appropriate skill level for your students' abilities. Before you ask your students to solve a problem that is not from your textbook, it is important that *you* solve it to determine the skills necessary for its solution. If the solution requires more mathematical background than your students presently have, either adapt the problem to their level or put it aside for future use. Be sure that the language is appropriate for your students' reading level; if possible, replace any vocabulary that is too difficult and shorten any sentences that are too lengthy. As a rule of thumb, most of your students should be able to understand the problem when you present it and should feel comfortable attempting the solution.

Children need not only to develop their *ability* to solve problems, but also to develop their *confidence* in this ability. If they are to become good problem solvers, we must present good problems to them.

Presenting Problems

There are many ways to present problems other than to simply refer your students to a written problem in a textbook or workbook. Different techniques have different advantages, and their proper use can be a tremendous aid to both you and your students. Let's look at some of these techniques and consider how you might use them in your classroom.

The Chalkboard

Writing a problem on the chalkboard is perhaps the most traditional technique. A chalkboard display is easily seen, and the problem is readily available for reference throughout the problem solving process. When using this technique, though, you may find it helpful to try to write the problem on the chalkboard before class or when your students are engaged in some other activity; children sometimes become restless, impatient, or disinterested when they have to wait for a problem to be written.

Since the chalkboard technique seems to invite worthwhile classroom discussion, an interesting variation is occasionally to leave a blank or blanks in the problem in the place of an important word or piece of data. You might also try providing all the data, but omitting the final question. Then have your students suggest appropriate words, data, or questions. Involving children in the creation of problems often enhances their understanding of the solution of problems. You may find that it also prompts some lively and thought-provoking class discussions.

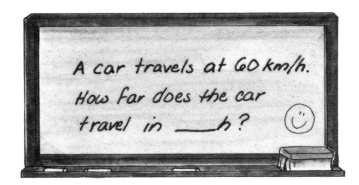

Another advantage of the chalkboard is that a problem can be left on display for more than one day. You might even wish to keep a special section of the chalkboard reserved for an especially challenging "Problem of the Week" for which an immediate solution is not expected.

The Overhead Projector

Another technique for presenting a problem is to write it on a transparency for use on an overhead projector. If you have a projector available to you, you will find that with it you can use most of the ideas recommended for the chalkboard.

The overhead projector does have some advantages over the chalkboard. For example, using a transparency can eliminate concern about finding an appropriate time to prepare the display of a problem, since you can prepare a transparency at the same time that you are planning your lesson. You may also find that it takes you less time to write a problem on a transparency, especially if the problem involves a graph, diagram, or geometric figure. Furthermore, once you have prepared a transparency of a problem, there is no need to erase it. This means that you can store the problem in a file and have it immediately available for use when you need it again.

When presenting a problem with the overhead projector, you may of course project the entire problem at once. At times, though, you may wish to present a problem line-by-line, using a piece of opaque paper to mask those parts of the transparency that you do not yet want your students to see. This method of presentation serves to temporarily focus your students' attention on each of the individual components of a problem, and you may find it helpful in pinpointing any sources of difficulty in their understanding of the problem.

Duplicated Sheets

Sometimes you may prefer to present a problem by duplicating it onto individual sheets so that each student receives a copy. Besides the fact that duplicated sheets can save you precious class time, you will also find that some students simply find it easier to refer to a problem this way. Duplicated sheets also eliminate the possibility of student error in copying a problem from the chalkboard or overhead projector.

Used properly, a duplicated sheet can be a valuable instructional aid. For example, if you are teaching your students how to deal with problems that contain too much information, having the problems at hand gives students the opportunity to physically cross out extraneous information and highlight essential information. When your students are working with problems that require a chart or graph, it sometimes is helpful to use the duplicated sheet to supply a partially-completed chart or graph beside the problem.

When you expect your students to work directly on a duplicated sheet, be sure to leave enough blank space for necessary computations or diagrams. You may also want to consider providing answer blanks, since they can save you time in helping your students by making their answers easier to locate.

Oral Presentation

Presenting a problem by reading it aloud is a little-used technique, yet it provides needed practice in screening out extraneous information. It also helps to sharpen children's listening and note-taking skills.

Before you present a problem orally, explain to your students that you will read the problem a given number of times—perhaps three. The first time, instruct them to just listen. The second time they may take notes, but stress the fact that their notes should contain just the information that is important to solving the problem. The third time, students should listen to make sure that their notes are accurate and that they understand the question. Using their notes, your students should then be able to proceed with solving the problem.

Helping Students

How much help should you give your students in their problem solving efforts? Too much help will leave them with little or nothing to do. Too little help may result in frustration and lack of progress. The right amount of help is such that it allows your students to experience the challenge of a problem and the pleasure of discovering its solution.

Whenever possible, give your students the opportunity to work on a problem independently. If they have trouble getting started, do not tell them which strategy to use; try only to ask questions that will lead *them* to choose an appropriate strategy. Be aware that some children mistakenly believe successful problem solvers are those who are able to immediately determine a strategy for solving and carry it out. Help your students to realize that they may need to test several strategies before an appropriate one is found. When children understand that it is all right to experience some difficulty in this process, they are more likely to approach problem solving with interest and enthusiasm.

When your students have arrived at an answer for a problem, encourage them to whisper it in your ear; if answers are blurted out, other students may feel that the challenge is gone and may be deterred from continuing to work on the solution. Respond to a whispered answer by saying "Correct," "Close," "Try again," or something similar. Try to avoid expressions such as "No," "Wrong," or "No good," which tend to discourage children. Always remember to give your students praise—it is still an excellent motivation.

Using Calculators and Computers

Some children are blocked from carrying out their problem solving plan by their weakness in computational skills. Calculators and computers can help overcome this obstacle for many children. Used properly, they make it possible for children to spend less time on computation and more time on the other steps of the problem solving process.

The availability of calculators and computers has opened up a broader range of problems to children. For example, you may find that your students are more inclined to attempt problems that involve large numbers if they have access to a calculator or computer. Because calculators and computers can be used to store and retrieve information, your students also may feel more comfortable attempting problems that involve large amounts of data.

The speed and accuracy of calculators and computers can bring a wider variety of problems within the reach of a greater number of children. However, be sure that your students are aware of the fact that calculators and computers do not solve problems—people do.

Answers to the problems discussed in this section can be found in Appendix 1 at the back of the book.

Some Problem Solving Strategies

Drawing a Picture or Diagram

When a problem is not illustrated, it is sometimes helpful to draw your own picture or diagram. A picture of the situation may reveal conditions that are not obvious when you just read the problem. If the situation is not easily pictured, a simple diagram using symbols to represent the situation may help to clarify the problem for you. Pictures and diagrams are also useful in keeping track of the various stages of a multi-step problem.

The Tournament

The eight teams of the City League will determine this season's champion with a single-elimination tournament. That is, each team will be out of the tournament after one loss. How many tournament games will the championship team have to play?

One good way to approach this problem is to diagram the progress of the tournament. Use symbols such as an × to represent a team and a bracket (⎯⎯⎯⎯>) to represent a game played.

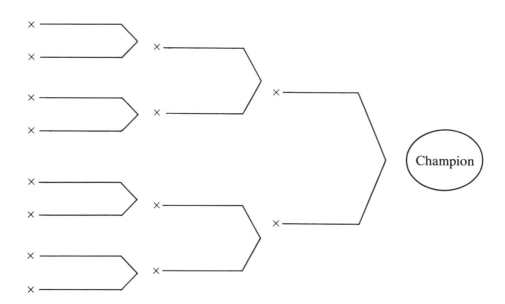

Answer: The championship team will have to play three tournament games in all.

Rod Measures

The lengths of three rods are 6 cm, 9 cm, and 11 cm. How can you use these rods to measure a length of 14 cm?

Sketching a picture of various placements for the rods may help you arrive at the solution most quickly.

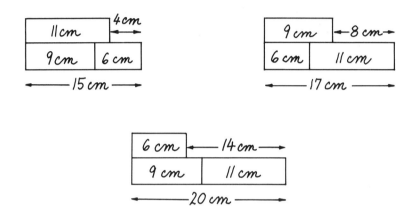

Answer: The picture at the bottom shows how to place the rods to measure a length of 14 cm.

Problems

1. How many tournament games will the champion have to play if there are sixteen teams competing in a single-elimination tournament?

2. How can you use four rods that measure 2 cm, 5 cm, 7 cm, and 9 cm to measure a length of 1 cm?

3. Making cuts across the diameter, a lumberjack can cut a log into four pieces in twelve minutes. How long would it take to cut a log of the same size and shape into six pieces?

4. Three containers have capacities of three, five, and nine liters. How can you use these containers to measure exactly seven liters of water?

5. Assuming that each corner must be tacked, what is the least number of tacks that you need to display four rectangular pictures of the same size and shape so that they can all be seen?

Finding a Pattern

One of the most frequently used problem solving strategies is that of recognizing and extending a pattern. As we shall see, there are many times that this is used as a strategy in conjunction with other problem solving strategies. For this discussion, though, we will look at some problems that can be solved by identifying a pattern in given data and simply applying that pattern to the problem situation.

Operation Diamond

Suppose that there is a mathematical operation called "diamond" in which each of the following statements is true.

$$2 \diamond 4 = 8$$
$$5 \diamond 3 = 13$$
$$3 \diamond 5 = 11$$
$$9 \diamond 7 = 25$$

What is the value of $7 \diamond 3$?

Do you observe any pattern that applies to *all* the given examples? The statement $2 \diamond 4 = 8$ may lead you to think that the pattern is one of multiplication, but you can soon see that this does not apply to the other examples. The fact that $5 \diamond 3$ does not have the same value as $3 \diamond 5$ indicates that the order of the numbers makes a difference. Pause to consider whether a *combination* of operations might be involved. Try doubling the first number. Did you conclude that operation "diamond" consists of doubling the first number, then adding the second number to that result?

Answer: $7 \diamond 3 = 2 \times 7 + 3 = 17$

Secret Code

Decode this message.

9   5–14–10–15–25   18–1–9–14–25   4–1–25–19.

A code such as the one used in this message usually is based on a pattern of relationships between each letter of the alphabet and a number, symbol, or other letter. Code patterns range from the very simple to the very complex.

Can you find the code pattern for this message? Notice that "9" stands alone to form a one-letter word, and the most common one-letter words are *a* and *I*. Since *I* is the 9th letter of the alphabet, consider substituting each letter for the number of its position in the alphabet. Did you get this result?

Answer: I ENJOY RAINY DAYS.

Problems

1. For each of the following sets of statements, determine the pattern of the operation. Then apply that pattern to complete the last two statements.

   a. $4 \bigcirc 2 = 8$

      $5 \bigcirc 3 = 11$

      $3 \bigcirc 5 = 13$

      $1 \bigcirc 7 = 15$

      $4 \bigcirc 3 = \blacksquare$

      $7 \bigcirc \blacksquare = 17$

   (Hint:
   Try doubling.)

   b. $3 \triangle 1 = 9$

      $1 \triangle 3 = 9$

      $2 \triangle 2 = 12$

      $5 \triangle 1 = 15$

      $3 \triangle 4 = \blacksquare$

      $\blacksquare \triangle 3 = 18$

   (Hint:
   Try tripling.)

   c. $2 \square 4 = 8$

      $4 \square 2 = 18$

      $3 \square 1 = 10$

      $2 \square 3 = 7$

      $5 \square 1 = \blacksquare$

      $\blacksquare \square 4 = 13$

   (Hint:
   Try squaring.)

2. Decode each of the following messages. (Each message has a different code.)

   a. IBWF   B   OJDF   EBZ!

   b. 7–19–18–8   18–8   26   20–12–12–23   11–9–12–25–15–22–14.

   c. GSRH   RH   Z   SZIW   NVHHZTV   GL   WVXLWV.

3. Each of the following begins with a set of four true statements. Complete the fifth statement of each set *without computing.*

   a.
   $$9 \times 1 + 2 = 11$$
   $$9 \times 12 + 3 = 111$$
   $$9 \times 123 + 4 = 1111$$
   $$9 \times 1234 + 5 = 11{,}111$$
   $$9 \times 12{,}345{,}678 + 9 = \blacksquare$$

   b.
   $$1 \times 8 + 1 = 9$$
   $$12 \times 8 + 2 = 98$$
   $$123 \times 8 + 3 = 987$$
   $$1234 \times 8 + 4 = 9876$$
   $$\blacksquare \times 8 + 9 = 987{,}654{,}321$$

   c.
   $$3 \times 37{,}037 = 111{,}111$$
   $$6 \times 37{,}037 = 222{,}222$$
   $$9 \times 37{,}037 = 333{,}333$$
   $$12 \times 37{,}037 = 444{,}444$$
   $$\blacksquare \times 37{,}037 = 999{,}999$$

Making an Organized List

A useful problem solving strategy is organizing information into some type of list, a technique that may serve a variety of purposes. When a problem requires you to generate a large amount of data, a list may help you account for all possibilities and avoid repetitions.

Bull's Eye!

Three darts are thrown at the target shown below. Assume that each of the darts lands within one of the rings or within the bull's eye. How many different point totals are possible?

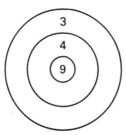

Notice that, since we are interested in *totals,* the *order* in which the darts hit the target does not matter. There are many ways to organize a list of the possible totals. For our list, let's focus on the number of darts that might hit the bull's eye.

3 Darts Hit Bull's Eye	2 Darts Hit Bull's Eye	1 Dart Hits Bull's Eye	0 Darts Hit Bull's Eye
9 + 9 + 9 = 27	9 + 9 + 4 = 22	9 + 4 + 4 = 17	4 + 4 + 4 = 12
	9 + 9 + 3 = 21	9 + 4 + 3 = 16	4 + 4 + 3 = 11
		9 + 3 + 3 = 15	4 + 3 + 3 = 10
			3 + 3 + 3 = 9

Answer: Ten different point totals are possible.

Words, Words, Words!

How many different three-letter code words can you make using the letters *P*, *Q*, and *R* if repetition of a letter is not permitted?

Let's identify all the possible code words by using a special type of organized listing called a **tree diagram.** This is a listing technique that is preferred by some people because the lines of the "tree" visually help them account for all possibilities. Notice that, in this problem, the order of the letters *does* make a difference.

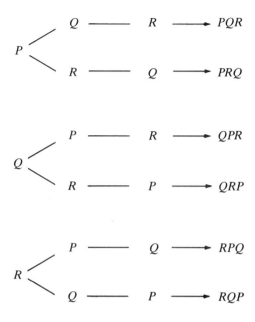

Answer: You can make six different code words using the letters
P, Q, and R if repetition of a letter is not permitted.

Problems

1. Suppose that the three regions of a target like the one pictured on page 24 are assigned point values of 3, 5, and 7. How many different point totals are possible if three darts are thrown and each lands on this target?

2. Suppose that *four* darts are thrown at the target described in problem 1. How many different point totals are possible if each lands on this target?

3. How many different three-letter code words can you make using the letters P, Q, and R if repetition of the letters *is* permitted?

4. Ken has a white shirt, a tan shirt, a pair of brown pants, a pair of black pants, a pair of blue pants, a plaid sport coat, and a tweed sport coat. How many different three-piece outfits can he make?

5. A domino has two square spaces on its face. Each of the two square spaces is marked with 1, 2, 3, 4, 5, or 6 dots, or it is left blank. A complete set of dominoes consists of one domino for each of the possible combinations of these markings. How many dominoes are in a complete set?

Making a Table

When a problem involves data that has more than one characteristic, an effective problem solving strategy is organizing the data into a table. A table displays data so that it is easily located, and missing data becomes obvious. If you are not given the data for a problem and must generate it yourself, a table is an excellent device for recording what you have done so you don't repeat your efforts. A table also can be an invaluable aid in detecting significant patterns.

Take a Chance!

Suppose that you roll two number cubes, each of which has faces numbered from 1 through 6. What are your chances of rolling a sum of 8?

To solve this problem you need to determine not only how many different numerical sums are possible, but also in how many ways it is possible for the two number cubes to form the sums. A table such as the one at the right helps to produce the data and display it in an organized manner.

Can you see that there are 36 possible ways the number cubes could land when you roll them? Of these 36 possibilities, there are 5 possibilities that have a sum of 8.

First Cube

+	1	2	3	4	5	6
1	2	3	4	5	6	7
2	3	4	5	6	7	8
3	4	5	6	7	8	9
4	5	6	7	8	9	10
5	6	7	8	9	10	11
6	7	8	9	10	11	12

(Second Cube)

Answer: There are 5 chances out of 36 that you will roll a sum of 8.

Barnyard Brainstorming

I know that there are 18 animals in the barnyard. Some are chickens and some are cows. I counted 50 legs in all. How many of the animals are chickens and how many are cows?

Let's make a table that displays *some* of the ways that there could be 18 animals. Counting 2 legs for each chicken and 4 legs for each cow, we'll also calculate the total number of legs.

number of chickens	1	2	3	4	5	. . .	?
number of cows	17	16	15	14	13	. . .	?
number of legs	70	68	66	64	62	. . .	50

Examining the data in the table, a pattern emerges. Reading from left to right, each time we "exchange" one cow for one chicken there are 2 fewer legs in the total. Therefore, to reduce 70, the first number of legs, to 50, we must "exchange" 10 of the 17 cows, since this will give us $10 \times 2 = 20$ fewer legs.

Answer: There are 7 cows and 11 chickens in the barnyard.

Problems

1. Suppose that you roll two number cubes, each of which has faces numbered from 0 through 5. What are your chances of rolling a sum of 8?

2. Suppose that you roll two triangular pyramids, each of which has faces numbered from 1 through 4.

   a. Make a table of the possible sums of the two faces that rest on the surface.
   b. What are your chances of rolling a sum of 5?

3. This week a carpenter made some three-legged stools and some four-legged chairs. The total number of stools and chairs was 30, and the carpenter used 103 legs in all. How many chairs did the carpenter make?

4. Using one or more of the coins, how many different amounts of money can be made from a collection of coins that consists of four pennies, one nickel, and one dime?

5. The toll for an automobile crossing a certain bridge is 50¢. The machines in the "exact change" lanes accept any combination of coins that total exactly 50¢, but they do not accept pennies or half dollars. In how many different ways can a driver pay the automobile toll in an "exact change" lane?

6. A collection of thirty coins consists of dimes and quarters and has a total value of $4.35. How many of each type of coin are in this collection?

Solving a Simpler Problem

When you are faced with a problem that appears difficult or complicated, you may find it helpful to first solve one or more similar problems that have simpler conditions. Sometimes the solutions of simpler problems may lead to the solution of the more difficult problem. At other times, solving a *series* of simpler problems may lead you to a pattern that provides a basis for solving the original problem.

Lucky Sevens

The houses on Main Street are numbered consecutively from 1 to 150. How many house numbers contain at least one digit 7?

You could of course examine each house number from 1 to 150, but this entails more work than is necessary. Let's see how you might separate this problem into two simpler problems.

How many house numbers contain the digit 7 in the ones' place? This occurs once in every set of 10 consecutive numbers. For houses numbered 1 to 150, there are 15 distinct sets of 10 consecutive numbers, so 15 house numbers contain the digit 7 in the ones' place.

How many house numbers contain the digit 7 in the tens' place? There are 10 such numbers, from 70 to 79. However, note that we already counted 77 among the house numbers with the digit 7 in the *ones'* place, so we will only add 9 of these numbers to our total.

Answer: For houses numbered from 1 to 150, there are 15 + 9 = 24 house numbers that contain at least one digit 7.

Note that, for young children, solving a simpler problem sometimes involves substituting simpler *numbers* into the problem until they are able to determine an appropriate procedure for solving.

Odds and Ends

What is the sum of the following series of numbers?

$$1 + 3 + 5 + \ldots + 97 + 99$$

At first this may seem like a fairly tedious exercise in addition. Rather than proceeding with this lengthy calculation, though, we'll first consider the sums of a few simpler series of numbers related to the given series and list the data.

Series	Sum
1	1
1 + 3	4
1 + 3 + 5	9
1 + 3 + 5 + 7	16
1 + 3 + 5 + 7 + 9	25

The above table of simpler series has a pattern. Did you observe that the entries in the "Series" column are all series of odd numbers, while the entries in the "Sum" column are all perfect-square numbers? To relate the series to its sum, notice that the sum of the first 1 odd number is $1^2 = 1$; the sum of the first 2 odd numbers is $2^2 = 4$; the sum of the first 3 odd numbers is $3^2 = 9$; the sum of the first 4 odd numbers is $4^2 = 16$; and the sum of the first 5 odd numbers is $5^2 = 25$.

Now extend this pattern. The series $1 + 3 + 5 + \ldots + 97 + 99$ contains the first 50 odd numbers. Therefore, its sum is $50^2 = 2500$.

Answer: $1 + 3 + 5 + \ldots + 97 + 99 = 2500$

Problems

1. Suppose that the houses on Main Street are numbered consecutively from 1 to 150. How many house numbers contain at least one digit 9? 4? 1?

2. What is the sum of each of the following series of numbers?
   a. $1 + 3 + 5 + \ldots + 997 + 999$ b. $2 + 4 + 6 + \ldots + 98 + 100$

3. If $1^2 + 2^2 + 3^2 + \ldots + 9^2 + 10^2 = 385$, what is the sum of $2^2 + 4^2 + 6^2 + \ldots + 18^2 + 20^2$?

4. What is the ones' digit of the product when one hundred 7s are multiplied?

5. What is the remainder when the product of one hundred 5s is divided by 7?

Trial and Error

An effective way to solve certain problems is to make a reasonable guess of the answer, then check the guess against the conditions of the problem. This is what we refer to as the "trial." Sometimes your first trial will yield the correct answer, and other times you will have to go through many trials before you succeed. However, even when your guess is an "error," you make progress in solving the problem by eliminating one possible answer and obtaining other information that may lead to the correct answer.

Triangle Sums

Arrange the counting numbers from 1 to 6 in the circles at the right so that the sum of the numbers along each side of the triangle is 10.

A few trials should lead you to the conclusion that there are only three ways to obtain the sum of 10: $1 + 3 + 6$, $1 + 4 + 5$, and $2 + 3 + 5$. Since each of the numbers 1, 3, and 5 appears in two of these sums, each of these three numbers must be placed in the circles at the corners of the triangle. The numbers 2, 4, and 6 can then be placed in the appropriate circles on the sides of the triangle.

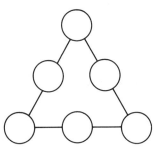

Answer: Any one of these six arrangements is correct.

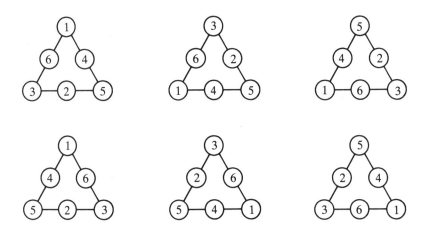

(Note that these are all variations of the *same* basic arrangement.)

Four!

How can you use four 4s to create an expression that has a value equal to 1?

Although this may sound impossible at first, remember that you have available to you a wide range of arithmetic operations: addition, subtraction, multiplication, division, square root, raising to a power, and so on. Try various operations, such as $4 + 4 = 8$, $4 - 4 = 0$, $4 \times 4 = 16$, $4 \div 4 = 1$, and $\sqrt{4} = 2$. Observe that the sum of $4 - 4$ and $4 \div 4$ is $0 + 1$ and is an answer.

Answer: The expression $4 - 4 + 4 \div 4$ has a value equal to 1.

Note that there are many *different* correct answers. The following are a few of these.

$$\frac{44}{44} \qquad \frac{4 \times 4}{4 \times 4} \qquad \frac{4 + 4}{4 + 4} \qquad \frac{4 + 4}{\sqrt{4} \times 4} \qquad 4^{\left(\frac{4 - 4}{4}\right)}$$

Problems

1. Arrange the counting numbers from 1 to 6 in the circles pictured on page 30 so the numbers along each side of the triangle add to each of the following sums.

    a. 9   b. 11   c. 12

2. Arrange the counting numbers from 1 to 7 in the circles at the right so that the sum of the numbers along each line is 10.

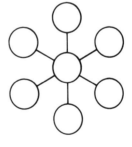

3. A **magic square** is a square grid of distinct numbers in which the sum of the numbers along each row, column, and major diagonal is the same number. Arrange the counting numbers from 1 to 9 in the 3 by 3 grid at the right to form a magic square.

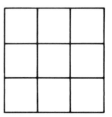

4. Use four 4s to create an expression that has a value equal to each of the following numbers.

    a. 0   b. 2   c. 3   d. 4   e. 255

5. Replace each ▨ with an operation symbol to make the following a true statement.

$$1 \ ▨ \ 2 \ ▨ \ 3 \ ▨ \ 4 \ ▨ \ 5 \ ▨ \ 6 \ ▨ \ 7 \ ▨ \ 8 \ ▨ \ 9 \ = 100$$

6. When a certain landowner died, this L-shaped plot of land was left to be shared among four children. The only stipulation of the will was that the land must be separated into four congruent plots. Show how this can be done.

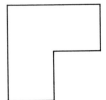

Experimenting

Problems involving geometric configurations or spatial relationships are sometimes solved by experimenting with a physical model in which concrete objects may be manipulated.

Bowling Pin Blues

The bowling pins shown at the right have been arranged incorrectly, with the triangle pointing away from the bowler. Can you make the triangle point toward the bowler by repositioning just three pins?

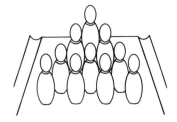

Many people find it difficult to visualize the movement of the pins to new positions while simultaneously "erasing" the old positions. You may find that the most direct method of solving this problem is to duplicate the arrangement with ten small objects such as coins, as shown at the right. Then try various movements of the objects.

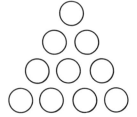

Answer:

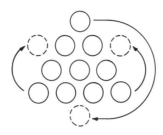

Toothpick Puzzler

The figure at the right shows twelve toothpicks arranged to form three squares. How can you form five squares by moving only three toothpicks?

This problem involves not only a rearrangement of the given objects, but also some careful observation of geometric relationships. For a number of people, the simplest approach is to gather twelve toothpicks, arrange them as shown, and experiment.

Answer:

(Notice that one of the squares is formed by the outer boundary of the arrangement. There was no requirement that each of the five squares must be congruent to each of the others.)

Problems

1. Six shrubs are planted as shown below at the left. Show how you could transplant only two shrubs to get the arrangement at the right.

2. Sixteen toothpicks are arranged as shown. Remove four toothpicks so that only four congruent triangles remain.

3. Show how to arrange these shapes to form a rectangle.

4. Moving two adjacent coins at a time, rearrange the top row to look like the bottom row in just four moves. The coins you move must stay together and remain in the same order.

5. Describe how to fold this "map" so that the numbered sections lie on top of one another in order from 1 to 8.

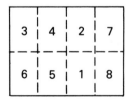

Acting Out the Problem

There may be times when you experience difficulty in visualizing a problem or the procedure necessary for its solution. In such cases, you may find it helpful to physically act out the problem situation. You might use people or objects exactly as described in the problem, or you might use items that *represent* the people or objects. Acting out the problem may itself lead you to the answer, or it may lead you to find another strategy that will help you find the answer. Acting out the problem is a strategy that is very effective for young children.

Trading Stamps

Suppose that you buy a rare stamp for $15, sell it for $20, buy it back for $25, and finally sell it for $30. How much money did you make or lose in buying and selling this stamp?

Many people erroneously conclude that you make $15. To see why this answer is wrong, it may help to act out the problem with a friend, using slips of paper to represent the money and the stamp.

Let your friend have the stamp, while you start with a certain amount of money in your "pocket," such as $50. (Your friend will need some money, too, but there is no need to keep track of that amount.) Trade your friend $15 for the stamp; you have $50 − $15 = $35 remaining. Now trade the stamp for $20 from your friend; you have $35 + $20 = $55. Trade again, this time giving your friend $25 in exchange for the stamp; you have $55 − $25 = $30 remaining. Finally, trade the stamp for $30 from your friend; the transaction is finished, and you have $30 + $30 = $60 in your "pocket." The amount of your profit is the difference between this amount and the amount of money in your "pocket" at the beginning.

Answer: In buying and selling the stamp, you made $60 − $50 = $10.

Evens Up

A class of 32 students counted off by 1s beginning with the number 1. Each student who counted an even number stood up. Then the students who were still seated counted off by 1s again. Each student who counted an even number this time also stood up. After the second counting was completed, how many students remained seated?

For young children especially, solving this problem with pencil and paper may make it seem more difficult that it actually is. Acting out the problem in the classroom can help your students realize that the solution is not all that complicated. Since half of the 32 numbers are even numbers, half of the 32 students stand up on the first counting; this is 16 students. On the second counting, half of the *remaining* 16 students stand up; this is 8 students.

Answer: After the second counting, 8 students remain seated.

Problems

1. Suppose that you buy a rare stamp for $15, sell it for $20, buy it back for $22, and finally sell it for $30. How much money did you make or lose in buying and selling this stamp?

2. A class of 27 students counted off by 1s beginning with the number 1. Each student who counted a number that was a multiple of 3 stood up. Then the students who were still seated counted off by 1s again. Each student who counted a number that was a multiple of 3 stood up. This procedure was repeated one more time. After the third counting was completed, how many students were standing?

3. An old-fashioned toaster like the one pictured at the right will toast two slices of bread at once, but it only toasts one side of each slice of bread at a time. You like each side of your bread to be toasted for exactly one minute. How can you toast three slices of bread in three minutes?

4. There is a duck in front of two ducks, a duck behind two ducks, and a duck between two ducks. What is the least number of ducks that there could be in this group?

Working Backwards

Some problems involve a sequence of actions: the final result of the actions is known, and you are asked to determine the beginning conditions of the problem. An effective way to solve this type of problem is to consider the actions in reverse order.

Money Wise

Ana gave Bill and Clare as much money as each had. Then Bill gave Ana and Clare as much money as each had. Then Clare gave Ana and Bill as much money as each had. Then each of the three people had $24. How much money did each have to begin with?

This problem has four stages.

1. Ana gives Bill and Clare as much money as each has.
2. Bill gives Ana and Clare as much money as each has.
3. Clare gives Ana and Bill as much money as each has.
4. Each has $24.

The only amount of money that is known is in the fourth stage, which is the final outcome. Therefore, try starting your solution there and working backwards. Consider the stages in reverse order, making a table of how much money each person must have in each stage.

As you work backwards, keep two facts in mind. Each time a person gives each of the others "as much money as each had," each of the others will have *half* as much money as in the preceding stage. Also note that the total amount of money can be computed from the final stage (3 × $24 = $72), and this total must remain the same throughout the problem.

	Ana	Bill	Clare
4. *Each has $24.*	$24	$24	$24
3. *Clare gives Ana and Bill as much money as each has.*	$12	$12	$48
2. *Bill gives Ana and Clare as much money as each has.*	$6	$42	$24
1. *Ana gives Bill and Clare as much money as each has.*	$39	$21	$12

Answer: To begin with, Ana had $39, Bill had $21, and Clare had $12.

Inverse Flow

What number belongs in the START circle of this "flow chart"?

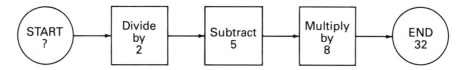

To find the starting number, the most direct procedure may be to begin with the *ending* number and work backwards. Use the inverse of each of the operations along the way.

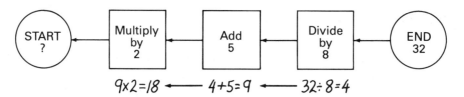

$$9 \times 2 = 18 \longleftarrow 4 + 5 = 9 \longleftarrow 32 \div 8 = 4$$

Answer: The number in the START circle is 18.

Problems

1. I went into a store and spent half of my money and then $20 more. I went into a second store and spent half of my remaining money and then $20 more. Then I had no money left. How much money did I have when I went into the first store?

2. What number belongs in the START circle of this "flow chart"?

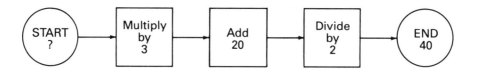

3. At the end of one school day a teacher had 17 crayons left. The teacher remembered giving out 14 crayons in the morning, getting 12 crayons back at recess, and giving out 11 crayons after lunch. How many crayons did the teacher have at the start of the day?

4. I have a Magic Money Box that will double any amount of money placed in it and add $5 to the doubled amount. Today I placed a certain amount of money in the box, got a new amount, then placed the new amount back in the box. Then I got $43. How much money did I first place in the Magic Money Box?

5. A cooperative farm has three subdivisions, A, B, and C; the subdivisions loan equipment to each other as needed. In the beginning A loaned B and C as many reapers as each then had. Several months later B loaned A and C as many reapers as each then had. The following spring C loaned A and B as many reapers as each then had. Each subdivision then had 16 reapers. How many reapers did each have to begin with?

Writing an Equation

Algebra involves the use of a mathematical "shorthand" to represent different quantities and the relationships among them. Usually letters of the alphabet are used as variables to represent unknown quantities in the problem, and the conditions of the problem are represented by an equation or inequality. Solving the equation or inequality then leads to the solution of the problem.

Name that Number!

The triple of what number is sixteen greater than the number?

Let's use the variable n to represent the unknown number. We can then translate the problem into one simple equation.

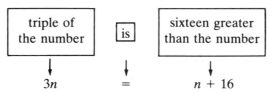

Now let's solve the equation.

$$3n = n + 16$$
$$3n - n = n + 16 - n$$
$$2n = 16$$
$$\frac{2n}{2} = \frac{16}{2}$$
$$n = 8$$

Answer: The number is 8: the triple of 8 is 24; 24 is 16 greater than 8.

A Weighty Question

Two apples weigh the same as a banana and a cherry. A banana weighs the same as nine cherries. How many cherries weigh the same as one apple?

This time we have three unknown quantities, so we'll need to use three variables. Let's choose a, b, and c to represent the weights of one apple, one banana, and one cherry, respectively. We can then translate the given information into *two* equations.

Two apples weigh the same as a banana and a cherry.

$$2a = b + c$$

A banana weighs the same as nine cherries.

$$b = 9c$$

Although it may seem that we have too many variables and equations, you may recall that, in algebra, one quantity may always be replaced by an equal quantity. Since $b = 9c$, we can substitute $9c$ for b in $2a = b + c$.

$$2a = 9c + c$$

We can now solve this equation for a, the weight of one apple.

$$2a = 9c + c$$
$$2a = 10c$$
$$\frac{2a}{2} = \frac{10c}{2}$$
$$a = 5c$$

The last equation gives us an expression for the weight of one apple in terms of the weight of one cherry.

Answer: Five cherries weigh the same as one apple.

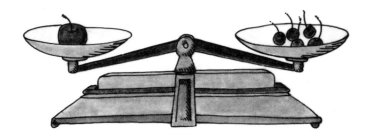

Problems

1. Find each of the following numbers.
   a. Four times a number is twelve greater than the number.
   b. Five times a number decreased by one is twice the number increased by eleven.
   c. A number multiplied by two is the same as two decreased by the number.
   d. One-third of a number increased by eleven is seven less than the number.

2. Three pears weigh the same as a quince. A quince weighs as much as eighteen raspberries. How many raspberries weigh the same as a pear?

3. I have twice as many nickels as quarters. The total value of all my nickels and quarters is $4.20. How many quarters do I have?

4. Ten years from now Sophia's age will be three times her present age. How old is Sophia now?

5. Find four consecutive numbers such that the sum of the first three numbers is twelve more than the fourth number.

Using Deduction

Deduction is the process of reaching a conclusion through logic, or reasoning. Sometimes this strategy takes the form of a process of elimination—that is, considering all solutions that *might* be possible and showing them to be impossible one-by-one until only one possibility remains. Because it is such a powerful technique, deduction is a frequently-used strategy in mathematics.

Fruitful Thinking

Three apples and two pears cost 78¢. But two apples and three pears cost 82¢. What is the total cost of one apple and one pear?

Some people experience difficulty with this type of problem because they try to find the cost of one apple and the cost of one pear. Notice that this is not necessary: you only need to find the *combined* cost of an apple and a pear. Therefore, consider combining the given information to obtain the fact that *five* apples and *five* pears must cost 78¢ + 82¢, or $1.60. Therefore, one apple and one pear must cost only one fifth as much.

Answer: The cost of one apple and one pear is $\frac{1}{5} \times$ $1.60, or 32¢.

Network News

The first figure below shows the **network** for a certain number cube. That is, this figure shows how the number cube would look if it were a box and could be "unfolded." One of the figures below the network is a drawing of this number cube. Which one is it?

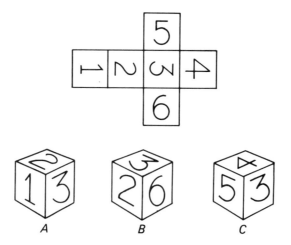

Consider if it is possible to eliminate any of the possible answers. In Figure *A*, the numbers 2 and 3 are positioned incorrectly in relation to one another; the same is true of the numbers 3 and 5 in Figure *C*. This leaves Figure *B* as the only possibility. Upon careful examination, we note that the numbers 2, 3, and 6 in Figure *B* are positioned exactly as in this network.

Answer: Figure *B* is the drawing of the number cube for this network.

Problems

1. Five oranges and a banana cost 87¢. An orange and five bananas cost 99¢. What is the total cost of two oranges and two bananas?

2. Nine coins look exactly alike, but you know that one of them is counterfeit and weighs slightly less than the others. The only equipment that you have available is a balance scale like the one pictured at the right. How can you find out which is the counterfeit coin by making just two weighings on this scale?

3. The six faces of a cube are marked with the following patterns.

Here are three different views of the cube.

Which pattern appears on the face that is directly opposite each of the following faces?

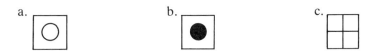

4. The native inhabitants of a certain island country have a strange characteristic: those who are swimmers always tell the truth, but those who are nonswimmers always lie. Suppose that you visit the island and meet a group of three people who are native inhabitants. You ask the first person, "Are you a swimmer?" The answer is unintelligible. The second person immediately says, "That was 'Yes.' I am a swimmer, too." The third person says, "They are both lying." Is each of these three people a swimmer or a nonswimmer?

5. What numbers must appear on the faces of two number cubes so that you have the same chance of rolling each of the numbers from 1 to 12?

Changing Your Point of View

Occasionally you may find that you are blocked in your attempts to solve a particular problem. Sometimes this type of difficulty arises from developing a "mind set." That is, you may have decided that there is only one way to approach the solution, or perhaps you made an incorrect assumption about the given information. If you reach this point, it often helps to read the problem once again and try to change your point of view.

Chain Links

You have four pieces of chain with three links apiece. A jeweler will charge you $2 to open a link and $3 to close a link. How can you have the four pieces joined to form a continuous-chain bracelet for only $15?

Many people are baffled by this problem because they think of the four pieces of chain as fixed units, as shown below. If one link at each of the four "corners" of this arrangement is opened, then closed, the total cost would be $20.

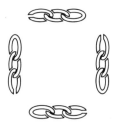

Obviously, a change of approach is needed. Consider cutting apart one of the pieces to get three individual links, and the solution becomes apparent.

Answer: Open all three links of one piece of chain. Use these three links to join the ends of the remaining pieces, as shown below. The cost to open and close just three links is $15.

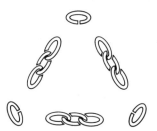

Connect the Dots

Show how to draw four line segments through the nine dots shown at the right without lifting your pencil from the paper.

Nearly everyone who attempts this problem becomes frustrated by assuming that the line segments must lie within the confines of the 3 by 3 array, much like a child's dot-to-dot picture. Removing this unnecessary restriction opens the door to the solution shown on the next page.

Answer:

Problems

1. You have six sticks of **equal length**. Without altering the sticks in any way, show how to arrange **them** end-to-end to form four equilateral triangles.

2. Show how to plant ten apple trees in five rows with only four trees in each row.

3. Every day a commuter takes a train that arrives at her station at precisely 6:00 P.M. She is met at the station by her husband, who also arrives at precisely 6:00 P.M. He always drives the same route to the station and never varies his speed. One day the commuter takes an earlier train and arrives at the station at precisely 5:00 P.M. She decides to begin walking home along her husband's usual route. They meet, she gets into the car, and they drive home. They arrive home precisely ten minutes earlier than usual. How long had the commuter been walking?

4. The 303 members of the chess club are planning a single-elimination tournament to determine a regional champion. How many tournament games will have to be played?

5. The measure of a radius of this circle is 10 cm. Point O is the center. If $OPQR$ is a rectangle, what is the measure of segment PR?

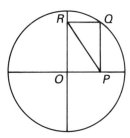

6. Show how to place twenty-seven sheep into four pens so there is an odd number of sheep in each pen.

Solutions to Problems of Part B

Drawing a Picture or Diagram
Page 21

1.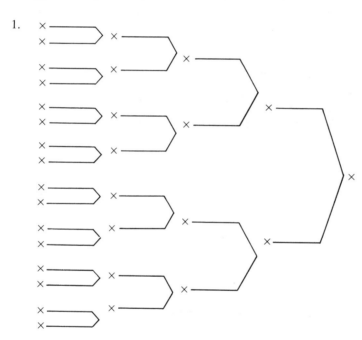

The championship team will have to play four tournament games.

2.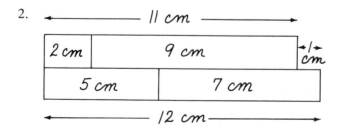

3. To obtain 4 pieces, the lumberjack needs to make only 3 cuts. Since 3 cuts take 12 min, each cut takes $12 \div 3 = 4$ min.

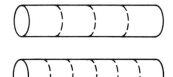

To obtain 6 pieces, the lumberjack will have to make 5 cuts. Since each cut takes 4 min, 5 cuts will take $5 \times 4 = 20$ min.

4. Fill the 9-L container with water, then empty as much of this water as possible into the 5-L container. The amount remaining in the 9-L container will be $9 - 5 = 4$ L. Fill the 3-L container with water. Combine the 3 L of water with the 4 L of water in the 9-L container for a total of $3 + 4 = 7$ L.

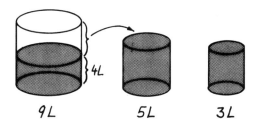

9L   5L   3L

5. The least number of tacks you need is 9, using the arrangement shown below.

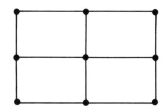

Finding a Pattern
Page 23

1. a. Add the first number to the double of the second number.

   $4 \bigcirc 3 = 4 + 2 \times 3 = 4 + 6 = 10$

   $7 \bigcirc 5 = 17$, since $7 + 2 \times 5 = 7 + 10 = 17$

   b. Triple the product of the two numbers.

   $3 \triangle 4 = 3 \times (3 \times 4) = 3 \times 12 = 36$

   $2 \triangle 3 = 18$, since $3 \times (2 \times 3) = 3 \times 6 = 18$

c. Add the second number to the square of the first number.

$5 \square 1 = 5^2 + 1 = 25 + 1 = 26$

$3 \square 4 = 13$, since $3^2 + 4 = 9 + 4 = 13$; or

$^-3 \square 4 = 13$, since $(^-3)^2 + 4 = 9 + 4 = 13$

2. a. Replace each letter with the letter that immediately precedes it in order in the alphabet.

I BWF	B	OJDF	EBZ!
HAVE	A	NICE	DAY!

b. Each counting number from 1 to 26 represents a corresponding letter of the alphabet, but in reverse order (1 = Z, 2 = Y, 3 = X, . . . , 26 = A).

7–19–18–8	18–8	26	20–12–12–23	11–9–12–25–15–22–14.
T H I S	I S	A	G O O D	P R O B L E M.

c. The letters of the alphabet are paired with each other in reverse order (A = Z, B = Y, C = X, . . . , Z = A).

GSRH	RH	Z	SZIW	NVHHZTV	GL	WVXLWV.
THIS	IS	A	HARD	MESSAGE	TO	DECODE.

3. a. 111,111,111   b. 123,456,789   c. 27

Making an Organized List
Page 25

1. 3 Darts Hit Bull's Eye: $7 + 7 + 7 = 21$

   2 Darts Hit Bull's Eye: $7 + 7 + 5 = 19$
   $7 + 7 + 3 = 17$

   1 Dart Hits Bull's Eye: $7 + 5 + 5 = 17$
   $7 + 5 + 3 = 15$
   $7 + 3 + 3 = 13$

   0 Darts Hit Bull's Eye: $5 + 5 + 5 = 15$
   $5 + 5 + 3 = 13$
   $5 + 3 + 3 = 11$
   $3 + 3 + 3 = 9$

Seven different point totals are possible: 21, 19, 17, 15, 13, 11, and 9.

2. 4 Darts Hit Bull's Eye: $\quad 7 + 7 + 7 + 7 = 28$

   3 Darts Hit Bull's Eye: $\quad 7 + 7 + 7 + 5 = 26$
   $\qquad\qquad\qquad\qquad\qquad 7 + 7 + 7 + 3 = 24$

   2 Darts Hit Bull's Eye: $\quad 7 + 7 + 5 + 5 = 24$
   $\qquad\qquad\qquad\qquad\qquad 7 + 7 + 5 + 3 = 22$
   $\qquad\qquad\qquad\qquad\qquad 7 + 7 + 3 + 3 = 20$

   1 Dart Hits Bull's Eye: $\quad 7 + 5 + 5 + 5 = 22$
   $\qquad\qquad\qquad\qquad\qquad 7 + 5 + 5 + 3 = 20$
   $\qquad\qquad\qquad\qquad\qquad 7 + 5 + 3 + 3 = 18$
   $\qquad\qquad\qquad\qquad\qquad 7 + 3 + 3 + 3 = 16$

   0 Darts Hit Bull's Eye: $\quad 5 + 5 + 5 + 5 = 20$
   $\qquad\qquad\qquad\qquad\qquad 5 + 5 + 5 + 3 = 18$
   $\qquad\qquad\qquad\qquad\qquad 5 + 5 + 3 + 3 = 16$
   $\qquad\qquad\qquad\qquad\qquad 5 + 3 + 3 + 3 = 14$
   $\qquad\qquad\qquad\qquad\qquad 3 + 3 + 3 + 3 = 12$

   Nine different point totals are possible: 28, 26, 24, 22, 20, 18, 16, 14, and 12.

3.

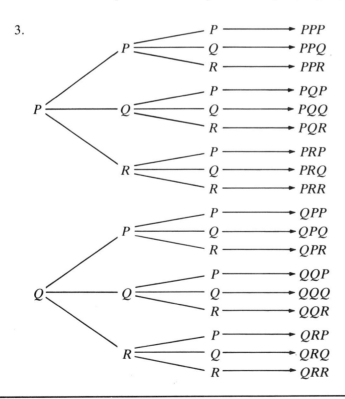

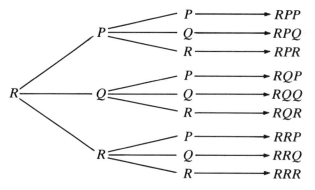

There are twenty-seven possible code words.

4. <u>Shirt</u>   <u>Pants</u>   <u>Coat</u>   <u>Outfit</u>

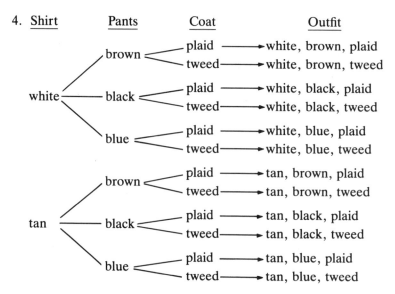

Ken can make twelve different three-piece outfits.

5. 0, 0
   0, 1   1, 1
   0, 2   1, 2   2, 2
   0, 3   1, 3   2, 3   3, 3
   0, 4   1, 4   2, 4   3, 4   4, 4
   0, 5   1, 5   2, 5   3, 5   4, 5   5, 5
   0, 6   1, 6   2, 6   3, 6   4, 6   5, 6   6, 6

There are twenty-eight dominoes in a complete set.

Making a Table
Pages 27-28

1. **First Cube**

		0	1	2	3	4	5
	+	**0**	**1**	**2**	**3**	**4**	**5**
	0	0	1	2	3	4	5
	1	1	2	3	4	5	6
Second Cube	**2**	2	3	4	5	6	7
	3	3	4	5	6	7	8
	4	4	5	6	7	8	9
	5	5	6	7	8	9	10

Your chances of rolling a sum of 8 are 3 out of 36, or 1 out of 12.

2. a. **First Pyramid**

	+	**1**	**2**	**3**	**4**
	1	2	3	4	5
Second Pyramid	**2**	3	4	5	6
	3	4	5	6	7
	4	5	6	7	8

   b. Your chances of rolling a sum of 5 are 4 out of 16, or 1 out of 4.

3.

number of stools	1	2	3	. . .	?
number of chairs	29	28	27	. . .	?
number of legs	119	118	117	. . .	103

Each time one chair is "exchanged" for one stool, there is one fewer leg in the total. To reduce the first number of legs, 119, to 103, 16 of the 29 chairs must be "exchanged" for stools. Therefore, the carpenter made 29 − 16 = 13 chairs.

4.

Number of Dimes	Number of Nickels	Number of Pennies	Total Value
1	1	4	19¢
1	1	3	18¢
1	1	2	17¢
1	1	1	16¢
1	1	0	15¢
1	0	4	14¢
1	0	3	13¢
1	0	2	12¢
1	0	1	11¢
1	0	0	10¢
0	1	4	9¢
0	1	3	8¢
0	1	2	7¢
0	1	1	6¢
0	1	0	5¢
0	0	4	4¢
0	0	3	3¢
0	0	2	2¢
0	0	1	1¢

It is possible to make nineteen different amounts.

5.

Quarters	Dimes	Nickels
2	0	0
1	2	1
1	1	3
1	0	5
0	5	0
0	4	2
0	3	4
0	2	6
0	1	8
0	0	10

There are ten different ways that a driver can pay the toll.

6.

quarters	1	2	3	. . .	?
dimes	29	28	27	. . .	?
total value	$3.15	$3.30	$3.45	. . .	$4.35

Each time one dime is "exchanged" for one quarter, the total value increases by $0.15. To increase the first total, $3.15, to $4.35, 8 of the 29 quarters must be "exchanged" for dimes, since this increases the total by 8 × $0.15 = $1.20. Therefore, there are 29 − 8 = 21 dimes and 1 + 8 = 9 quarters in this collection.

Solving a Simpler Problem
Page 29

1. 9: 15 numbers have 9 in the ones' place.
   10 − 1 = 9 other numbers have 9 in the tens' place.
   15 + 9 = 24 house numbers contain at least one digit 9.

   4: 15 numbers have 4 in the ones' place.
   20 − 2 = 18 other numbers have 4 in the tens' place.
   15 + 18 = 33 house numbers contain at least one digit 4.

   1: 15 numbers have 1 in the ones' place.
   20 − 2 = 18 other numbers have 1 in the tens' place.
   51 − 14 = 37 other numbers have 1 in the hundreds' place.
   15 + 18 + 37 = 70 house numbers contain at least one digit 1.

2. a. The series 1 + 3 + 5 + . . . + 997 + 999 contains the first 500 odd numbers. Its sum is $500^2 = 250,000$.

b.

Series	Sum	Pattern
2	2	$1^2 + 1 = 1 + 1 = 2$
2 + 4	6	$2^2 + 2 = 4 + 2 = 6$
2 + 4 + 6	12	$3^2 + 3 = 9 + 3 = 12$
2 + 4 + 6 + 8	20	$4^2 + 4 = 16 + 4 = 20$
2 + 4 + 6 + 8 + 10	30	$5^2 + 5 = 25 + 5 = 30$

According to the table above, the sum of the first n even numbers is $n^2 + n$. The series 2 + 4 + 6 + . . . + 98 + 100 contains the first 50 even numbers, so its sum is $50^2 + 50 = 2500 + 50 = 2550$.

3.

Series	Sum	Series	Sum
1^2	1	2^2	4
$1^2 + 2^2$	5	$2^2 + 4^2$	20
$1^2 + 2^2 + 3^2$	14	$2^2 + 4^2 + 6^2$	56
$1^2 + 2^2 + 3^2 + 4^2$	30	$2^2 + 4^2 + 6^2 + 8^2$	120
$1^2 + 2^2 + 3^2 + 4^2 + 5^2$	55	$2^2 + 4^2 + 6^2 + 8^2 + 10^2$	220

According to the table above, the sum of the squares of the first n even numbers is 4 times as great as the sum of the squares of the first n counting numbers. The series $1^2 + 2^2 + 3^2 + \ldots + 9^2 + 10^2$ contains the squares of the first 10 counting numbers, while the series $2^2 + 4^2 + 6^2 + \ldots + 18^2 + 20^2$ contains the squares of the first 10 even numbers. Therefore, the sum of the second series is 4 times as great as the sum of the first, or $4 \times 385 = 1540$.

4. $7 = 7$

$7 \times 7 = 49$

$7 \times 7 \times 7 = 343$

$7 \times 7 \times 7 \times 7 = 2401$

$7 \times 7 \times 7 \times 7 \times 7 = 16,807$

$7 \times 7 \times 7 \times 7 \times 7 \times 7 = 117,649$

From the above series of simpler problems, we see that the ones' digits of the products repeat in a cycle of four: 7, 9, 3, 1, 7, 9, 3, 1, . . . Every fourth product has 1 as its ones' digit, and so, when one hundred 7s are multiplied, the ones' digit will be 1.

5. $5 \div 7 = 0$ R5

$5 \times 5 \div 7 = 3$ R4

$5 \times 5 \times 5 \div 7 = 17$ R6

$5 \times 5 \times 5 \times 5 \div 7 = 89$ R2

$5 \times 5 \times 5 \times 5 \times 5 \div 7 = 446$ R3

$5 \times 5 \times 5 \times 5 \times 5 \times 5 \div 7 = 2232$ R1

$5 \times 5 \times 5 \times 5 \times 5 \times 5 \times 5 \div 7 = 11,160$ R5

$5 \times 5 \times 5 \times 5 \times 5 \times 5 \times 5 \times 5 \div 7 = 55,803$ R4

From the above series of simpler problems, we see that the ones' digit of the quotients repeat in a cycle of six: 5, 4, 6, 2, 3, 1, 5, 4, 6, 2, 3, 1, . . . Every sixth quotient has a remainder of 1, and so when the product of ninety-six 5s is divided by 7, the remainder will be 1. Therefore, when the product of one hundred 5s is divided by 7, the remainder will be the fourth number in the cycle, which is 2.

Trial and Error
Pages 31-32

1. a.   b. 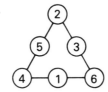 c.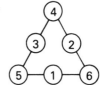

2.

3.

2	7	6
9	5	1
4	3	8

4. Answers may vary. One possible solution is given.

   a. $44 - 44$ b. $\dfrac{4 \times 4}{4 + 4}$ c. $\dfrac{4 + 4 + 4}{4}$ d. $\dfrac{4 + 4}{4} + \sqrt{4}$ e. $4^4 - \dfrac{4}{4}$

5. Answers may vary. One possible solution is given.
   $1 + 2 + 3 + 4 + 5 + 6 + 7 + 8 \times 9 = 100$

6.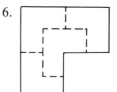

Experimenting
Pages 33-34

1. 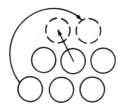   2.

3.

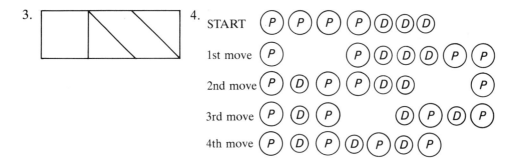

4.

5. Fold forward along the left vertical fold so that section 3 rests on top of section 4 and section 6 rests on top of section 5. Now fold the entire bottom half backward so that section 5 is behind section 4, section 1 is behind section 2, and section 8 is behind section 7. Fold forward along the left vertical fold so that section 3 rests on top of section 2. Finally, fold forward along the remaining vertical fold so that section 7 rests on top of section 6. The sections now lie on top of one another so that they are numbered 1 to 8 in order from the back.

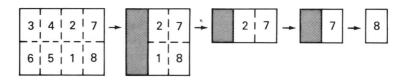

Acting Out the Problem
Page 36

1. Suppose that you start with $25. After the first trade, you have the stamp and $25 − $15 = $10. After the second trade you have $10 + $20 = $30. After the third trade you have the stamp and $30 − $22 = $8. After the final trade you have $8 + $30 = $38. In buying and selling the stamp you made $38 − $25 = $13.

2. After each counting, one third of the students who counted stood up. Therefore, after the first counting $\frac{1}{3}$ of 27 or 9 students stood up, leaving 27 − 9 = 18 students seated; after the second counting $\frac{1}{3}$ of 18 or 6 students stood up, leaving 18 − 6 = 12 students seated; and after the third counting $\frac{1}{3}$ of 12 or 4 students stood up, leaving 12 − 4 = 8 students seated. So after the third counting there were 27 − 8 = 19 students standing.

3. Call the slices *A*, *B*, and *C*. Toast side 1 of both slices *A* and *B*; this takes one minute. Turn slice *A*, remove slice *B*, and put in slice *C*. Toast side 2 of slice *A* and side 1 of slice *C*; this takes one more minute. Turn slice *C*, remove slice *A*, and put in slice *B*. Toast side 2 of both slices *C* and *B*; this takes one more minute. Both sides 1 and 2 of slices *A*, *B*, and *C* are now toasted, and the total amount of time was three minutes.

4. There only need to be three ducks in this group.

Working Backwards
Pages 38-39

1. Work backwards from \$0, the final amount. Each time that *half* of the remaining money was spent, consider that there was *twice* as much money previously.
   \$0 + \$20 = \$20; \$20 × 2 = \$40; \$40 + \$20 = \$60; \$60 × 2 = \$120.
   The speaker had \$120 to begin with.

2. Work backwards from 40, the number in the END circle.
   40 × 2 = 80; 80 − 20 = 60; 60 ÷ 3 = 20
   The number that belongs in the START circle is 20.

3. Work backwards from the 17 crayons that the teacher had at the end of the day.
   17 + 11 = 28; 28 − 12 = 16; 16 + 14 = 30
   The teacher had 30 crayons at the start of the day.

4. Work backwards from \$43, the final amount.
   \$43 − \$5 = \$38; \$38 ÷ 2 = \$19; \$19 − \$5 = \$14; \$14 ÷ 2 = \$7
   The speaker first placed \$7 in the box.

5. The problem has four stages. Work backwards from the final stage in which each subdivision has 16 reapers. Each time that a subdivision loans the others as many reapers as each had, consider that the others had only half as many reapers in the previous stage. Note that the total number of reapers in any stage must be 3 × 16 = 48.

	A	*B*	*C*
stage 4	16	16	16
stage 3	8	8	32
stage 2	4	28	16
stage 1	26	14	8

To begin with, *A* had 26 reapers, *B* had 14 reapers, and *C* had 8 reapers.

Writing an Equation
Page 41

1. Let n represent the unknown number in each case.

   a.
   $$4n = n + 12$$
   $$4n - n = n + 12 - n$$
   $$3n = 12$$
   $$\frac{3n}{3} = \frac{12}{3}$$
   $$n = 4$$

   The number is 4.

   b.
   $$5n - 1 = 2n + 11$$
   $$5n - 1 - 2n = 2n + 11 - 2n$$
   $$3n - 1 = 11$$
   $$3n - 1 + 1 = 11 + 1$$
   $$3n = 12$$
   $$\frac{3n}{3} = \frac{12}{3}$$
   $$n = 4$$

   The number is 4.

   c.
   $$2n = 2 - n$$
   $$2n + n = 2 - n + n$$
   $$3n = 2$$
   $$\frac{3n}{3} = \frac{2}{3}$$
   $$n = \frac{2}{3}$$

   The number is $\frac{2}{3}$.

   d.
   $$\tfrac{1}{3}n + 11 = n - 7$$
   $$\tfrac{1}{3}n + 11 - \tfrac{1}{3}n = n - 7 - \tfrac{1}{3}n$$
   $$11 = \tfrac{2}{3}n - 7$$
   $$11 + 7 = \tfrac{2}{3}n - 7 + 7$$
   $$18 = \tfrac{2}{3}n$$
   $$\tfrac{3}{2} \times 18 = \tfrac{3}{2} \times \tfrac{2}{3}n$$
   $$27 = n$$

   The number is 27.

2. Let p represent the weight of one pear, q represent the weight of one quince, and r represent the weight of one raspberry. Use the information in the problem to write two equations.

   $$3p = q \qquad q = 18r$$

   Since $q = 18r$, substitute $18r$ for q in the first equation, then solve for p.

   $$3p = q$$
   $$3p = 18r$$
   $$\frac{3p}{3} = \frac{18r}{3}$$
   $$p = 6r$$

   Six raspberries weigh the same as one pear.

3. If q is used to represent the number of quarters, then $2q$ can be used to represent the number of nickels. Since one quarter has a value of 25 cents, the value in cents of q quarters is $25q$. Since one nickel has a value of 5 cents, the value in cents of $2q$ nickels is $5 \times 2q$, or $10q$. You can now write and solve a simple equation, using 420 as the total value in cents.

$$25q + 10q = 420$$
$$35q = 420$$
$$\frac{35q}{35} = \frac{420}{35}$$
$$q = 12$$

The speaker has twelve quarters.

4. Let a represent Sophia's present age in years. Then $a + 10$ represents her age ten years from now, and $3a$ represents three times her present age. You can now write and solve a simple equation.

$$a + 10 = 3a$$
$$a + 10 - a = 3a - a$$
$$10 = 2a$$
$$\frac{10}{2} = \frac{2a}{2}$$
$$5 = a$$

Sophia is five years old.

5. Let n represent the first number. Then the three consecutive numbers that follow can be represented by $n + 1$, $n + 2$, and $n + 3$. You can now write and solve a simple equation.

$$n + (n + 1) + (n + 2) = (n + 3) + 12$$
$$3n + 3 = n + 15$$
$$3n + 3 - n = n + 15 - n$$
$$2n + 3 = 15$$
$$2n + 3 - 3 = 15 - 3$$
$$2n = 12$$
$$\frac{2n}{2} = \frac{12}{2}$$
$$n = 6$$

The four numbers are 6, 7, 8, and 9.

Using Deduction
Pages 42-43

1. Combine the given information to obtain the fact that *six* oranges and *six* bananas cost 87¢ + 99¢ = $1.86. Then *one* orange and *one* banana cost $\frac{1}{6}$ of $1.86, or 31¢, and *two* oranges and *two* bananas cost 2 × 31¢ = 62¢.

2. Separate the nine coins into three groups containing three coins apiece. Place one group of three coins in each pan of the balance scale. If the pans balance, the counterfeit coin is in the group of coins that is not in either pan. If the pans do *not* balance, the counterfeit coin is in the group of coins in the pan that is higher. Now use the group of three coins that you know contains the counterfeit coin. Place one of the three coins in each pan of the balance scale. If the pans balance, the counterfeit coin is the coin that is not in either pan. If the pans do *not* balance, the counterfeit coin is in the pan that is higher.

3. a. From the first and third views of the cube, the only face that is not *adjacent* to ⊙ is ■ . Therefore, ■ is *opposite* ⊙ .

   b. From the second and third views of the cube, the only face that is not *adjacent* to ● is □ . Therefore, □ is *opposite* ● .

   c. From the first and second views of the cube, the only face that is not *adjacent* to ⊞ is ⊠ . Therefore, ⊠ is *opposite* ⊞ .

4. The only possible answer to the question "Are you a swimmer?" is "Yes." A swimmer would tell the truth about this, while a nonswimmer would lie. Therefore, the second person has to be telling the truth: the first person is a swimmer, and so is the second person. Since both the first and second persons are swimmers they both tell the truth, so the third person's statement is a lie. The third person is a nonswimmer.

5. Each number cube has 6 faces, so there are 6 × 6 = 36 different ways that the cubes could land when you roll them. Since you need to have an equal chance of rolling each of 12 sums, there must be 36 ÷ 12 = 3 ways that the cubes could land to form each sum. One combination of numbers that will produce this result is shown in the table on the following page. The faces of one cube can be numbered 0, 1, 2, 3, 4, 5 and the faces of the other cube can be numbered 1, 1, 1, 7, 7, 7. There are other combinations.

First Cube

Second Cube

+	0	1	2	3	4	5
1	1	2	3	4	5	6
1	1	2	3	4	5	6
1	1	2	3	4	5	6
7	7	8	9	10	11	12
7	7	8	9	10	11	12
7	7	8	9	10	11	12

Changing Your Point of View
Page 45

1. It is not possible to solve this problem if you restrict yourself to a single plane surface. Arrange the sticks in the three-dimensional triangular pyramid shown below; the four equilateral triangles are the four faces of the pyramid.

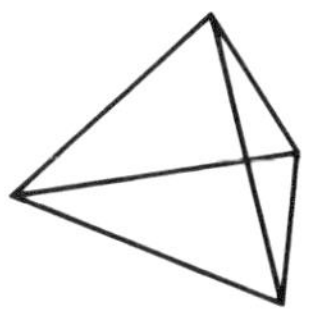

2. Since $5 \times 4 = 20$, it is not possible to plant the 10 trees in 5 distinct rows; some of the trees must appear in more than one row. Arrange the trees in the star-shape shown below.

3. Consider the situation not from the viewpoint of the commuter, but rather from the viewpoint of her husband. If they arrive home exactly ten minutes earlier than usual, then her husband's round trip was shortened by ten minutes, and his one-way trip was shortened by *five* minutes. This means that the commuter's husband met her at 5:55, five minutes earlier than his usual 6:00 arrival time at the station. Therefore, the commuter was walking for 55 minutes, from 5:00 to 5:55.

4. Since it will be a single-elimination tournament, each member will be out of the tournament after just one loss. Since there are 303 members in all, 302 members will each have to lose one game. This means that 302 tournament games will have to be played.

5. Segment *PR* is one of two diagonals of rectangle *OPQR;* the other diagonal is segment *OQ*. Segment *OQ* is a radius of the circle, and so its measure is 10 cm. Since the two diagonals of a rectangle have the same length, the measure of segment *PR* is also 10 cm.

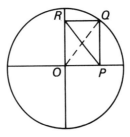

6. If you consider the four pens to be separate, there is no way to solve this problem. Try positioning one or more of the pens within a larger pen. The diagram below then shows one of many possible solutions.

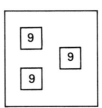

Part C

Some Topics in Problem Solving

1 | Number Patterns

1.1 Addition Patterns
Dollars and Sense

The symbol used for a dollar in United States currency is most commonly drawn as an uppercase S with a vertical stroke through it. The stroke separates the S into 4 parts, as shown at the right.

Sometimes the dollar symbol is drawn as an uppercase S with 2 vertical strokes through it. These 2 strokes separate the S into 7 parts.

Suppose that the symbol could be drawn with 100 vertical strokes. Into how many parts will the S be separated?

One way to solve this problem is to actually draw the dollar symbol with 100 strokes, then count the parts. However, the drawing would be far too complicated, your counting could be inaccurate, and the entire process would be lengthy. The following is an alternate approach.

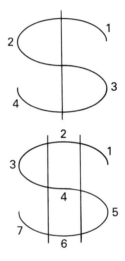

Consider the fact that we already know the number of parts for 1 and 2 strokes. It would not be difficult to gather some data for other simple problems, such as those associated with 3, 4, and 5 strokes. In a situation like this, a very effective strategy is to look for a pattern. Let's see if one emerges as we organize the data for these simpler problems into a table.

	$\$$	$\$$	$\$$	$\$$	$\$$
number of strokes	1	2	3	4	5
number of parts	4	7	10	13	16

If you study the data in the table, you will find that there is a simple pattern: the difference between two consecutive numbers of parts is always 3. How can you use this pattern to determine the number of parts for 100 strokes?

The constant difference of 3 means that each time a new stroke is drawn, the number of parts increases by 3. If you wish you could start at 16, the last entry in the table, and add 3s until you reach the entry for 100 strokes. However, this is a process that could become very time-consuming. Instead, let's rewrite each number of parts on the table as a number of 3s added to the original 4 parts.

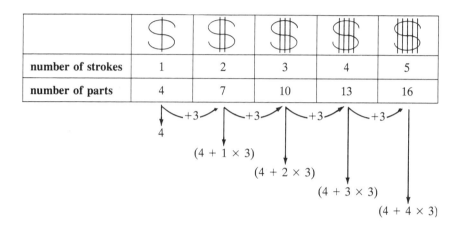

Do you see that the number of 3s being added is always one less than the number of strokes? Therefore, for 100 strokes you would have to add ninety-nine 3s to the original 4 parts. This is equivalent to $4 + 99 \times 3$, or $4 + 297 = 301$.

Answer: If the dollar symbol is drawn with 100 vertical strokes, the S will be separated into 301 parts.

Although we have solved the dollar-symbol problem, let's take this opportunity to look at the problem in more general terms.

In mathematics, a **sequence** is a set of numbers that is ordered according to some rule. In our problem, the numbers of parts into which the strokes separate the symbols are an example of a sequence. These numbers can be written using sequence notation.

$$4, 7, 10, 13, 16, \ldots$$

Each number in a sequence is called a **term** of the sequence. The position of a term in the sequence—1, 2, 3, 4, 5, and so on—is called the **order** of the term.

A sequence is an **arithmetic** (*a rith MET ik*) **sequence** if the difference between any two consecutive terms is the same constant number. The sequence in our problem is arithmetic, since we have identified in it a constant difference of 3.

In an arithmetic sequence, an interesting fact surfaces when the order of each term is multiplied by the constant difference between terms. Let's compare the numbers of parts in the dollar-symbol problem with the products you obtain by multiplying the order of each term by 3.

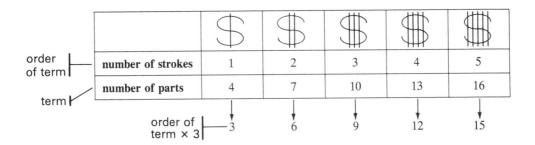

		$	$	$	$	$
order of term	number of strokes	1	2	3	4	5
term	number of parts	4	7	10	13	16
	order of term × 3	3	6	9	12	15

Do you see that each term is one greater than 3 times its order? A relationship such as this is called a **rule** for the sequence. If you can determine a rule for a sequence, you can then find the value of any term of that sequence.

How do all these facts relate to the solution of our problem? We have already identified the "number of parts" as a term of a sequence and the "number of strokes" as the order of that term. Therefore, in trying to determine the number of parts for 100

strokes, we are looking for the value of the 100th term of the sequence 4, 7, 10, 13, 16, . . . According to the rule, the 100th term of this sequence is one greater than 3 times 100. This gives us $3 \times 100 + 1$, or $300 + 1 = 301$. We have arrived at the same solution as before using a method that may be considered more direct.

Problems

1. Into how many parts will the *S* be separated if the dollar symbol is drawn with the number of vertical strokes given below?

    a. 6   b. 10   c. 75   d. 200

2. The symbol used for a cent in United States currency is most commonly drawn as a lowercase *c* with a vertical stroke through it (¢). The stroke separates the *c* into 3 parts.

    a. Into how many parts is the *c* separated if the cent symbol is drawn with 2 vertical strokes? 3? 4? 5?

    b. Use sequence notation to write a pattern for the number of parts into which the *c* is separated.

    c. Is the sequence formed by the numbers of parts an arithmetic sequence? If it is, write a rule for the sequence.

    d. Into how many parts is the *c* separated if the cent symbol is drawn with 100 vertical strokes?

    e. How many vertical strokes are drawn through the *c* if it is separated into 165 parts?

3. Write the next three terms of each of the following arithmetic sequences.

    a. 3, 7, 11, 15, 19, . . .

    b. 6, 7, 8, 9, 10, . . .

    c. 2, $2\frac{1}{2}$, 3, $3\frac{1}{2}$, 4, . . .

    d. 5, 5.3, 5.6, 5.9, 6.2, . . .

4. What is the 50th term of each sequence in problem 3?

5. Consider the arithmetic sequence 2, 7, 12, 17, 22, . . . Which term of the sequence is 102?

6. In a certain arithmetic sequence, the first term is 5 and the 10th term is 68. List the first ten terms of the sequence.

7. The figure below shows a rubber band wrapped twice around the blade of a pair of scissors. If the rubber band were now cut, 4 pieces would be formed. How many pieces would be formed if the rubber band were wrapped 50 times around the blade before being cut?

8. Under which letter would the number 999 appear if each of these patterns were continued?

a.

A	B	C	D	E	F	G
1	2	3	4	5	6	7
8	9	10	11	12	13	14
15	16	.	.	.		

b.

A	B	C	D	E	F	G
	2		3		4	
8		7		6		5
	9		10		11	
	.		.		.	12

9. If the 1st day of a certain month is a Tuesday, what day of the week is the 21st day of that same month?

10. If the 1st day of a certain year is a Friday, what day of the week is February 19th of that same year?

11. What is the date of the 100th day of any year that is not a leap year?

12. When we discussed the rule for the sequence 4, 7, 10, 13, 16, . . . on page 66, we said that "each term is one greater than 3 times its order." A shorthand way to state this rule using a variable is to describe the nth term as $(3 \times n) + 1$. However, when we first discussed this sequence in relation to the dollar-symbol problem on page 65, we said that "the number of 3s being added [to the original 4 parts] is always one less than the number of strokes." A shorthand way to state *this* rule is to describe the nth term as $4 + 3 \times (n - 1)$. Show that these two shorthand statements of the rule are equivalent.

1.2 Multiplication Patterns
An Odd Job

Suppose that you receive a very unusual job offer. You are told that your pay for the first day will be only 10¢. Each day after that your pay will be twice as much as it was the day before. What would your pay be at the end of a month on the job? (Consider one month to be 21 working days.)

Pause to estimate what you think the answer will be. Because the starting pay is only ten cents, many people guess that the most you could be making at the end of a month is just a few dollars. What really happens? Let's begin by making a table of the pay for each day of the first week (5 working days).

day	1	2	3	4	5
pay (in cents)	10	20	40	80	160

From the table you see that the pay on the 5th day would be 160 cents, or $1.60. This still isn't very much money, but notice that it is already *16 times* as much as the pay for the 1st day. Let's go on to calculate the pay for the 21st day.

At this point you could simply begin at 160, the pay for the 5th day, and extend the table until you reach the entry for the 21st day. However, let's first examine the table to see if there is a pattern that may be helpful. You know from the statement of the problem that the basic pattern is one of doubling, or multiplying by 2s. In the table below, you see that the pay can also be shown as the product of the beginning pay of 10 cents multiplied by a number of 2s.

day	1	2	3	4	5
pay (in cents)	10	20	40	80	160

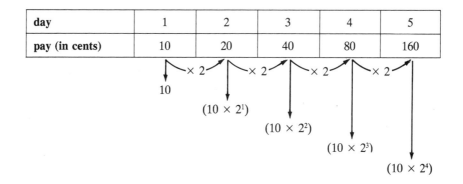

$$10$$
$$(10 \times 2^1)$$
$$(10 \times 2^2)$$
$$(10 \times 2^3)$$
$$(10 \times 2^4)$$

Notice that exponents were used as a shorthand way to show the number of times that 10 cents is multiplied by 2. Do you see that the exponent of 2 is always one less than the number of the day? Therefore, on the 21st day you would multiply the beginning pay of 10 cents by 2^{20}, which represents twenty 2s. This may be written as 10×2^{20}, or you may compute the standard form if a calculator is available. The surprise in this problem is how rapidly the numbers become very large: $10 \times 2^{20} = 10 \times 1{,}048{,}576 = 10{,}485{,}760$.

Answer: On the 21st working day your pay would be 10,485,760 cents, or $104,857.60.

Let's pause to look at this multiplication pattern in more general terms, as we did with the addition pattern in Section 1.1.

As before, we have encountered a set of numbers ordered according to a pattern. Therefore, this set of numbers forms a sequence, and we can label our data according to the basic definitions associated with a sequence.

order of term → day	1	2	3	4	5
term → pay (in cents)	10	20	40	80	160

sequence ——— 10, 20, 40, 80, 160, . . .

Recall that an arithmetic sequence is patterned by addition of a constant number, resulting in a constant difference between consecutive terms. The sequence shown above is patterned by *multiplication* by a constant number, which results in a constant *quotient* between consecutive terms. This type of sequence is called a **geometric sequence.**

Like an arithmetic sequence, any geometric sequence has a rule. In this case, we have already observed that the terms can be written as 10, 10×2^1, 10×2^2, 10×2^3, 10×2^4, ... Therefore, the rule of this sequence is that each term is the product of 10 multiplied by 2 raised to an exponent that is one less than the order of the term.

Although it may not seem so, this rule applies even to the first term, giving us 10×2^0. In mathematics, any number (except 0) with the exponent 0 is defined as being equal to 1. Consequently, $10 \times 2^0 = 10 \times 1$. This is equal to 10, which is indeed the first term of the sequence.

Problems

1. Consider a different job offer. You are told that your pay for the first day will be 5¢. Each day after that your pay will be three times as much as it was the day before.

   a. What will your pay be on the 2nd day? 3rd? 4th? 5th?

   b. Use sequence notation to write the pattern of pay for this job.

   c. Is the sequence formed by the pay for this job a geometric sequence? If it is, write a rule for the sequence.

   d. What would the pay be on the 10th day?

2. Write the next three terms of each of the following geometric sequences.

   a. 2, 6, 18, 54, 162, . . .

   b. 3, 15, 75, 375, 1875, . . .

   c. $\frac{2}{3}, \frac{4}{9}, \frac{8}{27}, \frac{16}{81}, \frac{32}{243}, \ldots$

   d. 5000, 500, 50, 5, 0.5, . . .

3. What is the 20th term of each sequence in problem 2? You may give your answer in exponent form.

4. Consider the geometric sequence 4, 12, 36, 108, 324, . . . Which term of the sequence is 8748?

5. In a certain geometric sequence, the first term is 2 and the 5th term is 1250. List the first five terms of this sequence.

6. A sheet of paper is torn in half and the pieces are placed on top of one another. These pieces together are torn in half, and the new pieces are placed on top of one another. Suppose that this process continues through 20 such tears. If the original piece of paper was 0.001 in. thick, how high is the final pile of pieces of paper?

7. An amoeba is a microscopic organism that reproduces itself in three minutes. One amoeba is placed in a jar, and in three hours the jar is filled. How long did it take for the jar to be half full?

1.3 More Addition Patterns
The Pumpkin Pyramid

The citizens of Hartville are creating a pumpkin pyramid as the central exhibit of this year's county fair. They plan to make the pyramid ten layers high. Each layer will have the shape of an equilateral triangle, so that each pumpkin above the bottom rests on three pumpkins below it. How many pumpkins will they need for the bottom layer?

One way to solve this problem is to draw a picture of the bottom layer and simply count the pumpkins. It may be hard to visualize, though, and the drawing could be inaccurate. Instead, let's take a look at some of the *top* layers to examine a pattern that may be helpful.

	○	🔾	🔾	🔾	🔾
layer	1	2	3	4	5
number of pumpkins	1	3	6	10	15

$$+2 \quad +3 \quad +4 \quad +5$$

Although the difference between successive numbers of pumpkins is not constant, there is a steady increase taking place. This time, it is the differences themselves that are constantly increasing by 1. Therefore, the pattern of differences can be continued to find the number of pumpkins in the 10th, or bottom, layer.

layer	1	2	3	4	5	6	7	8	9	10
number of pumpkins	1	3	6	10	15	21	28	36	45	55

$$+2 \quad +3 \quad +4 \quad +5 \quad +6 \quad +7 \quad +8 \quad +9 \quad +10$$

Answer: They will need 55 pumpkins for the bottom layer.

Notice that the number of pumpkins in the tenth layer is the same as the sum of all the counting numbers from 1 through 10: $1 + 2 + 3 + \ldots + 10$. We shall say more about such sums in Section 1.5.

The numbers of pumpkins in the layers of the pyramid form another type of sequence, which is neither arithmetic nor geometric. A rule for such a sequence is sometimes obtained by using an advanced technique called the *method of finite differences*.

Problems

1. Suppose that the pumpkin pyramid is constructed as described with 20 layers each in the shape of an equilateral triangle. How many pumpkins are in each of the following layers?
   a. 12th   b. 15th   c. 18th   d. 20th

2. Suppose that the pumpkin pyramid is constructed with 100 layers each in the shape of a *square*, so that each pumpkin above the bottom rests on *four* pumpkins below it. How many pumpkins are in each of the following layers?
   a. 12th   b. 15th   c. 50th   d. 100th

3. Each of these sequences has a pattern of successive differences increasing by a constant. Write the next three terms of each sequence.
   a. 2, 5, 9, 14, 20, . . .   b. 2, 5, 10, 17, 26, . . .
   c. 3, 7, 13, 21, 31, . . .   d. 2, 7, 16, 29, 46, . . .

4. Write a rule for each sequence. (*Hint:* Compare each term with the perfect square of its order.)
   a. 2, 5, 10, 17, 26, . . .   b. 0, 3, 8, 15, 24, . . .
   c. 2, 8, 18, 32, 50, . . .   d. 2, 6, 12, 20, 30, . . .

5. What is the 12th term of each sequence in problem 4?

6. The numbers of the triangular pyramid (1, 3, 6, 10, 15, . . .) are sometimes called the **triangular numbers,** since each number can be represented by an array of objects in the shape of an equilateral triangle.

1st   2nd   3rd   4th

Similarly, the numbers of the square pyramid (1, 4, 9, 16, 25, . . .) are called the **square numbers.**

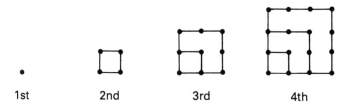

1st   2nd   3rd   4th

These numbers were so named over 2500 years ago by Greek mathematicians who were searching for a link between arithmetic and geometry.

a. Use these figures to help you list the first 10 **pentagonal numbers.**

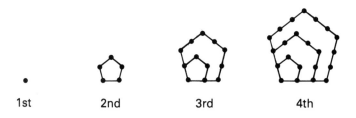

1st   2nd   3rd   4th

b. Use these figures to help you list the first 10 **hexagonal numbers.**

1st   2nd   3rd   4th

c. Use these figures to help you list the first 10 **rectangular numbers.**

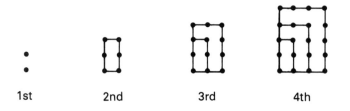

1st   2nd   3rd   4th

1.4 Unusual Patterns
About-Face!

What is the next number of this pattern?

$$1, 4, 9, 61, 52, 63, \ldots$$

At first you may feel that there has been a mistake. Like many people, you may think that number patterns are supposed to consistently increase or decrease. The consistency of a pattern, though, lies in the rule that is being followed. To discover the rule for this pattern, then, you may find that you need to change your point of view.

Let's start by examining the numbers to see if there is any element that is familiar. Did you recognize the first three numbers as the first three perfect-square numbers? Perhaps you did, but then abandoned this line of thinking when you saw the next three numbers. Look again. Are the next three numbers related in any way at all? Let's make a table to compare the six given numbers with the first six perfect-square numbers.

given numbers	1	4	9	61	52	63
perfect-square numbers	1	4	9	16	25	36

When the sets of numbers are placed side-by-side, the pattern that emerges is a simple reversal of the digits of the perfect-square numbers. The first three numbers appear the same, of course, because a single-digit number reads the same way backwards and forwards.

Answer: Since the next perfect-square number is 49, the next number of the given pattern is 94.

You may find that unusual patterns such as these provide some of your most challenging problem solving experiences, because the list of ways to create these patterns is almost endless. Sometimes you may have an insight that reveals the rule of the pattern to you immediately, and at other times the rule may elude you. A good way to become adept at working with these patterns is to try to solve many of them.

Problems

1. What are the next two numbers in each of the following patterns?
   a. 3, 6, 9, 21, 51, 81, . . .
   b. 0, 4, 8, 21, 52, 65, . . .
   c. 15, 26, 40, 16, 37, 58, . . .
   d. 5, 2, 6, 3, 9, 6, . . .

2. Sometimes the rule for a pattern is not numerical. What is the next item in each of the following patterns?
   a. *O, T, T, F, F, S, S,* . . .
   b. ⊓, ♡, 8, ⋈, ...

3. The number pattern 1, 1, 2, 3, 5, 8, 13, . . . has been given the special name of the **Fibonacci sequence.**
   a. What is the rule of the sequence?
   b. List the next three terms.
   c. Choose any three consecutive terms. Square the middle term and multiply the two outer terms. Compare the results. Repeat this process with other groups of three consecutive terms. What is the pattern?
   d. Choose any four consecutive terms. Multiply the two middle terms, then multiply the two outer terms. Compare the results. Repeat this process with other groups of four consecutive terms. What is the pattern?

4. When a single-stalk plant such as corn sprouts new leaves, it follows an upward spiraling pattern so that the new top leaves do not shade the older bottom leaves. The 2nd leaf sprouts $\frac{1}{2}$ of the way around the stalk from the 1st leaf, the 3rd leaf sprouts $\frac{2}{3}$ of the way around the stalk from the 2nd leaf, the 4th leaf sprouts $\frac{3}{5}$ of the way around the stalk from the 3rd leaf, the 5th leaf sprouts $\frac{5}{8}$ of the way around the stalk from the 4th leaf, and so on. Following this pattern, how far around the stalk from the 8th leaf will the 9th leaf sprout?

5. A curious biological fact is that a male bee has only one parent, a mother, whereas a female bee has both a mother and a father. How many 2nd generation ancestors (grandparents) does the male bee have? 3rd generation ancestors (great-grandparents)? 4th? 5th? 10th?

6. The figure below shows a special number pattern called the **Pascal triangle.** The number of a row or diagonal is counted from the top down. The first seven rows and diagonals are shown.

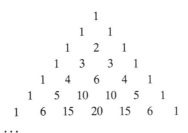

```
                  1
               1     1
            1     2     1
         1     3     3     1
      1     4     6     4     1
   1     5    10    10     5     1
1     6    15    20    15     6     1
   . . .
```

   a. What is the rule of this pattern?
   b. List the numbers in the 8th row.
   c. What are the next three numbers in the 1st diagonal? 2nd? 3rd? 4th?

7. A person named Pascal lives in the town pictured below. The streets are arranged in an orderly grid and are all either one-way south or one-way east, as shown.

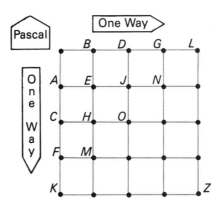

   a. How many different routes are there from Pascal's house to location *A*? *B*? *C*? *D*? *E*? *F*? *G*? *H*? *J*? *K*? *L*? *M*? *N*? *O*?
   b. How many different routes are there from Pascal's house to location *Z* on the other side of town?

8. The first figure below shows an example of a special type of number pattern called a **number bracelet.**

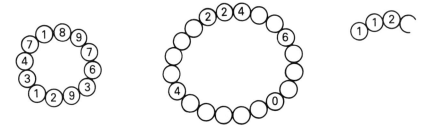

a. What is the rule for this pattern? (*Hint:* Some number patterns are formed by eliminating certain digits.)

b. Use this rule to fill in the missing links of the bracelet shown in the second figure.

c. Complete the bracelet that is begun in the third figure. (*Note:* There are 60 links in this bracelet!)

1.5 *Patterns and Sums*
A Child Prodigy

Karl Friedrich Gauss (1777–1855) was one of the world's greatest mathematicians. There is a story that, when Gauss was a nine-year-old schoolboy, the teacher of his class assigned the rather tedious task of finding the sum of all the counting numbers from 1 to 100. To the teacher's surprise, Gauss arrived at the correct answer within seconds. What is the sum?

How do you think Gauss performed the calculations so quickly and accurately? We can't be sure, of course, but one possibility is that he noticed this pattern.

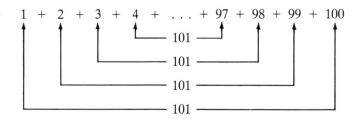

Do you see that the numbers pair to form sums of 101? How many such pairs are there? There are 50 in all, and so the sum is simply 50 × 101 = 5050.

It is also possible that Gauss used a strategy involving some very simple algebra, with a variable like S representing the unknown sum.

$$
\begin{array}{rccccccccc}
S = & 1 + & 2 + & 3 + & \ldots + & 98 + & 99 + & 100 \\
S = & 100 + & 99 + & 98 + & \ldots + & 3 + & 2 + & 1 \\
2S = & 101 + & 101 + & 101 + & \ldots + & 101 + & 101 + & 101
\end{array}
$$

Notice that the order of the addends was reversed in the second line. The third line was obtained by vertical addition, giving us the fact that $2S$ equals 100 sums of 101, or $100 \times 101 = 10{,}100$. To find the sum, solve for S in the resulting equation.

$$2S = 10{,}100$$

$$\frac{2S}{2} = \frac{10{,}100}{2}$$

$$S = 5050$$

Answer: The sum of all the counting numbers from 1 to 100 is 5050.

Problems

1. Find the sum of all the counting numbers within the indicated limits.
   - a. from 1 to 10
   - b. from 1 to 50
   - c. from 1 to 75
   - d. from 3 to 12
   - e. from 5 to 90
   - f. from 15 to 55

2. Your New Year's resolution is to put 1¢ into your savings on the 1st day of the year, 2¢ on the 2nd day, 3¢ on the 3rd day, 4¢ on the 4th day, and so on for all 365 days of the year. How much money in all will you have put into your savings by the end of the year?

3. In the game of bowling, ten pins are set up in a four-row triangular arrangement, as shown. Imagine a "super" bowling game in which a similar triangular arrangement contains *forty* rows of pins. What would be the total number of pins in this arrangement?

4. Draw two straight lines across this clock face so that the sum of the numbers in each region formed is the same.

5. For each of the following, distribute the eggs so that you have a different number of eggs in each basket.

   a. $\frac{1}{2}$ dozen eggs, 3 baskets   b. $6\frac{1}{2}$ dozen eggs, 12 baskets

   c. 3 dozen eggs, 9 baskets   d. 4 dozen eggs, 9 baskets

6. The indicated sum of the terms of an arithmetic sequence is called an **arithmetic series.** Find the sum of each of the following finite arithmetic series.
   a. 1 + 3 + 5 + . . . + 97 + 99   b. 1 + 5 + 9 + . . . + 93 + 97
   c. 1 + 5 + 9 + . . . + 145 + 149   d. 2 + 5 + 8 + . . . + 95 + 98

7. Last night there was a party, and the host's doorbell rang 20 times. The first time the doorbell rang, only one guest arrived. Each time the doorbell rang after that, two more guests arrived than had arrived on the previous ring. How many guests in all arrived at the party?

8. Rearrange the numbers in the "x" below so that the numbers on each of the two diagonals have the same sum.

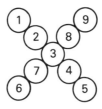

9. Suppose that you have a secret. One Sunday, you tell your secret to a friend. On Monday, your friend tells your secret to 2 other friends. On Tuesday, each of the friends who heard your secret on Monday tells it to 2 other friends. If this procedure continues from day to day, how many people in all will have been told your secret by the end of the following Sunday? Assume that no one is told your secret more than once. (*Hint:* Make a table and look for a pattern.)

10. The indicated sum of the terms of a geometric sequence is called a **geometric series.** Although a geometric series is infinite, a remarkable fact is that its sum is *finite* if the constant multiplier of the series is less than 1. Study this example, which shows how to find the sum of such a series.

Let:
$$S = \frac{1}{3} + \frac{1}{9} + \frac{1}{27} + \frac{1}{81} + \frac{1}{243} + \cdots$$

Multiply both sides by the constant:
$$\frac{1}{3}S = \frac{1}{9} + \frac{1}{27} + \frac{1}{81} + \frac{1}{243} + \cdots$$

Subtract:
$$S - \frac{1}{3}S = \frac{1}{3}$$

Then:
$$\frac{2}{3}S = \frac{1}{3}, \text{ or } S = \frac{1}{2}$$

Use the above method to find each of the following sums.

a. $\dfrac{1}{2} + \dfrac{1}{4} + \dfrac{1}{8} + \dfrac{1}{16} + \dfrac{1}{32} + \cdots$

b. $1 + \dfrac{1}{5} + \dfrac{1}{25} + \dfrac{1}{125} + \dfrac{1}{625} + \cdots$

c. $3 + \dfrac{3}{4} + \dfrac{3}{16} + \dfrac{3}{64} + \dfrac{3}{256} + \cdots$

d. $0.5 + 0.05 + 0.005 + 0.0005 + 0.00005 + \cdots$

e. $0.272727\ldots$
   (Hint: $0.272727\ldots = 0.27 + 0.0027 + 0.000027 + \cdots$)

Formulas for the sums of finite arithmetic and geometric series can be found in Appendix 2 at the back of the book.

2 Factors and Multiples

2.1 Factors
The Locker Room Problem

At a new junior high school, there are exactly 1000 students and 1000 lockers. The lockers are numbered in order from 1 to 1000. On April Fool's Day the students played the following prank. The first student to enter the building opened every locker. The second student closed every locker that had an even number. The third student *changed* every third locker, closing those that were open and opening those that were closed. The fourth student changed every fourth locker, and so on. After all 1000 students passed through the locker room, which lockers were open?

When a problem involves such a large amount of data, it is usually a good strategy to start by solving a simpler problem. In this case, let's examine what would happen if there were only 12 students and 12 lockers.

One way to organize the data for this simpler problem is to make a chart like the one below, following each student's progress through the locker room. Use graph paper if it is available.

locker numbers

students	1	2	3	4	5	6	7	8	9	10	11	12
1	O	O	O	O	O	O	O	O	O	O	O	O
2		C		C		C		C		C		C
3			C			O			C			O
4				O				O				C
5					C					O		
6						C						O
7							C					
8								C				
9									O			
10										C		
11											C	
12												C

O = locker open
C = locker closed

The diagonal entries on the chart show the final condition of each locker. As you can see, lockers 1, 4, and 9 are the only ones that remain open. What do you

notice about these numbers? Did you observe that they are the perfect-square numbers less than 12? Why are these lockers open, while those lockers whose numbers are not perfect squares are closed?

Let's examine what happened to locker 12. The column of entries on the chart shows us that locker 12 was either opened or closed by students whose numbers were 1, 2, 3, 4, 6, and 12. Do you see that each of these student numbers is a factor of 12 and that there are six factors in all? Furthermore, the factors can be paired so that the product of each pair is 12: 1×12, 2×6, and 3×4. Most numbers are like 12 and have an even number of factors. Therefore, most lockers will be changed by an even number of students and will be closed.

However, perfect-square numbers such as 1, 4, 9, and 16 each have one factor that must be multiplied by itself to produce the perfect square. For example, the factors of 16 are 1, 2, 4, 8, and 16. This is an odd number of factors. When we pair these factors so that the product of each pair is 16, we get 1×16 and 2×8. The remaining factor, 4, must be multiplied by itself to get 16. Every perfect-square number is like 16 and has one factor that must be multiplied by itself to produce the perfect square. Therefore, every perfect-square number has an odd number of factors. This means that the lockers with perfect-square numbers are changed by an odd number of students, and these are the lockers that will be open after all the students have passed through the locker room.

Answer: After all 1000 students changed the 1000 lockers, the lockers that were open were those numbered with the perfect-square numbers less than 1000: 1, 4, 9, 16, 25, . . . , 961.

Problems

1. List the numbers of the lockers that would be open after 200 students changed 200 lockers.

2. *How many* lockers would be open after 1000 students changed 1000 lockers?

3. Use the chart on page 82. How many lockers would be open if 12 lockers were changed by only 4 students? 6 students? 10 students?

4. How many lockers would be open if 50 lockers were changed by 4 students?

5. List the factors of 36. Pair the factors so that their product is 36. Which factor cannot be paired with another factor?

6. List all the ways that the number 90 can be expressed as the product of two factors. The order of the factors does not matter.

7. List all the ways that the number 24 can be expressed as the product of three whole numbers. The order of the numbers does not matter.

8. If a number written in standard form ends in one or more zeros, then those zeros are called **terminal zeros.** Find the number of terminal zeros in each of the following products when expressed in standard form.
   a. $700 \times 80{,}000$ b. 500×600
   c. $800 \times 30 \times 4000$ d. $5 \times 10^1 \times 10^2 \times 10^3$

9. The product of two whole numbers is 1,000,000, but neither number contains a zero. What are the numbers?

10. A convenient way to express the product of all the counting numbers from 1 to 5 inclusive is 5! Thus, $5! = 5 \times 4 \times 3 \times 2 \times 1$. Find the number of terminal zeros in each of the following when expressed in standard form.
   a. 5!   b. 10!   c. 17!   d. 25!

11. A recent census form included a space for residents to record the ages of all children in the household. One resident wrote, "I have three children. The product of their ages is 72. The sum of their ages is the same as our house number." The census worker who had to process the form phoned this resident to complain that this was not enough information. "I'm sorry," replied the resident. "I forgot to mention that my oldest child likes chocolate pudding." The census worker thanked the resident and hung up the phone. How old are the children? (*Hint:* List all the ways that 72 can be expressed as the product of three whole numbers.)

2.2 *Factors and Primes*
The Locker Room Revisited

Suppose that 1000 students change 1000 lockers according to the procedure described on page 82. How many students changed locker 432?

From our discussion in Section 2.1, we know that each locker is changed by those students who are assigned the factors of the locker number. Therefore, to determine how many students opened or closed any one locker is equivalent to counting all the factors of that locker number. In the case of a large number, though, the process of listing its factors may be tedious and sometimes inaccurate. The key to counting all the factors of a large number lies in first finding its *prime* factors.

Let us first consider a number whose prime factorization consists of just one prime factor, such as $16 = 2 \times 2 \times 2 \times 2 = 2^4$. The factors of 16 are 1, 2, 4, 8, and 16, which can be expressed as 1, 2^1, 2^2, 2^3, and 2^4. Do you see a relationship between the prime factorization of 16 and the number of factors it has? Observe that the number of factors is *five,* which is one more than the exponent of the prime factorization.

We can now extend this idea to find the number of factors of 432. A convenient way to find the prime factorization is to make a factor tree like the one below, which shows that $432 = 2^4 \times 3^3$.

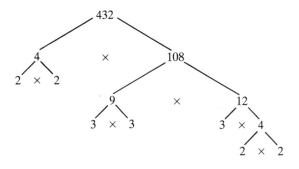

$$432 = 2 \times 2 \times 2 \times 2 \times 3 \times 3 \times 3$$
$$432 = 2^4 \times 3^3$$

We have already seen that 2^4 has 5 factors, and we can calculate that 3^3 has $3 + 1 = 4$ factors. Therefore, 432 has $5 \times 4 = 20$ factors.

Answer: Locker 432 was changed by 20 students.

We can also use the prime factorization shown on the previous page to determine exactly which students changed locker 432. This may be done by listing all the factors of 2^4 and 3^3 in the following way.

$$
\begin{array}{llll}
1 \times 1 = 1 & 1 \times 3^1 = 3 & 1 \times 3^2 = 9 & 1 \times 3^3 = 27 \\
2^1 \times 1 = 2 & 2^1 \times 3^1 = 6 & 2^1 \times 3^2 = 18 & 2^1 \times 3^3 = 54 \\
2^2 \times 1 = 4 & 2^2 \times 3^1 = 12 & 2^2 \times 3^2 = 36 & 2^2 \times 3^3 = 108 \\
2^3 \times 1 = 8 & 2^3 \times 3^1 = 24 & 2^3 \times 3^2 = 72 & 2^3 \times 3^3 = 216 \\
2^4 \times 1 = 16 & 2^4 \times 3^1 = 48 & 2^4 \times 3^2 = 144 & 2^4 \times 3^3 = 432 \\
\end{array}
$$

Therefore, locker 432 was changed by those students assigned numbers 1, 2, 3, 4, 6, 8, 9, 12, 16, 18, 24, 27, 36, 48, 54, 72, 108, 144, 216, and 432.

Problems

1. If 1000 students change 1000 lockers, how many times will each of the following lockers be changed?
   a. 29   b. 81   c. 100   d. 360

2. How many factors does the number 600 have?

3. List all the factors of 900.

4. If 50 students change 50 lockers, which lockers will be changed exactly two times? What property is common to the numbers of these lockers?

5. If 1000 students change 1000 lockers, what is the largest locker number of those lockers that are changed exactly two times?

6. The number 13 is prime. When you reverse its digits you get 31, which is also prime. Name four other pairs of "reversible" two-digit prime numbers.

7. The mathematician Christian Goldbach (1690–1764) made two guesses about whole numbers that no one has been able to prove as either true or false. These guesses are called **Goldbach's conjectures.** The first conjecture is that every even number greater than 2 can be written as the sum of two prime numbers. The second conjecture is that every odd number greater than 5 can be written as the sum of *three* prime numbers.
   a. What two prime numbers have a sum of 6? 10? 28? 38? 96?
   b. What three prime numbers have a sum of 9? 21? 29? 45? 61?

2.3 *Greatest Common Factor*
Checkers, Anyone?

A set of 36 red checkers and 60 black checkers is to be arranged into piles. Each pile may contain only red or only black checkers. All piles, both red and black, must contain the same number of checkers. What is the greatest number of checkers that each of the piles can have?

One approach to this problem is to make two lists of possible groupings, one for the red checkers and one for the black checkers. Then look for the largest number in a pile that is common to both red and black checkers.

Red Checkers	Black Checkers
1 pile of 36	1 pile of 60
2 piles of 18	2 piles of 30
3 piles of 12	3 piles of 20
4 piles of 9	4 piles of 15
6 piles of 6	5 piles of 12
9 piles of 4	6 piles of 10
12 piles of 3	10 piles of 6
18 piles of 2	12 piles of 5
36 piles of 1	15 piles of 4
	20 piles of 3
	30 piles of 2
	60 piles of 1

From the lists you can see that, in order to have piles of the same amount for both the red and black checkers, each pile may have 1, 2, 3, 4, 6, or 12 checkers.

Answer: The greatest number of checkers that can be in each pile is 12.

You may have noticed that the numbers of checkers in piles of the same amount are the *common factors* of 36 and 60. Therefore, in searching for the greatest number in a pile that is common to both red and black checkers, we are looking for the *greatest common factor (GCF)* of 36 and 60. This suggests that there may be other approaches to solving this problem.

One method of finding the GCF is a simple listing technique: list the factors of 36, list the factors of 60, list the common factors of 36 and 60, and identify the greatest of these common factors. However, since a factor may be overlooked in the process of listing, the method of prime factorization may be preferable. To use this method, first identify the prime factors that are common to both numbers; the GCF is the product of the least powers present for each of these primes.

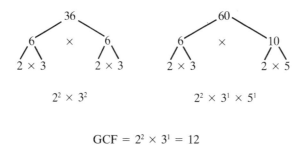

$$GCF = 2^2 \times 3^1 = 12$$

Another interesting technique is associated with the Greek mathematician Euclid, who lived more than two thousand years ago. It consists of a series of divisions, as shown below. The GCF is the divisor used in the last division.

Divide the greater number by the lesser number.

Divide the previous divisor by the remainder.

Repeat the process until the remainder is 0.

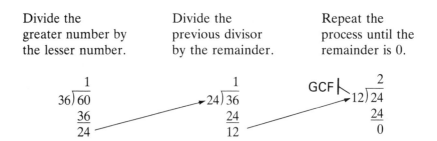

This method is called **Euclid's algorithm.** Although it may seem somewhat complicated, it can be especially helpful in finding the GCF of two large numbers.

Problems

1. Each of the following sets of red and black checkers is to be arranged into piles. Each pile may contain only red or only black checkers. All piles, both red and black, must contain the same number of checkers. What is the greatest number of checkers that each pile can have?
   a. 18 red, 30 black
   b. 84 red, 56 black
   c. 12 red, 60 black
   d. 21 red, 10 black

2. What is the GCF of each of the following pairs of numbers? Use Euclid's algorithm if other methods are not convenient.
   a. 54, 144
   b. 38, 95
   c. 629, 2257

3. To find the lowest terms of a given fraction, divide both the numerator and the denominator by their GCF. Use the GCF to write each of the following fractions in lowest terms.

   a. $\frac{54}{72}$
   b. $\frac{119}{391}$
   c. $\frac{1921}{2599}$

4. A North American fellowship conference is being attended by 96 students from the United States, 72 from Canada, and 48 from Mexico. What is the greatest number of discussion groups that can be formed so that the students from each country are distributed equally among all the groups? How many students from each country will be in each group?

5. A set of two or more numbers is **relatively prime** if each pair of numbers within the set has no common factor other than 1. Determine if each of the following sets of numbers is relatively prime.
   a. 27, 64
   b. 112, 175
   c. 18, 35, 75
   d. 13, 45, 56

6. A rectangular kitchen floor is covered by square tiles. A straight line is drawn from one corner to the corner that is diagonally opposite.

   a. How many tiles does the line cross if the floor measures exactly 2 tiles by 3 tiles? 4 tiles by 6 tiles? 6 tiles by 9 tiles? 8 tiles by 12 tiles? (*Note:* A tile is not considered to be crossed if the line intersects it only at a corner.)

   b. How many tiles does the line cross if the floor measures exactly 24 tiles by 40 tiles?

   c. State a rule for finding the number of tiles that the line crosses for any pair of whole-number dimensions of the kitchen floor.

   d. Use your rule to determine how many tiles the line crosses if the floor measures exactly 54 tiles by 96 tiles.

2.4 Multiples
The Marching Band

The members of the school marching band wanted to arrange themselves into rows with exactly the same number of band members in each row. They tried rows of 2, 3, and 4, but there was always one band member left over. Finally they were able to arrange themselves into rows with exactly 5 in each row. What is the least number of members in the marching band?

In mathematical terms, we are looking for a number that leaves a remainder of 1 when divided by 2, 3, or 4, and that is also a multiple of 5. A possible approach to this problem is to first identify those numbers that are multiples of 5, then examine the results of dividing those numbers by 2, 3, and 4. However, this process could be quite time-consuming. A more direct approach is to first find those numbers that are *common multiples* of 2, 3, and 4.

multiples of 2:	2, 4, 6, 8, 10, 12, 14, 16, 18, 20, 22, 24, . . .
multiples of 3:	3, 6, 9, 12, 15, 18, 21, 24, 27, 30, 33, 36, . . .
multiples of 4:	4, 8, 12, 16, 20, 24, 28, 32, 36, 40, 44, 48, . . .
common multiples of 2, 3, 4:	12, 24, 36, 48, 60, 72, 84, 96, 108, 120, 132, . . .

To leave a remainder of 1 when divided by 2, 3, and 4, a number would have to be 1 greater than a common multiple of 2, 3, and 4. Therefore, the list of numbers to be considered is the following.

13, 25, 37, 49, 61, 73, 85, 97, 109, 121, 133, . . .

The first of these that is a multiple of 5 is 25.

Answer: The least number of members in the marching band is 25.

Problems

1. The members of the flag squad wanted to arrange themselves into rows with exactly the same number of squad members in each row. They tried rows of 2, 3, and 4, but there was always one squad member missing. Finally they were able to arrange themselves into rows with exactly 5 in each row. What is the least number of members in the flag squad?

2. There are two sizes of tables in a banquet hall. One size seats exactly 5 people and the other size seats exactly 8 people. At tonight's banquet, exactly 79 people will be seated at less than one dozen tables, and there will be no empty places. How many tables of each size will there be?

3. If a certain number is divided by 2, 3, 4, or 5, the remainder is 1 in each case. What is the least number that satisfies these conditions?

4. If a certain number is divided by 2, 3, 4, or 5, the respective remainders are 1, 2, 3, and 4. What is the least number that satisfies these conditions?

5. What is the remainder when 3^{10} is divided by 5? (*Hint:* Solve some simpler problems and look for a pattern.)

6. A group of people is seated at a round table. They pass a tray of appetizers from person to person in order around the table. Helen takes the first appetizer, then every other person takes one appetizer each time the tray is passed around. Helen also takes the last appetizer.

   a. If the tray contains 25 appetizers, how many people could be seated around the table?

   b. If the tray contains 50 appetizers and Helen takes a total of 8, how many people are seated around the table?

2.5 Least Common Multiple
Broadway Bound

The choreographer of a big Broadway musical has requested that the producer hire enough chorus dancers so that, for various scenes, the dancers can be arranged in groups of 4, 6, or 9 with none left over. What is the least number of dancers that the producer must hire?

Let's first think of a simpler problem. If the choreographer wanted to arrange groups of only one size, such as 4, it follows that the producer would consider hiring a number of dancers that is a multiple of 4. However, since the choreographer wants the freedom to arrange the dancers in groups of 4, 6, or 9, then the producer must somehow be concerned with multiples of all three numbers. The least number of dancers that would satisfy these conditions is the *least common multiple* (*LCM*) of 4, 6, and 9.

One way to find the LCM is to list multiples for all the numbers involved until a common multiple appears.

multiples of 4:	4, 8, 12, 16, 20, 24, 28, 32, 36, . . .
multiples of 6:	6, 12, 18, 24, 30, 36, . . .
multiples of 9:	9, 18, 27, 36, . . .
LCM:	36

Answer: The producer must hire 36 dancers.

Another method of finding the LCM is a trial-and-error approach that focuses on the multiples of the greatest number only. Each of these multiples is divided by each of the smaller numbers until both quotients are whole numbers.

Multiples of 9	Divisible by 6?	Divisible by 4?
9	No	No
18	Yes	No
27	No	No
36	Yes	Yes
LCM = 36		

As you can see, methods involving the listing of multiples can become lengthy and time-consuming. A more direct approach consists of finding the prime factorization of each number. The LCM is then the product of the greatest powers of all the primes that are present.

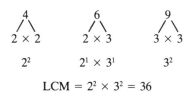

$$LCM = 2^2 \times 3^2 = 36$$

Problems

1. What is the LCM of each of the following pairs of numbers?
   a. 6, 10   b. 24, 54   c. 108, 126

2. What is the least number of dancers that a producer must hire if the choreographer wants to arrange them in groups of 4, 5, or 6 with none left over?

3. At the Fourth of July parade, the local scout troop found that they could arrange themselves in rows of exactly 6, exactly 7, or exactly 8, with no one left over. What is the least number of scouts in the troop?

4. I have a collection of pennies that can be arranged in piles that each contain exactly 9 pennies. My pennies can also be arranged in piles that each contain exactly 10 pennies, exactly 11 pennies, and exactly 12 pennies. What is the least number of pennies that can be in my collection?

5. Complete the calculations for each set of numbers. Then answer the questions.

   16×20=?   18×48=?
   GCF of 16 and 20=?   GCF of 18 and 48=?
   LCM of 16 and 20=?   LCM of 18 and 48=?
   GCF×LCM=?   GCF×LCM=?

   a. State a rule to describe the relationship between the product of two numbers and their GCF and LCM.
   b. Use your rule to describe a method for finding the LCM of two numbers if you already know their GCF.
   c. The GCF of 36 and 60 is 12. Show how to use your method to find the LCM of 36 and 60.

3 Divisibility

3.1 Divisibility by 2, 5, 10, and 100
One for the Books

The pages of a certain book are numbered consecutively from 1 to 300. How many page numbers contain the digit 5 and are also divisible by 5?

A whole number is **divisible** by another whole number if their quotient is a whole number. You may recall that there are "tests" that can help you determine certain divisibility properties of numbers without going through lengthy calculations. The following are some simple tests that may be familiar to you.

Number	Divisibility Test
2	The ones' digit is 0, 2, 4, 6, or 8.
5	The ones' digit is 0 or 5.
10	The ones' digit is 0.
100	The ones' and tens' digits are *both* 0.

One way to solve the problem is to list in order all the whole numbers from 1 to 300 that are divisible by 5 and then remove those listed numbers that do not contain the digit 5. Another way is to use the divisibility test from the table and to consider each of the two cases individually.

The ones' digit is 5. All such numbers will satisfy the conditions of the problem. We know that every set of ten consecutive whole numbers contains exactly one number whose ones' digit is 5. Since three hundred page numbers contain *thirty* sets of ten consecutive whole numbers, there are thirty different page numbers whose ones' digit is 5.

The ones' digit is 0. Such numbers will satisfy the conditions of the problem only if they have the digit 5 in the tens' place. There are only three of these: 50, 150, and 250.

Answer: There are thirty-three page numbers from 1 to 300 that contain the digit 5 and are also divisible by 5.

Problems

1. The pages of a certain book are numbered consecutively from 1 to 500. How many page numbers meet each of the following sets of conditions?

   a. The page numbers contain the digit 5 and are also divisible by 5.

   b. The page numbers contain the digit 5 but are *not* divisible by 5.

   c. The page numbers do not contain the digit 5 but are divisible by 5.

2. All whole numbers can be classified as either odd or even. If the number is divisible by 2 it is **even;** if the number is *not* divisible by 2 it is **odd.** Suppose that each of the following sets of numbers is added. Is the sum even or odd?

   a. two even numbers

   b. two odd numbers

   c. one even number and one odd number

   d. three even numbers

   e. three odd numbers

   f. ninety-nine odd numbers and one even number

   g. thirteen even numbers and twenty odd numbers

3. Suppose that the numbers in each of the sets of numbers described in problem 2 are *multiplied.* Is the product even or odd?

4. In the following tables for addition and multiplication, *E* represents any even number and *O* represents any odd number. Complete each table.

   a.

+	*E*	*O*
E		
O		

   b.

×	*E*	*O*
E		
O		

5. For each of the following books, how many page numbers contain the digit 2 but are not divisible by 2? (Assume that the pages of each book are numbered consecutively from 1 to the given number of pages.)

   a. 100 pages

   b. 200 pages

   c. 300 pages

6. State a rule for divisibility by each of the following numbers.

   a. 1000

   b. 10,000

   c. 10^n, where n is any whole-number exponent.

      (*Hint:* Notice that $10 = 10^1$, $100 = 10^2$, $1000 = 10^3$, $10,000 = 10^4$, and so on.)

3.2 Divisibility Principle for Sums and Differences
The "Week" Link

Does a period of 329 days form a whole number of 7-day weeks?

Notice that this problem does not require you to find *how many* 7-day weeks there may be. Rather, you are only asked whether 329 days forms a *whole number* of 7-day weeks. Therefore, you need only to determine if 329 is divisible by 7.

Obviously, you could solve the problem by performing the division $7\overline{)329}$ to find if the quotient is a whole number. However, let's use this problem as an opportunity to explore a basic principle of divisibility.

The number 329 can be written as $280 + 49$. We know that 280 and 49 are each divisible by 7: $280 = 7 \times 40$ and $49 = 7 \times 7$. The distributive property of multiplication over division now helps us make this observation.

$$
\begin{aligned}
329 &= 280 & + & \quad 49 \\
&= 7 \times 40 & + & \quad 7 \times 7 \\
&= 7 \times & & (40 + 7) \\
329 &= 7 \times & & \quad 47
\end{aligned}
$$

Since 329 can be written as 7×47, 329 is divisible by 7.

Answer: A period of 329 days does form a whole number of 7-day weeks.

The observations that we made in solving this problem are an example of applying a general rule that we shall call the **divisibility principle for sums and differences.**

For whole numbers *a*, *b*, and *c*, if *a* and *b* are each divisible by *c*, then the sum and the difference of *a* and *b* are each divisible by *c*.

The following is a related principle.

For whole numbers *a*, *b*, and *c*, if *a* is divisible by *c* but *b* is not, then neither the sum nor the difference of *a* and *b* is divisible by *c*.

Problems

1. Determine if each of the following sums and differences is divisible by 7.
   a. $56 + 21$ b. $42 + 65$ c. $210 - 49$ d. $770 - 540$

2. Does each of the following periods of days form a whole number of 7-day weeks? Show how to use the divisibility principle for sums and differences to determine the answer without dividing.
   a. 98 days   b. 154 days   c. 133 days   d. 693 days

3. Use the divisibility principle for sums and differences to determine if each of the following numbers is divisible by 11.
   a. 253   b. 784   c. 6589   d. 8777

4. Suppose that a person was born in 1945. Will the number of the year of that person's 62nd birthday be divisible by 5? Explain.

5. Neither 40 nor 32 is divisible by 9. However, the sum $40 + 32 = 72$ is divisible by 9. Does this contradict the divisibility principle for sums and differences?

6. Explain how the divisibility principle for sums and differences is the basis for the divisibility test for 5 discussed in Section 3.1.

7. How can you determine if a whole number is divisible by 25 without dividing?

8. How can you determine if a whole number is divisible by 125 without dividing?

3.3 Divisibility by Powers of 2
The Packaging Problem

A toy distributor has to package 19,836,472 marbles in boxes that will each contain 8 marbles. Will any marbles be left over?

We could of course divide 19,836,472 by 8 to see if there is a remainder. However, let's examine a different way to answer the question.

A fact that is useful in this situation is that 1000 is divisible by 8 (1000 ÷ 8 = 125). Let's rewrite the number of marbles as the following sum.

$$19,836,472 = 19,836,000 + 472$$

The left addend is a multiple of 1000, and so it is divisible by 8. The right addend is also divisible by 8, since 472 ÷ 8 = 59. Then according to the divisibility principle for sums, 19,836,472 is divisible by 8.

Answer: When packaged in boxes of 8, no marbles will be left over.

Suppose that the toy distributor has to package the 19,836,472 marbles in boxes that each contain *16* marbles. Will any marbles be left over?

In this case, the fact that is useful to us is that 10,000 is divisible by 16 (10,000 ÷ 16 = 625). Let's rewrite the number of marbles as a different sum.

$$19,836,472 = 19,830,000 + 6472$$

The left addend is a multiple of 10,000, and so it is divisible by 16. However, the right addend is *not* divisible by 16, since 6472 ÷ 16 = 404 R8. Therefore, 19,836,472 is not divisible by 16.

Answer: When packaged in boxes of 16, there will be marbles left over. Specifically, the number of marbles that will be left over is 8.

Look back at the packaging problems. What do 8 and 16 have in common? Did you notice that both are powers of 2? That is, $8 = 2^3$ and $16 = 2^4$. When we tested for divisibility by 8, or 2^3, we needed to test just the number formed by the last 3 digits. When we tested for divisibility by 16, or 2^4, we needed to test just the number formed by the last 4 digits. This suggests the following table of tests for divisibility by powers of 2.

Number	Divisibility Test
$2 = 2^1$	The number formed by the last 1 digit is divisible by 2.
$4 = 2^2$	The number formed by the last 2 digits is divisible by 4.
$8 = 2^3$	The number formed by the last 3 digits is divisible by 8.
$16 = 2^4$	The number formed by the last 4 digits is divisible by 16.

Problems

1. Can each of the following numbers of marbles be packaged in boxes that each contain 16 marbles with none left over?

   a. 841,600   b. 1,403,280   c. 250,036

2. Suppose that marbles are packaged in boxes that each contain 32 marbles.

   a. Use the pattern from the table above to state a test for divisibility by 32.

   b. Can 100,032 marbles be packaged in boxes that each contain 32 marbles with none left over? 2,306,420 marbles? 8,732,128 marbles?

3. Helsinki, Finland was the site of the Summer Olympic games either in 1952 or in 1954. Can you determine which is the correct year without consulting any reference?

4. After 25 tons of silver ore were processed, 2,197,216 ounces of pure silver were extracted. If the pure silver is then cast into one-pound ingots, will any pure silver be left over?

5. What values of the missing digit will make each of the following numbers divisible by 4? by 8?

   a. 47█6   b. 27,█12   c. 732,█82

6. Replace the missing digit in 1,876,9█2 so that the resulting number is divisible by 16.

7. A four-digit number contains the digits 1, 4, 5, and 7, but not necessarily in that order. Can the number be divisible by 4?

8. Which of the three-digit numbers whose digits are 6, 7, and 8 is divisible by 8?

9. List all the four-digit numbers that contain each of the digits 1, 2, 3, and 4 and are divisible by 4.

10. The pages of a certain book are numbered consecutively from 1 to 1000. How many page numbers have the digit 2 in the ones' place and are divisible by 8?

3.4 Divisibility by 3 and 9
The Faded Bill of Sale

Suppose that you see this old bill of sale on display in a museum. You notice that some of the digits of the numbers have faded. Can you tell what the numbers must be?

One way to solve this problem is to use trial and error, testing different digits in the faded spaces until you find a combination of digits that works. However, this is not necessarily the most direct approach. Is there another way?

For ɛ ·· sheep
Eac ·· :t $9
A t ··· al of
$ ·· 38
rec ·· by me
the ·· b th day

The problem provides a valuable clue. Since each sheep costs $9, the total cost of all the sheep must be a multiple of 9. How can you know if a number is a multiple of 9? Let's choose some examples to see if there is a pattern.

Multiple of 9	Sum of Digits
17 × 9 = 153	1 + 5 + 3 = 9
64 × 9 = 576	5 + 7 + 6 = 18
104 × 9 = 936	9 + 3 + 6 = 18
762 × 9 = 6858	6 + 8 + 5 + 8 = 27
4328 × 9 = 38,952	3 + 8 + 9 + 5 + 2 = 27

What do each of the sums of the digits have in common? Do you see that each sum is itself a multiple of 9? This suggest the following divisibility test for 9.

A number is divisible by 9 if the sum of its digits is divisible by 9.

Now let's return to the bill of sale. The total cost of the sheep must be a multiple of 9, and so we are looking for a number, ▮38, that is divisible by 9. We know that 8 + 3 = 11. The next multiple of 9 greater than 11 is 18, and therefore the missing digit of the total must be 18 − 11 = 7.

Answer: The total cost of the sheep is $738, and the number of sheep is 738 ÷ 9, or 82.

If you investigate multiples of 3 in the manner that we have just investigated multiples of 9, you will find that the sums of their digits are always multiples of 3. This leads us to a similar divisibility test for 3.

A number is divisible by 3 if the sum of its digits is divisible by 3.

Problems

1. Replace the missing digit so that the resulting number is divisible by 9.

   a. 1,456,█28   b. █649   c. 6,█54,321

2. For each number in problem 1, replace the missing digit so that the resulting number is divisible by 3.

3. Find all possible values for the missing digits in █5█ so that the resulting number is divisible by 9.

4. Find all possible values for the missing digits in █5█ so that the resulting number is divisible by 3.

5. How is the divisibility test for 9 helpful in remembering the multiplication facts from 2 × 9 through 9 × 9?

6. Some accountants use the divisibility test for 9 to determine a possible source of error in a ledger. Answer these questions to find how they use it.

   a. Compute these differences.

$51	$685
− 15	− 658

$40,752	$382,861
− 40,572	− 328,861

   b. Is each difference in part **a** divisible by 9?

   c. If a ledger is "off" by a number that is divisible by 9, what is a possible source of the error?

7. Suppose that one number contains the same digits as another number, but in reverse order. What is true of the difference of the two numbers? (*Hint:* Try some examples, such as 6281 and 1826.)

8. Is it possible to use each of the digits from 1 through 9 exactly once to create a nine-digit prime number? Why or why not?

3.5 Divisibility by 11
Search for a Pattern

These numbers are each divisible by 11: 99, 792, 4015, 87,263, 380,919, and 1,644,192. What do these number have in common?

In looking for something common to all these numbers, you are in fact looking for a divisibility test for 11. Where do you begin? You will probably find that organization is important in solving a problem such as this. Start by considering a number of simple cases, then proceed to more difficult ones and see if a pattern emerges along the way.

Let's begin with just the two-digit numbers that are divisible by 11: 11, 22, 33, 44, . . . , 99. They're easy to recognize, of course, because the two digits are the same. This leads to the observation that the sum of the digits for each number varies, but the *difference* of the digits is always 0.

Can we relate this observation in any way to three-digit numbers? Let's look at these numbers, which are all divisible by 11.

$$121 \qquad 319 \qquad 627 \qquad 792$$

Again, the sum of the digits for each number varies. A difference of the digits for each number also seems to have no meaning, since each number has three digits. Before you read on, though, try considering *both* addition and subtraction. Did you observe that when you *add* the digits in the ones' and hundreds' places and then *subtract* the digit in the tens' place, the result is either 0 or 11 for each number?

$$\overset{2}{\underset{1\ 2\ 1}{\sqcap}} \qquad \overset{12}{\underset{3\ 1\ 9}{\sqcap}} \qquad \overset{13}{\underset{6\ 2\ 7}{\sqcap}} \qquad \overset{9}{\underset{7\ 9\ 2}{\sqcap}}$$

$$2 - 2 = 0 \qquad 12 - 1 = 11 \qquad 13 - 2 = 11 \qquad 9 - 9 = 0$$

Let's go on to look at some four-digit numbers that are divisible by 11.

$$1034 \qquad 3916 \qquad 4015 \qquad 5060$$

Can you see how to apply the same pattern of sums and differences to these numbers? As before, begin by adding the digits in the ones' and hundreds' places.

Next add the digits in the tens' and thousands' places. Subtract one sum from the other. Once again, the difference is either 0 or 11.

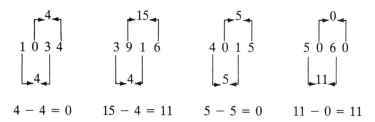

$$4 - 4 = 0 \qquad 15 - 4 = 11 \qquad 5 - 5 = 0 \qquad 11 - 0 = 11$$

Can you extend the pattern to these larger numbers? Each is divisible by 11.

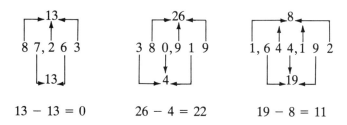

$$13 - 13 = 0 \qquad 26 - 4 = 22 \qquad 19 - 8 = 11$$

This time the differences between sums are 0, 11, and 22. Do you see that each of these differences is divisible by 11?

Let's introduce some vocabulary that will help us describe this pattern of sums and differences. We shall call the ones' place an **odd place** and the tens' place an **even place.** The places to the left of tens are then alternately called *odd place, even place, odd place, even place,* and so on, as shown at the right.

odd places

even places

We can now use this vocabulary to state the following divisibility test for 11.

A number is divisible by 11 if the difference between the sum of the odd-place digits and the sum of the even-place digits is divisible by 11.

Is 80,918,090 divisible by 11? Notice above that the sum of its odd-place digits is $0 + 1 + 0 + 0 = 1$. The sum of its even-place digits is $8 + 9 + 8 + 9 = 34$. The difference of these sums is $34 - 1 = 33$, which is divisible by 11.

Answer: The number 80,918,090 is divisible by 11.

Problems

1. Use the divisibility test to determine if each of the following numbers is divisible by 11.
   a. 1826   b. 7259   c. 82,907   d. 1,724,943

2. Replace the missing digit so that the resulting number is divisible by 11.
   a. 93▓   b. 37▓9   c. 39,▓21   d. ▓0,819

3. Replace the missing digits in ▓5▓ so that the resulting number is divisible by 11.

4. A four-digit number contains the digits 1, 4, 7, and 9, but not in that order. Arrange these digits so that the resulting number is divisible by 11. In how many ways can this be done?

5. Find the sum of all the four-digit numbers that contain the digits 1, 2, 3, and 4 and that are divisible by 11.

6. The number 1,234,567 is not divisible by 11, but you can change the order of the digits to form numbers that *are* divisible by 11. Find one such number.

7. There are 1500 students in the freshman class of Central State College. In the autumn they play intramural football with 11 freshmen on each team. If each freshman can play on just one team, what is the greatest number of freshmen that can play?

3.6 Combined Divisibility
Cheaper by the Dozen

Farmer Brown's chickens produced 9762 eggs today. Can these eggs be packed in cartons that each contain exactly one dozen eggs with none left over?

Since there are 12 eggs in a dozen, one way to solve this problem is to perform the division 9762 ÷ 12 to see if there is a remainder. However, let's use this problem to see how divisibility tests might be used.

Notice that 12 = 3 × 4. To test 9762 for divisibility by 12 then, we need to test for divisibility both by 3 *and* by 4.

9762 is divisible by 3, since the sum of its digits (9 + 7 + 6 + 2 = 24) is divisible by 3.

9762 is *not* divisible by 4, since the number formed by its last two digits (62) is not divisible by 4.

Therefore, 9762 is *not* divisible by 12.

Answer: The 9762 eggs cannot be packed in cartons that each contain exactly one dozen eggs with none left over.

Problems

1. Can each of the following numbers of eggs be packed in cartons that each contain exactly one dozen eggs with none left over?
   a. 5824   b. 7416   c. 12,054   d. 428,676

2. Can Farmer Brown's 9762 eggs be packed in cartons that each contain exactly one half dozen eggs with none left over?

3. Is each of the following numbers divisible by 18?
   a. 972   b. 8946   c. 9081   d. 15,018

4. Describe a divisibility test for 15.

5. For each of the following, find *all* pairs of replacements for the missing digits so that the resulting number meets the given condition.
   a. ▦23▦ is divisible by 45.
   b. ▦31▦ is divisible by 72.
   c. ▦47▦ is divisible by 36.
   d. ▦47▦ is divisible by 55.

6. List all the three-digit numbers that are divisible by 99.

3.7 *Divisibility by 7, 11, and 13*
License Plate Lookout

When traveling with her family, Helen enjoys looking at the license plates of passing cars to see if she can identify any special properties of the numbers on them. When she saw this license plate she said, "That number is divisible by 7 and by 13, but it's not divisible by 11."

How can you determine this without dividing?

It would seem that Helen knows one special test that determines divisibility by all three numbers. To discover this test, let's consider the fact that $7 \times 11 \times 13 = 1001$. Do you see that, since 1001 is divisible by 7, 11, and 13, any multiple of 1001 is also divisible by 7, 11, and 13? Many multiples of 1001, such as 5005, 27,027, and 863,863, are easy to recognize and therefore are easy to test for divisibility by 7, 11, and 13.

How was Helen able to apply this test to the license plate number above? She may have recognized that $497{,}406 = 497{,}497 - 91$, then used this special divisibility test in combination with the divisibility principle for sums and differences.

> *Answer:* 497,497 and 91 are each divisible by 7 and by 13, so 497,406 is divisible by 7 and by 13.
>
> 497,497 is divisible by 11, but 91 is *not* divisible by 11, so 497,406 is not divisible by 11.

Notice that the special divisibility test for 11 discussed in Section 3.5 also applies to 1001 and multiples of 1001.

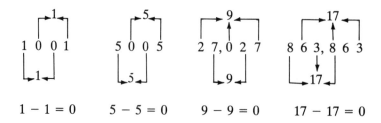

Problems

1. Use the special divisibility test to determine if each of the following numbers is divisible by 7, by 11, and by 13.

   a. 180,124   b. 621,595   c. 236,346

   d. 430,445   e. 583,660   f. 900,869

   g. 98,126   h. 63,078   i. 52,143

2. The number of the year 2002 has four different prime factors. What are they?

3. What is the least number that has six different prime factors?

4. The special test for divisibility by 7, 11, and 13 can be extended to numbers with more than six digits by using this procedure.

   – Starting at the right, place the digits in groups of three.
   – Working from the right, alternately subtract and add the numbers formed by the groups of three digits.
   – Test the final result for divisibility by 7, 11, and 13.

   Use this procedure to test each of the following numbers for divisibility by 7, 11, and 13.

   a. 270,060,340   b. 600,515,134   c. 29,482,531

5. The budget figure $125,811,738 has been allocated for thirteen different departments. Can the departments receive equal amounts?

   A further discussion of the divisibility tests for 3, 9, and 11 can be found in Appendix 3 at the back of the book.

4 Fractions

4.1 Unit Fractions
Ancient Arithmetic

The Rhind Papyrus is an ancient document containing evidence that fractions were in use as early as four thousand years ago in the Egyptian system of numeration. However, the Egyptians seemed to work primarily with the **unit fraction**, which is a fraction with a numerator of 1 and a denominator that is any counting number. It is believed that they tried to avoid computational difficulties by representing all fractions except $\frac{2}{3}$ as the *sum* of unit fractions.

The Papyrus begins with a table that shows how to write fractions of the form $\frac{2}{n}$ as the sum of distinct unit fractions for all odd values of n from 5 to 101. Here are a few of the sums.

$$\frac{2}{5} = \frac{1}{3} + \frac{1}{15} \qquad \frac{2}{7} = \frac{1}{4} + \frac{1}{28} \qquad \frac{2}{11} = \frac{1}{6} + \frac{1}{66}$$

There are many interesting theories to explain how the Egyptians obtained these sums. One of the theories is based on a pattern among the denominators. What is this pattern? How might the pattern be used to write $\frac{2}{13}$ as the sum of two distinct unit fractions?

As you study the given sums, one element of the pattern may seem fairly obvious. Did you observe that the denominator of the second unit fraction is the product of the denominator of the given fraction and the denominator of the first unit fraction?

$$5 \times 3 = 15 \qquad 7 \times 4 = 28 \qquad 11 \times 6 = 66$$

The problem that remains is how to find the denominator of the *first* unit fraction. Study the examples again. Do you see that the denominator of the first unit fraction is equal to one half of the sum of the denominator of the given fraction and 1?

$$\frac{1}{2} \times (5 + 1) = 3 \qquad \frac{1}{2} \times (7 + 1) = 4 \qquad \frac{1}{2} \times (11 + 1) = 6$$

For $\frac{2}{13}$, then, the denominator of the first unit fraction is one half of $(13 + 1)$, or 7. This means that the denominator of the second unit fraction is $13 \times 7 = 91$.

Answer: $\frac{2}{13} = \frac{1}{7} + \frac{1}{91}$

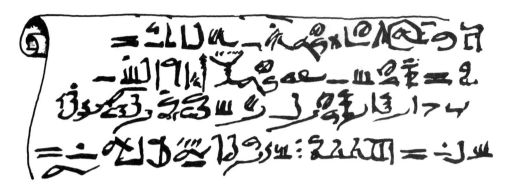

The Egyptians' accomplishments with unit fractions lead us to a related question: can a unit fraction itself be written as the sum of two other unit fractions? Let's investigate by trying to find such sums for $\frac{1}{2}$, $\frac{1}{3}$, and $\frac{1}{5}$.

To begin with, every unit fraction can be written as the sum of two *equal* unit fractions, like this.

$$\frac{1}{2} = \frac{1}{4} + \frac{1}{4} \qquad \frac{1}{3} = \frac{1}{6} + \frac{1}{6} \qquad \frac{1}{5} = \frac{1}{10} + \frac{1}{10}$$

Can you describe these results in general terms? Use a variable such as n to represent the denominator of the original unit fraction. Is this your conclusion?

$$\frac{1}{n} = \frac{1}{2n} + \frac{1}{2n}$$

However, this is not the only type of sum that is possible. An unusual property of any unit fraction is that it also can be written as the sum of two *distinct* unit fractions. Look at these examples.

$$\frac{1}{2} = \frac{1}{3} + \frac{1}{6} \qquad \frac{1}{3} = \frac{1}{4} + \frac{1}{12} \qquad \frac{1}{5} = \frac{1}{6} + \frac{1}{30}$$

Can you detect a pattern among these equalities? Once again, try to describe it before reading ahead, using the variable n to represent the denominator of the original unit fraction. Did you get this result?

$$\frac{1}{n} = \frac{1}{n + 1} + \frac{1}{n \times (n + 1)}$$

This fact is sometimes referred to as the **unit fraction principle.**

Problems

1. Use the pattern discussed for $\frac{2}{n}$ to write each of the following fractions as the sum of two distinct unit fractions. Check your results.

   a. $\frac{2}{3}$ b. $\frac{2}{9}$ c. $\frac{2}{15}$ d. $\frac{2}{25}$

2. Use the unit fraction principle to write each of the following unit fractions as the sum of two distinct unit fractions. Check your results.

    a. $\frac{1}{4}$ b. $\frac{1}{7}$ c. $\frac{1}{10}$ d. $\frac{1}{11}$

3. Write $\frac{1}{3}$ as the indicated sum of *four* distinct unit fractions.

4. Show two ways to write $\frac{1}{2}$ as the indicated sum of three distinct unit fractions.

5. **Consecutive unit fractions** are unit fractions whose denominators are consecutive numbers, such as $\frac{1}{2}, \frac{1}{3}, \frac{1}{4}, \frac{1}{5}$, and $\frac{1}{6}$. An immediate consequence of the unit fraction principle is the following fact about the *difference* of two consecutive unit fractions.

$$\frac{1}{n} - \frac{1}{n+1} = \frac{1}{n \times (n+1)}$$

Use this fact to compute each of the following differences.

    a. $\frac{1}{2} - \frac{1}{3}$ b. $\frac{1}{4} - \frac{1}{5}$ c. $\frac{1}{7} - \frac{1}{8}$ d. $\frac{1}{9} - \frac{1}{10}$

6. Write $\frac{1}{12}$ as the indicated difference of two consecutive unit fractions.

7. Write each of the following indicated sums as a simple fraction in lowest terms.

    a. $\frac{1}{1 \times 2} + \frac{1}{2 \times 3} + \ldots + \frac{1}{9 \times 10}$ b. $\frac{1}{1 \times 3} + \frac{1}{3 \times 5} + \ldots + \frac{1}{9 \times 11}$

8. When the denominator of a unit fraction is a composite number, it is possible to write that unit fraction as the indicated sum of two distinct unit fractions in many different ways. If we choose a and b to represent any factor pair for the composite number, the following statements can be shown to be true.

$$\frac{1}{a \times b} = \frac{1}{a \times (a+b)} + \frac{1}{b \times (a+b)}$$

$$\frac{1}{a \times b} = \frac{1}{a \times (b+1)} + \frac{1}{a \times b \times (b+1)}$$

$$\frac{1}{a \times b} = \frac{1}{b \times (a+1)} + \frac{1}{a \times b \times (a+1)}$$

Write each of the following unit fractions as the indicated sum of two unit fractions in as many ways as possible.

    a. $\frac{1}{6}$ b. $\frac{1}{10}$ c. $\frac{1}{4}$ d. $\frac{1}{12}$

9. Use trial and error to write each of the following fractions as the indicated sum of two distinct unit fractions.

    a. $\frac{3}{4}$ b. $\frac{5}{6}$ c. $\frac{3}{5}$ d. $\frac{2}{7}$

4.2 Complex Fractions
Heart Arithmetic

Suppose that there is a different kind of arithmetic in which the expression $a \heartsuit b$ has the same meaning as the expression $\frac{a}{b}$ in our arithmetic. What is the value of $\frac{2}{3} \heartsuit \frac{4}{7}$ written as a simple fraction in lowest terms?

To begin with, let's rewrite $\frac{2}{3} \heartsuit \frac{4}{7}$ using the meaning given in the problem.

$$\frac{2}{3} \heartsuit \frac{4}{7} = \frac{\frac{2}{3}}{\frac{4}{7}}$$

Obviously, the result is not a simple fraction. In fact, a fraction such as this in which either the numerator or denominator itself contains a fraction is called a **complex fraction**. Can we find a simple fraction value for a complex fraction?

Recall that the value of any fraction is not changed if you multiply *both* its numerator and denominator by the same nonzero number. For this complex fraction, let's see what happens when we multiply the numerator and denominator by the reciprocal of the fraction in the denominator.

$$\frac{\frac{2}{3}}{\frac{4}{7}} = \frac{\frac{2}{3} \times \frac{7}{4}}{\frac{4}{7} \times \frac{7}{4}} = \frac{\frac{14}{12}}{1} = \frac{14}{12} = \frac{7}{6}$$

If you wish, you could choose a technique that involves multiplying both the numerator and denominator of the complex fraction by the LCM of the two denominators, 3 and 7, or by 21. As you can see, the result is the same.

$$\frac{\frac{2}{3}}{\frac{4}{7}} = \frac{\frac{2}{3} \times 21}{\frac{4}{7} \times 21} = \frac{14}{12} = \frac{7}{6}$$

Answer: As a simple fraction in lowest terms, the value of $\frac{2}{3} \heartsuit \frac{4}{7}$ is $\frac{7}{6}$.

Problems

1. Suppose that $a \heartsuit b$ is defined as $\frac{a}{b}$. What is the value of each of the following written as a simple fraction in lowest terms?

   a. $\frac{3}{4} \heartsuit \frac{4}{5}$ b. $\frac{5}{6} \heartsuit \frac{3}{8}$ c. $1\frac{1}{3} \heartsuit 2\frac{1}{4}$ d. $\frac{1}{2} \heartsuit \left(\frac{1}{3} \heartsuit \frac{1}{4}\right)$

2. Suppose that $a \blacklozenge b$ is defined as $\frac{b}{a}$. What is the value of each of the expressions in problem 1 in lowest terms if each $\heartsuit$ is changed to $\blacklozenge$?

3. What is the value of each of the following complex fractions written as a simple fraction in lowest terms?

a. $\dfrac{\frac{1}{1}}{\frac{1}{2}}$ b. $\dfrac{\frac{1}{3}}{\frac{3}{5}}$ c. $\dfrac{\frac{1}{2\frac{1}{4}}}{\,}$ d. $\dfrac{\frac{1}{3.7}}{\,}$

4. The reciprocal of 3 is $\frac{1}{3}$. What is the reciprocal of $\frac{1}{3}$?

5. What is the reciprocal of the reciprocal of $\frac{3}{8}$?

6. What is the value of each of the following complex fractions written as a simple fraction in lowest terms?

a. $\dfrac{\frac{2}{5}+\frac{1}{2}}{3}$ b. $\dfrac{3}{4+\frac{1}{5}}$ c. $\dfrac{\frac{3}{4}+\frac{1}{3}}{\frac{1}{2}+\frac{4}{5}}$ d. $\dfrac{2-\frac{1}{2}}{2+\frac{1}{2}}$

7. What is the value of each of the following expressions written as a simple fraction in lowest terms, given that $a = \frac{1}{2}$ and $b = \frac{1}{3}$?

a. $\dfrac{a+b}{a-b}$ b. $\dfrac{a+b}{3}$ c. $\dfrac{a-b}{4}$

8. If $a \# b$ is defined as $\dfrac{a+b}{2}$, what is the value of $\frac{1}{3} \# \left(\frac{1}{5} \# \frac{1}{7}\right)$ written as a simple fraction in lowest terms?

4.3 Continued Fractions
Repeat Performance

What is the value of the expression at the right?

This expression is an example of a special type of complex fraction that is called a **continued fraction**. It is possible to write its value as a simple fraction. How can this be done?

$$\cfrac{1}{2+\cfrac{1}{2+\frac{1}{2}}}$$

Examine the expression to see if any *part* of it can be simplified. Did you observe that $2 + \frac{1}{2}$ at the bottom is equal to $2\frac{1}{2}$, or $\frac{5}{2}$? You can use this fact to rewrite the expression in a simpler form.

$$\cfrac{1}{2+\cfrac{1}{2+\frac{1}{2}}} = \cfrac{1}{2+\cfrac{1}{\frac{5}{2}}}$$

Once again, look for any part of the expression that can be simplified. Did you notice this reciprocal at the bottom?

$$\frac{1}{\frac{5}{2}} = \frac{2}{5}$$

You can now rewrite the expression again.

$$\cfrac{1}{2 + \cfrac{1}{\frac{5}{2}}} = \cfrac{1}{2 + \frac{2}{5}}$$

Finally, repeat the process of performing the indicated addition and evaluating the resulting reciprocal.

$$\cfrac{1}{2 + \frac{2}{5}} = \frac{1}{2\frac{2}{5}} = \frac{1}{\frac{12}{5}} = \frac{5}{12}$$

Answer: Written as a simple fraction in lowest terms, the value of the given expression is $\frac{5}{12}$.

Problems

1. Write each of the following expressions as a simple fraction in lowest terms.

   a. $\cfrac{1}{3 + \cfrac{1}{3 + \frac{1}{3}}}$

   b. $\cfrac{1}{1 + \cfrac{1}{1 + \cfrac{1}{1 + \frac{1}{3}}}}$

   c. $2 + \cfrac{1}{1 + \frac{1}{2}}$

   d. $1 + \cfrac{1}{1 + \cfrac{1}{2 + \frac{1}{3}}}$

2. It is possible to write any simple fraction as a continued fraction by simply reversing the process we discussed in this section. Here is an example.

$$\frac{5}{17} = \frac{1}{\frac{17}{5}} = \cfrac{1}{3 + \frac{2}{5}} = \cfrac{1}{3 + \cfrac{1}{\frac{5}{2}}} = \cfrac{1}{3 + \cfrac{1}{2 + \frac{1}{2}}}$$

   Write each of these simple fractions as a continued fraction. (*Hint:* A continued fraction terminates when a unit fraction occurs in one of the denominators.)

   a. $\frac{3}{7}$ b. $\frac{13}{30}$ c. $\frac{8}{13}$ d. $\frac{14}{3}$

4.4 Fractional Parts
What's My Number?

If $\frac{2}{3}$ of my number is 18, what's my number?

Many methods can be used to solve problems that involve fractional parts of whole numbers. One strategy that may be especially helpful for young children is drawing a diagram. Therefore, let's see how to approach this problem using a figure such as a rectangle to represent the unknown number.

Since the fraction in the problem is two *thirds*, separate the rectangle into three congruent parts. Each part represents one third of the number.

Now place the given information on the diagram, and add any conclusions you can draw from this information.

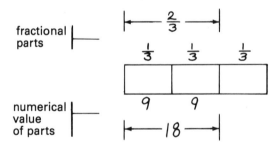

Since two congruent parts of the rectangle represent a total value of 18, do you see that each of these parts should be labeled with a value of 9? This means that the third congruent part must also have a value of 9, and therefore the value represented by the entire rectangle is $3 \times 9 = 27$.

Answer: If $\frac{2}{3}$ of a number is 18, the number must be 27.

Problems

1. What's my number?

   a. $\frac{3}{5}$ of my number is 21.

   b. $\frac{2}{7}$ of my number is 14.

   c. The product of $1\frac{1}{2}$ and my number is 12.

   d. If 56 is added to $\frac{1}{4}$ of my number, the result is the double of my number.

   e. If 6 is added to $2\frac{1}{2}$ times my number, the result is the triple of my number.

   f. If my number is multiplied by 4, the result is the same as adding 15 to $3\frac{1}{4}$ times my number.

2. Dave spent $\frac{3}{5}$ of his money and then had $12 left. How much money did Dave originally have?

3. Anne spent $\frac{1}{3}$ of her money and then lost $\frac{1}{2}$ of what she had left. She then had only 10¢. How much money did Anne originally have?

4. Insert two fractions between $\frac{1}{6}$ and $\frac{1}{5}$ so that the four fractions are in arithmetic sequence. (Recall that arithmetic sequences were discussed in Section 1.1.)

5. Insert three fractions between $\frac{1}{3}$ and $\frac{1}{2}$ so that the five fractions are in arithmetic sequence.

6. There is an old story that a certain farmer died, leaving 17 cows. According to the terms of the will, the farmer's eldest child was to receive $\frac{1}{2}$ of the cows, the second child was to receive $\frac{1}{3}$ of the cows, and the youngest child was to receive $\frac{1}{9}$ of the cows. The children were puzzled about how to carry out the terms of their father's will, since none of these fractional parts of 17 cows was a whole number. Finally, a generous neighbor offered to loan a cow to the children. They then had 18 cows: $\frac{1}{2}$ of 18 cows was 9 cows, $\frac{1}{3}$ of 18 cows was 6 cows, and $\frac{1}{9}$ of 18 cows was 2 cows. The total, $9 + 6 + 2$, was the original 17 cows. The 18th cow remained for the children to return to the neighbor with their thanks. How was this possible?

5 Geometry and Measurement

5.1 Squares and Rectangles
The Checkerboard Problem

How many squares are on a checkerboard?

Many people count just the small squares and answer 64. Others remember that the entire board is one large square and answer 65. In fact, there are more than 200 distinct squares! Where are all these other squares? How do we count them?

One way to solve a problem that may seem complicated is to consider one or more problems that are related, but simpler. Let's begin by imagining that there are simpler checkerboards and counting the squares on them.

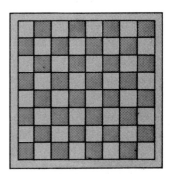

The figures below show a series of simpler checkerboards. Each board is a square, and each of the small boxes within the boards is also a square. Notice that we name the boards according to the lengths of their sides: a 1 by 1 board measures 1 square along each side, a 2 by 2 board measures 2 squares along each side, and so on.

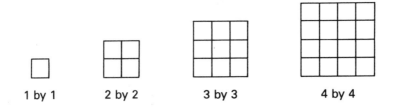

| 1 by 1 | 2 by 2 | 3 by 3 | 4 by 4 |

Clearly, there is only one square in the first figure. How many squares are in the second figure? No, not just four. We'll have to remember to count the large square. There are five squares in all.

Finding the number of squares on a 3 by 3 checkerboard may be more difficult. How many different *sizes* of squares are there? Do you see that there are three sizes: 1 by 1, 2 by 2, and 3 by 3? Now let's count the number of each of the different-sized squares and use a table to record the results.

Squares on a 3 by 3 Checkerboard	
Size of Square	**Number of Squares**
1 by 1	9
2 by 2	4
3 by 3	1
Total	14

Some people experience difficulty in counting the 2 by 2 squares. It may help to visualize these squares if we mask the board as shown below. In the classroom, this can be done very effectively by using translucent colored screens on an overhead projector.

Finding the number of squares on a 4 by 4 checkerboard is only slightly more complicated.

Squares on a 4 by 4 Checkerboard	
Size of Square	**Number of Squares**
1 by 1	16
2 by 2	9
3 by 3	4
4 by 4	1
Total	30

To visualize the nine 2 by 2 squares, we can again use a masking technique. You may find it helpful to focus your attention on two adjacent rows at a time, as shown below.

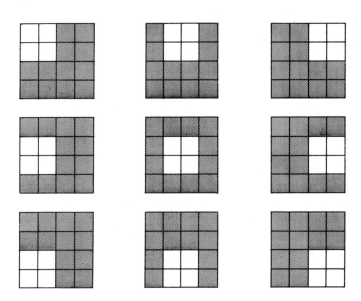

Similarly, to find the **four 3 by 3 squares** it may help you to look at *three* adjacent rows at a time.

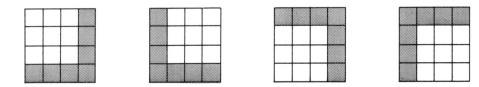

Now let's consider a 5 by 5 checkerboard. How many squares are on it? You could draw a picture and begin to count again, but this process could become time-consuming. When you reach a point such as this, it is sometimes helpful to organize and examine the facts you already know. Let's make a single table of all the data collected so far.

Squares on a Checkerboard				
	Type of Checkerboard			
Size of Square	1 by 1	2 by 2	3 by 3	4 by 4
1 by 1	1	4	9	16
2 by 2		1	4	9
3 by 2			1	4
4 by 4				1
Total	1	5	14	30

Within the structure of the table, a pattern begins to emerge. Do you see that certain numbers repeat along the diagonals of the table? Furthermore, observe that each of these numbers is a perfect-square number: $1 = 1^2$, $4 = 2^2$, $9 = 3^2$, and $16 = 4^2$. This suggests a second way to display the data, as shown in the table below. Notice that we were able to extend the pattern to learn without counting that there are 55 squares on a 5 by 5 checkerboard.

Squares on a Checkerboard					
	Type of Checkerboard				
Size of Square	1 by 1	2 by 2	3 by 3	4 by 4	5 by 5
1 by 1	1^2	2^2	3^2	4^2	5^2
2 by 2		1^2	2^2	3^2	4^2
3 by 3			1^2	2^2	3^2
4 by 4				1^2	2^2
5 by 5					1^2
Total	1	5	14	30	55

You can now use this pattern to solve the original checkerboard problem. A standard checkerboard is an 8 by 8 board. If the pattern in the table were extended, what would be the entries in the "8 by 8" column? Do you agree that the entries will be the squares of each of the whole numbers from 8 down to 1?

$$8^2 + 7^2 + 6^2 + 5^2 + 4^2 + 3^2 + 2^2 + 1^2 = 204$$

Answer: There are 204 squares on a checkerboard.

Problems

1. Suppose that you have a 6 by 6 checkerboard. How many squares of each of the following sizes are on it?

    a. 1 by 1   b. 2 by 2

    c. 3 by 3   d. 4 by 4

    e. 5 by 5   f. 6 by 6

2. What is the total number of squares on each of these checkerboards?

    a. 6 by 6   b. 7 by 7

    c. 9 by 9   d. 10 by 10

3. Each small box is a square. What is the total number of squares in each figure?

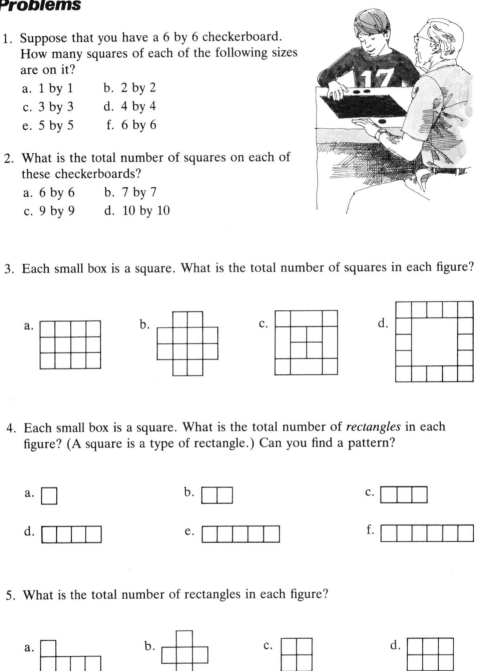

    a.   b.   c.   d.

4. Each small box is a square. What is the total number of *rectangles* in each figure? (A square is a type of rectangle.) Can you find a pattern?

    a.   b.   c.

    d.   e.   f.

5. What is the total number of rectangles in each figure?

    a.   b.   c.   d.

5.2 Triangles
The Triangle Tangle

How many triangles are in this picture?

After our discussion of the checkerboard problem in Section 5.1, you may immediately realize that the answer is not simply 6 or 7. The triangle tangle is similar to the checkerboard problem in many ways. However, the arrangement of the triangles suggests that a different method of counting may be appropriate to this situation.

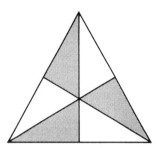

One counting device is that of using a different letter of the alphabet to identify each of the distinct parts formed by the lines of the figure. One way to do this is shown in the figure below, in which the parts have been lettered alphabetically. As we shall see, this system is helpful in organizing information and avoiding duplications.

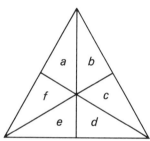

Clearly, each of the six parts we have identified by a letter is itself a triangle. Let's begin by calling these triangles 1-part triangles and listing them by letter: *a*, *b*, *c*, *d*, *e*, and *f*.

Using this device, other triangles in the figure may be described as 2-part triangles. Can you identify them? There are three, as shown below. We will name these triangles by combining the letters of the two parts that form them: *f–a*, *b–c*, and *d–e*.

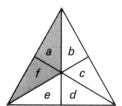
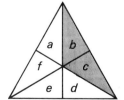
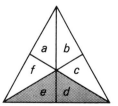

How many 3-part triangles are there? Can you name them? There are six: *a–b–c*, *b–c–d*, *c–d–e*, *d–e–f*, *e–f–a*, and *f–a–b*.

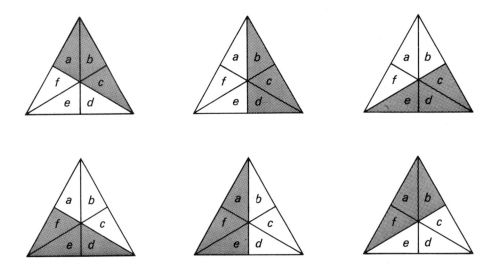

Can you see that there are no 4-part or 5-part triangles? However, the listing is not yet complete. Remember that the entire figure is a triangle, so that there is one 6-part triangle: *a–b–c–d–e–f*.

Notice that in all the listings the letters for the parts have been named in a clockwise order. This practice makes it easier to compare listings and to reduce the occurrence of repetitions.

Let's summarize by organizing all the data into one table.

Triangle Tangle	
Type of Triangle	**Number of Triangles**
1-part	6
2-part	3
3-part	6
6-part	1
Total	16

Answer: Altogether, there are 16 triangles in the tangle.

Problems

1. What is the total number of triangles in each figure? List them.

a.   b. 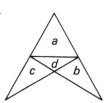   c.   d.

2. What is the total number of triangles in each figure? Can you find a pattern?

a.    b.    c.

d.    e.    f.

3. How do your answers to problem 2 above compare with your answers to problem 4 on page 120?

4. What is the total number of triangles in each figure?

a.   b.   c.   d.

5.3 Circles
Pieces of Pie

Can you cut a pie into seven pieces with just three straight cuts?

People frequently think that this problem is impossible. Do you? If you restrict yourself to the conventional way of cutting a pie, then it is indeed impossible. The most you can get is six pieces, as shown at the right.

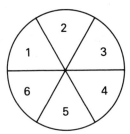

Sometimes we hinder our own problem solving efforts by making false assumptions. In this case, you may have incorrectly assumed that the pieces of pie must be equal in size. Notice that this is *not* a condition of the problem. Removing this unnecessary restriction opens a new line of thinking to us.

Let's look at the problem again. One way to cut the pie is to make three cuts independent of each other, with no cut intersecting any other. There are many ways to place these cuts, but as these placements show, they produce only four pieces of pie.

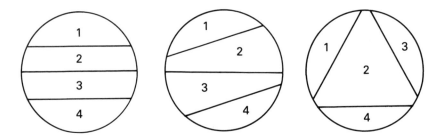

Therefore, to get seven pieces of pie the cuts cannot be independent. Let's see what happens if we place the cuts so that two of them intersect each other.

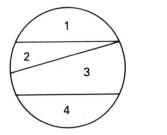
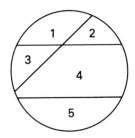

Notice that the cuts may intersect either at the edge of the pie or inside the pie. When the cuts intersect inside, more pieces are formed. When only two cuts intersect, though, the greatest number of pieces you can get is five. Thus it would seem that all three cuts must intersect each other if we are to get seven pieces.

Answer: When the three cuts intersect each other at three different points *inside* the pie, there are seven pieces of pie. The figure at the right shows one possible placement of the three cuts.

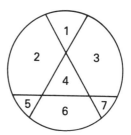

Problems

1. What is the greatest number of pieces of pie you can get with the given number of straight cuts?

   a. one   b. two   c. four   d. five

2. Complete the table using your answers to problem 1.

Number of Straight Cuts	Greatest Number of Pieces of Pie
0	1
1	?
2	?
3	7
4	?
5	?

3. Use the completed table from problem 2 to answer the questions.

   a. Subtract each number in the right-hand column from the number just below it. If your answers are correct, there is a pattern. What is it?

   b. What is the greatest number of pieces of pie you can get if you make eight straight cuts? Use the pattern to find the answer.

4. What is the greatest number of pieces of pie you can get if you make three straight cuts in a pie that is shaped like a *rectangle*?

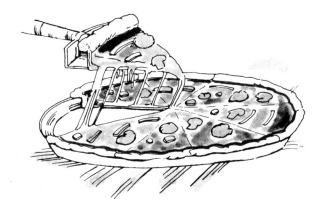

5. When two circles intersect, they may do so in either one or two points. If they intersect in only one point they form two regions. If they intersect in two points they form three regions.

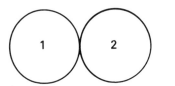
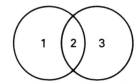

    a. What is the greatest number of regions formed when three circles intersect?

    b. Complete the table.

Number of Intersecting Circles	Greatest Number of Regions Formed
1	1
2	3
3	?
4	?
5	?

    c. What is the greatest number of regions formed when eight circles intersect?

6. Certain types of cheese are packaged in large "wheels" such as the one shown at the right. Show how to cut a wheel of cheese into eight *equal* pieces with just three straight cuts.

5.4 Perimeter
The Missing Dimension

To prepare an estimate for some work on a city lot, a builder asked the client for the dimensions of the lot.

"I can't remember," said the client. "It's shaped like a rectangle, and I know that they needed ninety meters of fencing to enclose it. Oh, yes! The crew putting up the fence remarked that the lot is exactly twice as long as it is wide."

"Thank you," said the builder. "That's all the information I need."

How did the builder know the dimensions? Can you find the length and width of the lot?

In solving a problem like this, it is important to identify the information that is essential. The core problem can in fact be stated in a *simpler* way.

The perimeter of a rectangle is ninety meters.
The length is twice the width.
Find the dimensions of the rectangle.

There are many ways to solve this problem. For example, you may use trial and error, somewhat like this.

The length is twice the width. Try a width of 10 and a length of 20.

Perimeter = 10 + 20 + 10 + 20
= 60

The first guess is too small. Try doubling the dimensions.

Perimeter = 20 + 40 + 20 + 40
= 120

The second guess is too large, but now we know that the width is between 10 and 20 and that the length is between 20 and 40. Try 15 and 30.

Perimeter = 15 + 30 + 15 + 30
= 90

It works!

Answer: The width of the lot is 15 m and the length is 30 m.

Another approach to this problem involves organizing a few trial values into a table and using the table to determine a pattern. Let's begin again with a width of 10 and a length of 20 and see what happens as the width is *gradually* increased.

width	10	11	12	13	. . .	?
length	20	22	24	26	. . .	?
Perimeter	60	66	72	78	. . .	90

Do you see that, each time the width is increased by 1, the length is increased by 2 and the perimeter is increased by 6? To arrive at a perimeter of 90, you would continue the pattern by making five increases of 6 over 60, the first perimeter in the table. This means that you would also have to increase the width five times by 1 and increase the length five times by 2. This leads to a width of $10 + 5 \times 1 = 15$ and a length of $20 + 5 \times 2 = 30$.

The use of trial and error or a table puts this type of problem within the grasp of even very young children. There is another method of solution that involves the use of some simple algebra.

Choose w to show the width. The length is twice the width, so 2w shows the length. Now you can write and solve an equation.

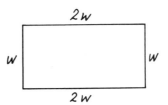

$$w + 2w + w + 2w = 90$$
$$6w = 90$$
$$\frac{6w}{6} = \frac{90}{6}$$
$$w = 15$$

Since w = 15, 2w = 30. The width is 15 m and the length is 30 m.

We have discussed three ways to approach the solution of this problem. As you read on, you may notice that some methods help to solve a problem more efficiently than others. It is important to realize, though, that the method appropriate for you is the one that you best understand and that leads you successfully to the solution.

Problems

1. The perimeter of a rectangular plot of land is forty-two meters. What are the dimensions of the plot given each of the following conditions?
   a. The length is twice the width.
   b. The length is three meters more than the width.
   c. The length is three meters less than twice the width.
   d. The width is one fifth the length.

2. Assume that the length and width of a rectangle are restricted to whole-number measures.
   a. How many rectangles of different shape have a perimeter of 10? 12? 14? 16? 24?
   b. State a rule for finding the number of rectangles of different shape that have a given perimeter.
   c. Is it possible for the perimeter to have an odd-number measure? Why or why not?

3. Assume that the sides of a *triangle* are restricted to whole-number measures. How many different triangles are there that have a perimeter of 10?

4. Each of the small boxes in these figures is a square. All the squares are the same size. If the perimeter of the figure at the right is 30, what is the perimeter of each figure below?

a. 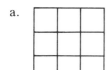   b. 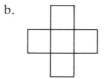   c. 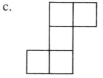   d.

5. *PQRS* is a square. Imagine that it can be folded.
   a. *P* is folded onto *Q*. Then *Q* is folded onto *R*. If the perimeter of *PQRS* is 1, what is the perimeter of the new figure?
   b. *Q* is folded onto *R* to form a figure with a perimeter of 24. What is the perimeter of *PQRS*?
   c. *Q* is folded onto the midpoint of side *QR*. The perimeter of the smaller figure formed is 15. What is the perimeter of *PQRS*?

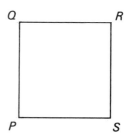

5.5 Circumference
"Circular" Reasoning

Suppose that you just completed a nonstop bicycle trip of 5.5 km. You know that each wheel of your bicycle has a radius of 35 cm. How many times did each wheel turn during this trip?

Often a problem may seem complex, yet you discover that there is a relatively simple problem at its core. In this instance, the key question is: how far does each wheel travel in just one turn? Let's draw a picture of the progress of a wheel through one turn to see how you might determine this distance.

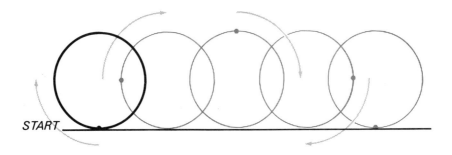

The starting position of the wheel in this picture is at the left, and here the point of the wheel that is touching the ground has been marked. The wheel is then drawn turning toward the right. When the marked point again touches the ground, you can see that the wheel has traveled a distance equal to its perimeter.

The special name for the perimeter of a circle is the **circumference.** Recall that the formula used to calculate circumference is $C = 2\pi r$, where π is a number approximately equal to $\frac{22}{7}$ or 3.14 and r is the length of the radius of the circle. To find the circumference of a wheel of your bicycle, substitute $\frac{22}{7}$ for π and 35 for r. Then $C \approx 2 \times \frac{22}{7} \times 35$, which is 220. Therefore, each wheel travels approximately 220 cm in just one turn.

To find how many times each wheel turned in the entire trip of 5.5 km, you now need only to calculate how many 220-cm lengths there are in 5.5 km.

Before you proceed, note that one measure is named in centimeters and the other is named in kilometers. The numbers involved should be rewritten so that each of them names the same type of unit. There are usually different ways to do this. In this problem, one way is to rename the 5.5 km as 550,000 cm.

To find the number of 220-cm lengths in 550,000 cm, perform the division $220\overline{)550,000}$. The quotient is 2500.

Answer: Each wheel of your bicycle turned approximately 2500 times.

Problems

1. Suppose that each wheel of your car has a radius of 42 cm.
   a. How far does each wheel travel in just one turn?
   b. How many turns does each wheel make in a nonstop 5.5-km trip?

2. One wheel of a tractor turns 240 times in a one-mile trip. What is its radius?

3. A racetrack is in the shape of a 70- by 100-yd rectangle with a semicircle attached to each of the 70-yd sides. What is the distance around the track?

4. Gears A, B, and C rotate on fixed axes, and they form the gear train shown at the right. Gear A has 40 teeth, Gear B has 20 teeth, and Gear C has 30 teeth.

   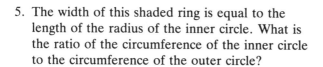

   a. If Gear A turns in a clockwise direction, in which direction does Gear B turn?
   b. If Gear A turns in a clockwise direction, in which direction does Gear C turn?
   c. If Gear A makes 3 complete turns, how many complete turns does Gear B make?
   d. If Gear A makes 3 complete turns, how many complete turns does Gear C make?

5. The width of this shaded ring is equal to the length of the radius of the inner circle. What is the ratio of the circumference of the inner circle to the circumference of the outer circle?

6. The hour hand of a certain clock is 4 in. long and the minute hand is 6 in. long. How far does the tip of each hand travel in a 24-hour period?

7. The figure at the right shows a crate being moved along the ground by rolling it on cylinders. If the circumference of each cylinder is 75 cm, how far does the crate move for each complete turn of the cylinders?

   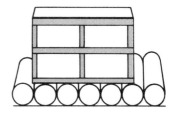

5.6 Area of Rectangles and Squares
Garden Variety

Suppose that you bought a carton of thirty-six one-foot sections of decorative garden fencing to enclose a rectangular flower garden. What is the largest garden you can enclose with the fencing that you bought?

Before attempting to solve this problem, you may again find it helpful to identify the essential information and to use it to state a simpler problem. To do this, you need to understand that the fencing represents the *perimeter* of a rectangle and that the size of your garden is associated with the *area* of that rectangle.

The perimeter of a rectangle is thirty-six feet.
Find the greatest area that the rectangle can have.

Recall that the area formula for a rectangle is *Area = length × width*, or $A = l \times w$. The diagram below helps us realize that the sum of a single length and width is half the perimeter, or 18. Furthermore, the length and width are restricted to whole-number measures because the fencing is made in one-foot sections. Therefore, you only need to consider pairs of whole numbers whose sum is 18.

$$\ell$$
$$w \boxed{\ell \times w = ?} w$$
$$\ell$$

$$\ell + \ell + w + w = 36$$
$$\ell + w = 18$$

Since the number of possible lengths and widths is limited, an effective strategy to use is organized listing. Let's make a table of the possible lengths, widths, and corresponding areas.

length	17	16	15	14	13	12	11	10	9
width	1	2	3	4	5	6	7	8	9
Area	17	32	45	56	65	72	77	80	81

Answer: The largest rectangular garden you can make has the shape of a square whose sides each measure 9 ft. Its area is 81 ft².

Problems

1. A certain brand of garden fencing is sold in cartons of twenty-four one-foot sections.

   a. What is the area of the largest rectangular garden you can enclose if you buy one carton of the fencing? two cartons? three cartons?

   b. State a rule for finding the area of the largest rectangular garden you can enclose with a given number of cartons of this fencing.

   c. What is the least number of cartons of this fencing that you need to buy if you want to enclose a rectangular garden of exactly 32 ft²? 128 ft²?

2. The surface of a swimming pool is rectangular in shape and measures 12 m by 20 m. A concrete walk 2 m wide is to be built around the surface of the pool. What will be the surface area of the walk?

3. Find the area of the floor in each floor plan. All angles are right angles.

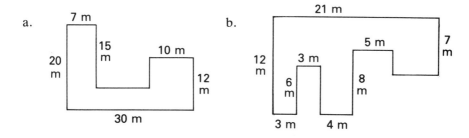

4. How many square feet of plywood will be needed to build an open-top bin if it is to be 3 ft wide, 5 ft long, and 2 ft high?

5. *PQRS* is a square. Imagine that it can be folded.

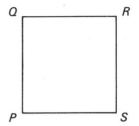

   a. *P* is folded onto *Q*. Then *Q* is folded onto *R*. If the area of *PQRS* is 1, what is the area of the new figure?
   b. *P* is folded onto the midpoint of side *PQ*. If the area of *PQRS* is 16, what is the area of the new figure?
   c. *Q* is folded onto *R*. If the perimeter of the new figure is 24, what is the area of *PQRS*?

6. Concrete walks, 3 ft wide, are constructed diagonally across a square lawn as shown at the right. What is the total lawn area that remains, as represented by the shaded region?

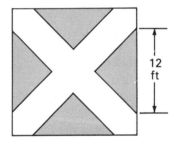

7. *ABCD* is a square with sides that measure 2. *E*, *F*, *G*, and *H* are the midpoints of the sides. What is the area of *EFGH*?

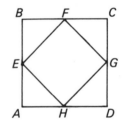

8. The area and perimeter of a square are numerically equal. What is the length of a side of the square?

9. If you double the measure of each side of a square, do you double the area of the square, also?

10. The figure at the right shows a square separated into the seven pieces of an ancient puzzle called the **tangram**. If the area of the entire square is one square unit, what is the area of each of the seven tangram pieces?

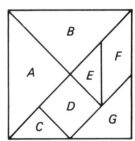

5.7 *Area of Circles*
Tin Pan Tally

To make a baking pan, a tinsmith is planning to cut the largest possible circular disk from a square sheet of tin that measures 30 cm on each side. What will be the area of the leftover scraps of tin?

This is an example of a problem whose solution has a number of smaller problems embedded within it. In this case, it may help you to identify these problems if you begin by drawing a picture such as the one at the right. Looking at the picture, can you see that these are the questions that need to be answered?

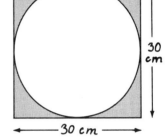

– What is the area of the entire sheet of tin?
– What is the area of the circular disk?
– What is the area of the leftover scraps of tin?

Let's answer these questions one by one.

What is the area of the entire sheet of tin? Apply the area formula for a square.

$$\text{Area of Square} = \text{side} \times \text{side}$$
$$= 30 \text{ cm} \times 30 \text{ cm} = 900 \text{ cm}^2$$

What is the area of the circular disk? From the picture above, you can see that the diameter of the largest disk possible has the same length as a side of the square sheet of tin. This means that the diameter of the circle measures 30 cm and its radius measures 15 cm. To approximate the area of the circular disk, remember that you can substitute 3.14 or $3\frac{1}{7}$ for π in the area formula.

$$\text{Area of Circle} = \pi \times r^2$$
$$\approx 3.14 \times (15 \text{ cm})^2$$
$$\approx 3.14 \times 225 \text{ cm}^2 \approx 706.5 \text{ cm}^2$$

What is the area of the leftover scraps of tin? Use subtraction to parallel the physical process of cutting the circular disk from the square sheet of tin.

$$\text{Area of Scraps} = \text{Area of Square} - \text{Area of Circle}$$
$$\approx 900 \text{ cm}^2 - 706.5 \text{ cm}^2$$
$$\approx 193.5 \text{ cm}^2$$

Answer: There will be approximately 193.5 cm² of tin left over.

Problems

1. The figure at the right shows a plan for cutting a piece of tin shaped like part of a circle from a square sheet of tin that measures 30 cm on each side. What will be the area of the leftover scraps of tin?

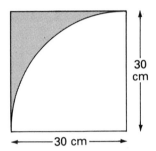

30 cm

30 cm

2. A certain rectangular sheet of tin measures 4 ft by 8 ft.

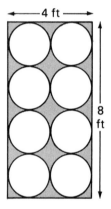

4 ft

8 ft

   a. Suppose that a tinsmith cuts eight circular disks from the sheet as shown in the figure at the right. What will be the area of the leftover scraps of tin?

   b. What is the greatest possible number of circular disks that could be cut from this sheet if each disk must have a 1-ft diameter? 2-ft radius? 6-in. diameter? 8-in. radius?

   c. For each size of circular disk in part **b**, what would be the area of the leftover scraps of tin after the greatest possible number of circular disks was cut?

3. Suppose that you have a square piece of paper. You draw the largest possible circle, cut it out, and discard the leftover scraps of paper. Inside the circle you draw the largest possible square, cut it out, and discard the leftover scraps of paper. How much of the original square have you discarded in all?

4. A Norman window is shaped like a rectangle that is surmounted by a semicircle. What is the area in square centimeters of a Norman window with the dimensions shown at the right?

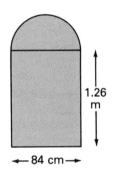

1.26 m

84 cm

5. The figure at the right is formed by two circles with a common center. The diameter of the inner circle is 10 units, and the width of the shaded ring is also 10 units. What is the area of the shaded ring?

6. The inner boundary of a racetrack is formed by two opposite sides of a 400-yd square joined by two semicircles, as shown in the figure at the right. What is the area of the shaded region?

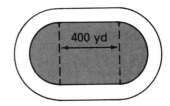

7. In the figure at the right, segment *AB* is the diameter of the large circle. Points *X* and *Y* are the centers of the small circles. What is the ratio of the area of the shaded region to the area of the large circle?

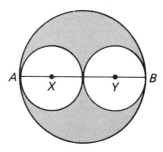

8. A square barn measures 42 ft on each side. A goat is tethered outside by a rope that is attached to one corner of the barn, as shown in the sketch at the right.

   a. Suppose that the length of the rope is 28 ft. On how many square feet of land is the goat able to graze?

   b. Suppose that the rope is made twice as long as in part **a.** On how many square feet of land is the goat now able to graze?

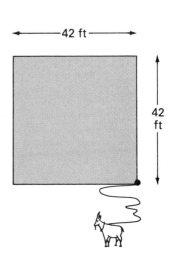

9. A goat is tethered to the outside corner of a barn as in problem 8, but this barn is rectangular in shape and measures 28 ft by 21 ft. If the length of the rope is 35 ft, on how many square feet of land is this goat able to graze?

5.8 Geometric Patterns
Tromino Theory

Just about everyone knows what a domino shape looks like. It's basically a plane figure formed by two congruent squares that share a common side. As you can see, there are many ways that a domino can be positioned, but the basic pattern remains the same. There is only one *type* of domino.

When *three* congruent squares share common sides, the resulting figure is called a **tromino.** How many different types of tromino are there?

A problem that involves the manipulation of shapes is often best approached by some simple experimenting. In this case, a good way for you to find all the trominoes may be to physically move three squares on a flat surface. Use pattern blocks if they're handy, or simply cut the squares out of paper.

As you manipulate the squares, you will probably realize that there are literally dozens of ways to arrange them. However, you will notice that most of the arrangements do not fulfill the conditions of our problem. In patterns like these, for example, the squares do not share common sides; they only share single points or *parts* of their sides.

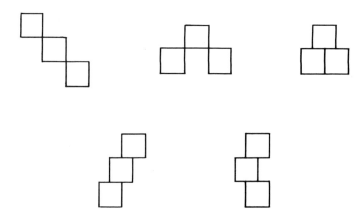

There is an arrangement that is most obviously a tromino. When the three squares are joined together end-to-end, we see a tromino pattern that is very similar to the familiar domino. Again, there are many ways that this tromino can be positioned, but they do not change the shape of the tromino.

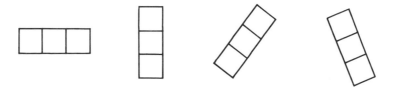

Can you find a second type of tromino? Did you discover that the only other way to fulfill the requirements is to arrange the squares into an L-shape? Your pattern may be positioned in many ways, but these are all positions of the same L-shaped tromino.

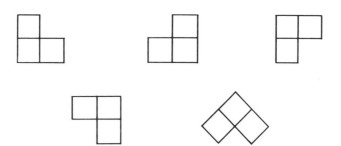

Answer: There are only two types of tromino: the end-to-end shape and the L-shape.

Problems

1. A **tetromino** is formed by *four* congruent squares that share common sides.
   a. How many different types of tetromino are there? Sketch them.
   b. Which tetromino has the least perimeter?

2. Suppose that the squares in our dominoes, trominoes, and tetrominoes are replaced by congruent equilateral triangles. How many different types of each are there? Sketch them.
   a. triangle-dominoes
   b. triangle-trominoes
   c. triangle-tetrominoes

3. In the trapezoid below, each of the three short sides has the same length, and the longest side is exactly twice as long as a short side. How many trapezoid-dominoes can you make with this figure? Sketch them.

4. A **pentomino** is formed by five congruent squares that share common sides.
   a. There are twelve different types of pentomino. Sketch them.
   b. Which of the pentomino patterns could be folded to make a box with an open top?
   c. Draw the twelve pentominoes on graph paper and cut them out. Using the pentominoes like pieces of a jigsaw puzzle, assemble them into a 6 by 10 rectangle.

5. Suppose that the nine small squares of a 3 by 3 tick-tack-toe grid are each congruent to the individual squares of a set of dominoes. Can the grid be covered completely by placing a whole number of dominoes on it with no overlapping?

6. Suppose that the sixty-four small squares of an 8 by 8 checkerboard are each congruent to the individual squares of a set of dominoes. Two squares are removed from diagonally opposite corners of the checkerboard. Can the remaining board be covered completely by placing a whole number of dominoes on it with no overlapping?

   A listing of geometric formulas is provided as a reference in Appendix 4 at the back of the book.

6 | Trains, Books, Clocks, and Things

6.1 Motion Problems
Trains of Thought

Two trains leave from the same station at the same time, but they are moving in opposite directions. One train averages 56 mi/h and the other averages 64 mi/h. How far apart will the trains be at the end of three hours? How much time will it take for the trains to be 600 mi apart?

A problem such as this is called a **motion problem** because it concerns the behavior of one or more moving objects. In solving a motion problem you generally need to consider three items: the *rate* at which each object is moving, the *time* interval during which each object moves, and the *distance* that each object moves. The relationship among these three items is summarized by this formula.

$$\text{Distance} = \text{rate} \times \text{time}$$
$$D = r \times t$$

For the given problem, let's start by considering a simpler problem: how far apart will the trains be at the end of just one hour? To answer this question you may find it helpful to draw a diagram of the situation, somewhat like this one.

Station

Train 1	Train 2
56 mi	64 mi

Can you see that at the end of one hour the distance between the trains will be $56 + 64 = 120$ mi? Therefore, the two trains are separating at the rate of 120 mi each hour.

Answer: At the end of three hours, the distance between the trains will be $3 \times 120 = 360$ mi.

For the trains to be 600 mi apart, the amount of time needed will be $600 \div 120 = 5$ h.

Suppose that the two trains described in our problem start from the same station at the same time and move in the *same* direction along parallel tracks. How far apart will the trains be at the end of three hours? How much time will it take for the trains to be 80 mi apart?

As before, let's approach this problem by considering how far apart the trains will be at the end of one hour. A diagram may again prove to be helpful.

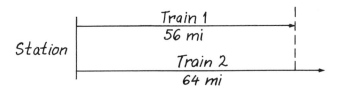

This time, do you see that the distance between the trains at the end of one hour will be 64 − 56 = 8 mi? Although they are moving in the same direction, the trains are separating at the rate of 8 mi each hour.

Answer: At the end of three hours, the distance between the two trains moving in the same direction will be 3 × 8 = 24 mi.

For the two trains to be 80 mi apart, the amount of time needed will be 80 ÷ 8 = 10 h.

These train problems are examples of two basic principles of motion.

When two objects move from the same point at the same time, but in opposite directions, they separate from each other at a rate equal to the *sum* of their two individual rates.

When two objects move from the same point at the same time and in the same direction, they separate from each other at a rate equal to the *difference* of their two individual rates.

Problems

1. Two trains leave from the same station at the same time, moving in opposite directions. One train averages 95 km/h and the other averages 105 km/h.
   a. How far apart will the trains be at the end of $2\frac{1}{2}$ h?
   b. How much time will it take for the trains to be 350 km apart?

2. Two trains leave from the same station at 10:00 A.M. and move in the same direction along parallel tracks. One train averages 72 km/h and the other averages 108 km/h.
   a. How far apart will the trains be at 1:05 P.M. of the same day?
   b. At what time will the trains be 270 km apart?

3. Riding their bicycles, Helen and Kenji leave from two different places at the same time and ride directly toward each other. Helen rides at 6 mi/h and Kenji rides at 8 mi/h. If they meet in $\frac{1}{2}$ h, how far apart were they when they started?

4. A man left his home and drove along a certain road at 48 km/h. One hour later his son left the same home and drove along the same road in the same direction at 72 km/h. In how many hours will the son overtake his father?

5. Lisa can row a boat at the rate of 3 mi/h in still water. However, the river in which she is rowing has a current that flows at the rate of 1 mi/h. Lisa rows 8 mi downstream, then turns and rows back upstream to her starting point. How much time does her entire trip take?

6. A passenger train and a freight train leave at the same time from stations that are 270 km apart. The trains are traveling toward each other, and the rate of the passenger train is twice the rate of the freight train. If the trains pass each other in three hours, what is the rate of each train?

7. A train that is 1 km long is traveling at 30 km/h. If the train enters a tunnel that is 1 km long, how much time will it take the train to clear the tunnel?

8. A passenger train traveling at 40 mi/h passes a freight train traveling in the opposite direction at 20 mi/h. Leo, riding on the passenger train, notes that the freight train passes him in 15 seconds. What is the length of the freight train?

9. Two passenger trains traveling in opposite directions meet and pass each other. Each train is $\frac{1}{12}$ mi long and is traveling at 50 mi/h. How many seconds after the front parts of the trains meet will their rear parts pass each other?

10. Two trains leave at the same time from stations that are 60 km apart. The trains travel toward each other, one at 55 km/h and the other at 65 km/h. At the same time, a bee flying at a constant rate of 80 km/h starts at the front of one train, flies to the front of the other train, immediately turns and flies back to the front of the first train, and so on. When the two trains meet, what is the total distance that the bee will have flown?

6.2 Book Problems
A Pressing Problem

Suppose that a printer is using an old-style printing press and needs one piece of type for each digit in the page numbers of a book. How many pieces of type will the printer need to number pages from 1 through 250?

One way to solve this problem is to consider the structure of the counting numbers assigned to the pages of the book. Here is how you might proceed.

How many one-digit page numbers are there? There are 9, of course, since the first pages would be assigned counting numbers 1 through 9. For these, 9 pieces of type will be necessary.

How many two-digit page numbers are there? These consist of the 90 two-digit counting numbers from 10 through 99. The printer will need $90 \times 2 = 180$ pieces of type for these.

How many three-digit page numbers are there? The page numbers to be considered begin at 100 and go through 250. Notice that there are 151 pages in this set. Therefore, $151 \times 3 = 453$ pieces of type will be needed for these page numbers.

Answer: For page numbers 1 through 250, the printer will need
$9 + 180 + 453 = 642$ pieces of type.

Now let's consider an extension of this problem. Using one piece of type for each digit, how many 2s will the printer need in printing page numbers from 1 through 250?

You may find it helpful to once again focus on the structure of the counting numbers. This time, though, we'll consider the numbers place-by-place.

How many times will the digit 2 appear in the ones' place? This occurs once in every group of 10 consecutive counting numbers. For page numbers 1 through 250 there are 25 such groups, so 2 appears in the ones' place 25 times.

$$2, 12, 22, 32, 42, \ldots, 242$$

How many times will the digit 2 appear in the tens' place? This happens 10 times in every group of 100 consecutive counting numbers. For pages numbered 1 through 250, this is 30 times.

$$20, \; 21, \; 22, \; 23, \; 24, \ldots, \; 29$$
$$120, 121, 122, 123, 124, \ldots, 129$$
$$220, 221, 222, 223, 224, \ldots, 229$$

How many times will the digit 2 appear in the hundreds' place? This occurs in each of the last 51 numbers.

$$200, 201, 202, 203, 204, \ldots, 250$$

Answer: The total number of 2s that the printer will need is
$$25 + 30 + 51 = 106.$$

Problems

1. Suppose that a printer is using an old-style printing press and needs one piece of type for each digit in the page numbers of a book. A certain book contains pages numbered from 1 to 375.

   a. What is the total number of pieces of type that the printer will need to print these page numbers?

   b. How many 3s will the printer need?

   c. How many 4s will the printer need?

   d. How many 8s will the printer need?

2. Suppose that the printer uses a total of 402 pieces of type in numbering the pages of a certain book. If the first page number is 1, how many numbered pages does this book contain?

3. A book is opened, and the product of the two page numbers that appear is 1190. What are the two page numbers?

4. One section of a certain book contains six pages. The sum of all the page numbers in this section is 513. What are the page numbers?

6.3 Work Problems
On the Job

Working alone, Dan can do a certain job in three hours and Stan can do the same job in two hours. How long would it take Dan and Stan to do this job working together?

Problems such as the one above are often referred to as **work problems.** Since work problems can be associated with fractional parts, let's approach this problem by drawing a diagram, which was the strategy that we applied to fractional parts problems in Section 4.4. In this case, we choose a rectangle to represent the entire job and draw two rectangles—one for Dan and one for Stan.

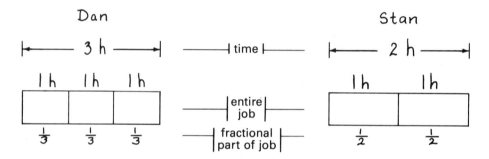

When we use the diagram to interpret the given information, we observe that Dan can do $\frac{1}{3}$ of the job in one hour and Stan can do $\frac{1}{2}$ of the job in one hour. If they work together they can do $\frac{1}{2} + \frac{1}{3} = \frac{5}{6}$ of the job in one hour.

We now know how long it would take Dan and Stan together to do $\frac{5}{6}$ of the job. We still need to determine how long it would take them to do the *entire* job. At this point, let's draw a new diagram that represents their *combined* work.

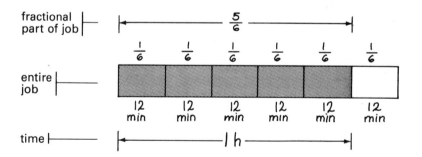

As you can see from the diagram, since $\frac{5}{6}$ of the job requires one hour, $\frac{1}{6}$ of the job requires $\frac{1}{5}$ of one hour. This is twelve minutes. Therefore, the additional $\frac{1}{6}$ of the job requires an additional twelve minutes.

Answer: Dan and Stan together can do the job in one hour and twelve minutes, which is equal to seventy-two minutes.

For a different job, Dan is able to work at the same rate as Stan. Together they can complete this job in six days. Suppose that they are joined by Fran, who can also work at the same rate. How long would it take Dan, Stan, and Fran together to do this job?

Notice that each of the individuals involved in this problem works at the same rate. Although we could again use a diagram to solve the problem, let's see how a different strategy might be used.

Consider a simpler question: how long would it take any one of these people working *alone* to do this job? Since we know that two people working together require six days, it follows that one person working alone would need twice as much time, or twelve days.

Now consider another question: how much of the job can any one of these people working alone do in just one day? Since one person can do the job in twelve days, that person alone can do one *twelfth* of the job in one day. Therefore, three people working together can do *three* twelfths of the job in one day. This is equal to one fourth of the job. If one fourth of the job is done each day, it will take four days to complete the job.

Answer: Dan, Stan, and Fran together can do the job in four days.

Problems

1. Working alone, an adult requires three hours to do a certain job. A child working alone requires seven hours to do the same job. How long will it take the adult and child working together to do this job?

2. An old-model machine can stamp 1000 parts in four hours. A new-model machine can stamp 1000 parts in just two hours. How long will it take one old-model and one new-model machine to stamp 1000 parts working together?

3. Laura needs three days to do a certain job, Eric needs four days to do the same job, and Connie also needs four days to do the job. How long will it take Laura, Eric, and Connie working together to do this job?

4. It takes three minutes to fill a tub to the top and four minutes to drain the full tub. If the faucet and drain are both open, how long will it take to fill the tub?

5. It takes nine days for eight workers to pave a stretch of road. If each worker works at the same rate as each of the others, how long will it take twelve workers to pave the same stretch of road?

6. A group of six scouts purchases rations sufficient for a fifteen-day camping trip. If three more scouts join the group but no additional rations are purchased, how many days will the rations last?

7. Four duplicating machines together require six minutes to make a certain number of copies. Each machine has the same capability. If one of the machines becomes inoperative, how long will it take the remaining machines to make the same number of copies?

8. A company payroll is prepared by two computers in $13\frac{1}{3}$ min. Working alone, the faster of the two computers can prepare the payroll in 20 min. How much time does the slower computer alone require to prepare the payroll?

6.4 *Clock Problems*
As Time Goes By

A certain clock gains one minute of time every hour. If the clock shows the correct time now, when will it show the correct time again?

This type of clock problem concerns **elapsed time,** which is the amount of time that passes between two events. Elapsed time problems sometimes seem complicated, but they often can be solved by reasoning with familiar facts about time.

Here is one way to regard this problem. We know that a clock keeping time properly *always* shows the correct time. Therefore, let's consider an extreme: what about a clock that has stopped and is not keeping time at all? This clock, of course, shows the correct time only once in every twelve-hour interval.

The clock in our problem must then gain the *equivalent* of twelve hours before it once again shows the correct time. How much actual time will this take? Twelve hours contain $12 \times 60 = 720$ min. Since the clock gains one minute in one hour, it will gain 720 min in 720 h.

Answer: The clock will again show the correct time in 720 h, which is thirty days.

A different type of clock problem involves the positions of the hands of a clock in relation to each other. Here is an example.

How many times during the day do the hands of a clock coincide? (Assume that the clock is keeping time properly.)

Recall that the minute hand is moving faster than the hour hand, and each time the minute hand passes over thé hour hand they will coincide. How frequently does this happen?

If you have a watch or clock available, you may wish to experiment. Does it seem that the hour hand passes the minute hand once each hour? Be careful. Note that this is true for every hour *except* the eleventh hour, during which the hour hand does not pass the minute hand at all.

Answer: The hour hand and the minute hand of a clock coincide 11 times in each twelve-hour interval, or 22 times each day.

Problems

1. Suppose that a clock shows the correct time now. Under each of the following conditions, when will it show the correct time again?
   a. It gains three minutes every hour.
   b. It loses two minutes every hour.
   c. It gains two seconds every three hours.

2. At which *hours* do the hands of a clock form an angle that measures 60°?

3. How many times each day do the hands of a clock satisfy each of the following conditions?
   a. They lie directly opposite each other.
   b. They are perpendicular to each other.

4. Larry's clock has sixty marks that identify the sixty minutes of the hour. At a certain time Larry noticed that the hour hand pointed exactly to one of these marks while the minute hand pointed exactly to the mark beside it. What time was it?

5. One afternoon Maria observed that the time that had elapsed since noon was equal to half the time that remained until midnight. What time was it?

6. A certain digital clock constantly displays the digits for the hour and the minute. During how many minutes of the day is there at least one 2 in the display of this clock? (Assume that the clock is keeping time properly.)

7. A certain clock loses six minutes every hour. One day this clock is set to the correct time at 10:30 A.M. What will be the correct time when the clock first shows 12:00 on that same day?

6.5 Related Problems
Handshakes

Five people are introduced to each other, and each person shakes hands with each of the others exactly once. How many handshakes are exchanged altogether?

Where should you begin a problem like this? Try considering the simplest handshake problem of all: how many handshakes are exchanged when only two people are introduced? The answer, of course, is just one. Let's represent the people by A and B and use this notation to represent their handshake.

$$A, B$$

Suppose now that A and B are joined by a third person, C. Persons A and B already exchanged a handshake with each other, so only two new handshakes are necessary: A must shake hands with C and B must shake hands with C. A total of three handshakes have been exchanged. Let's make an organized list of these handshakes. We'll also make a table to record the totals, using n to represent the number of people and h to represent the number of handshakes.

$A,B \qquad A,C$

B,C

n	h	
2	1	$\Big) +2$
3	3	

What happens if a fourth person, D, joins the group? Do you see that three new handshakes are necesssary? Pause to list and record them all according to the scheme established above. Did you arrive at this list of six?

$A,B \qquad A,C \qquad A,D$

$B,C \qquad B,D$

C,D

n	h	
2	1	$\Big) +2$
3	3	
4	6	$\Big) +3$

Do you see that a pattern is emerging in the listing and in the table? How many handshakes will be added to the total if a fifth person joins this group? Each of the four people already in the group will have to shake hands with the new person, and so four handshakes will be added to the previous total of six. If we represent the fifth person by E, all ten handshakes can be listed as follows.

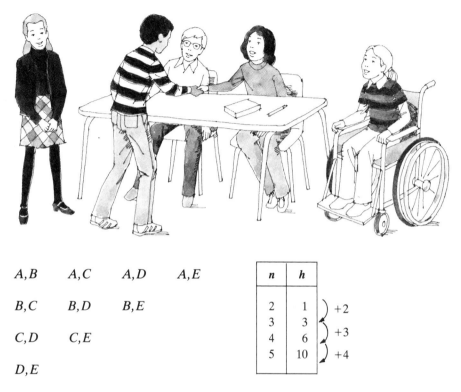

n	h
2	1
3	3
4	6
5	10

$\big)$ +2
$\big\}$ +3
$\big)$ +4

A,B A,C A,D A,E

B,C B,D B,E

C,D C,E

D,E

Answer: When five people are introduced to each other, a total of ten handshakes are exchanged in all.

Young children may enjoy solving this problem by acting out the procedure that we have just discussed.

One interesting aspect of the handshake problem is the variety of ways that it can be approached. For example, another way to make an organized list of all the handshakes is to make a tree diagram that focuses on the handshakes from the viewpoint of each of the five individuals.

Using this method of listing, it would seem that there is a total of $5 \times 4 = 20$ handshakes. However, notice that each handshake has been counted twice: a handshake between B and A is the same as a handshake between A and B; a handshake between C and A is the same as a handshake between A and C; and so on. Since each handshake is listed two times, the number of *distinct* handshakes is $20 \div 2 = 10$, which is the same as our previous conclusion.

Now consider a different problem: how many segments can be drawn connecting five points, no three of which lie on the same line?

Let's make a diagram showing five points that meet the conditions of the problem. We'll label the points *A*, *B*, *C*, *D*, and *E*. As shown below, you can then draw all the segments by connecting each pair of points.

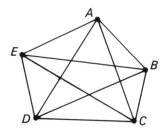

How many segments are there? Do you see that there are ten in all? To verify this, we can make an organized list.

$$\overline{AB} \qquad \overline{AC} \qquad \overline{AD} \qquad \overline{AE}$$

$$\overline{BC} \qquad \overline{BD} \qquad \overline{BE}$$

$$\overline{CD} \qquad \overline{CE}$$

$$\overline{DE}$$

We can also use the reasoning we employed with the tree diagram of the handshakes.

There are 5 points, and each one of the points is connected to the other 4 points. Thus there appear to be 5 × 4 = 20 segments. However, in this set of 20 segments, each segment has been counted twice. For example, $\overline{AB}$ and $\overline{BA}$ are the same segment, $\overline{AC}$ and $\overline{CA}$ are the same segment, and so on. Therefore, there are 20 ÷ 2 = 10 distinct segments.

Answer: Given five points, no three of which lie on the same line, ten segments can be drawn connecting them.

Looking back, does the list of ten segments seem familiar? It appears to be almost a duplicate of the list of handshakes exchanged by five people. Instead of handshakes that "connect" people, this problem involves segments that connect points. In each problem the total is the same: ten "connections." Though the two problems may seem very different, they are related because they are both instances of the same mathematical model.

Problems

1. Six people are introduced to each other, and each person shakes hands with each of the others exactly once. How many handshakes are exchanged altogether?

2. Using *A*, *B*, *C*, *D*, *E*, and *F* to represent six people, draw a tree diagram to verify your answer to problem 1.

3. Complete the following table.

Number of People	Number of Handshakes
2	1
3	?
4	?
5	10
6	?
7	?
8	?

4. In the completed table for problem 3, the entries in the "Number of Handshakes" column should form a familiar number pattern. Extend this pattern to determine the number of handshakes that would be exchanged by ten people.

5. Each person in a certain group of people shakes hands with each of the others exactly once, and 120 handshakes are exchanged altogether. How many people are in this group?

6. Twenty chess players hold a tournament in which each player plays just one game with each of the other players. How many games are played altogether?

7. How many segments can be drawn connecting each of the following numbers of points, if no three of the points lie on the same straight line?
   a. 6   b. 7   c. 8   d. 10

8. How many different segments can be named in this figure, using the labeled points as endpoints? List the segments.

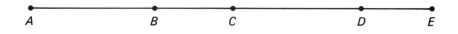

9. The figure below shows a ten-sided polygon, which is called a **decagon**. How many diagonals can be drawn in it?

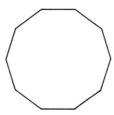

10. How many different rectangles are in each of the following figures? (All angles are right angles.)

a. 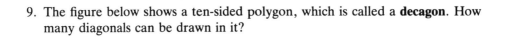   b.

c.   d.

e.   f.

11. Each of the small boxes in the following figures is a square. How many different rectangles are there in each figure? (Remember that a square is a type of rectangle.)

a.   b.   c.   d.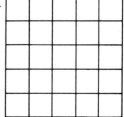

12. How many different rectangles are on a standard 8 by 8 checkerboard?

7 Logic

7.1 Cryptarithms
Aha!

In the addition at the right, *A* and *H* represent two different digits. What are the values of *A* and *H*?

$$\begin{array}{r} A \\ A \\ + A \\ \hline H\,A \end{array}$$

A problem such as the one above is called a **cryptarithm.** This is the special name given to a puzzle in which all or several digits of an arithmetic exercise have been replaced by some type of placeholder. In this case, the placeholders are letters of the alphabet. The challenge is to discover the missing digits represented by the letters.

How do you solve a cryptarithm? Perhaps the most common method is to use properties of numbers that are familiar to you and apply logical reasoning. Here is how you might regard the cryptarithm above.

The sum A + A + A has A as its ones' digit. The only digits for which this is true are 0 and 5.

The sum A + A + A is a two-digit number. This eliminates the possibility that *A* = 0, since 0 + 0 + 0 = 0. This sum could be written as 00, of course, but this form violates the condition that each letter of *HA* represents a different digit. Therefore, *A* must be 5.

Since we have found the value of *A*, we can substitute that value into the cryptarithm to discover the value of *H*.

$$\begin{array}{r} 5 \\ 5 \\ + 5 \\ \hline 1\,5 \end{array}$$

Answer: *A* = 5 and *H* = 1.

In solving the cryptarithm above, we remarked that different letters must represent different digits. It is equally important to note that these letters must each represent only *one* digit throughout the problem.

Other cryptarithms use blank boxes as placeholders for missing digits. Whereas letters of the alphabet may each represent only one digit, it is possible for blank boxes to represent many different digits.

Can you reconstruct this multiplication?

$$
\begin{array}{r}
3\blacksquare \longrightarrow \text{first factor} \\
\times\, \blacksquare 2 \longrightarrow \text{second factor} \\
\hline
\end{array}
$$

first partial product ⊢—— $\blacksquare 4$

second partial product ⊢—— $14\blacksquare$

product ⊢—— $\blacksquare\blacksquare\blacksquare 4$

Once again, let's use our knowledge of some simple number properties and follow a process of logical reasoning.

The missing digit in the first factor must be multiplied by 2 to produce a 4 in the first partial product. There are only two digits for which this is possible: 2 and 7.

The missing digit in the second factor must multiply the first factor 3$\blacksquare$ *to produce the second partial product 14*$\blacksquare$. The missing digit in the second factor must be 4.

$4 \times 32 = 128$ *and* $4 \times 37 = 148$. Therefore, the missing digit in the first factor must be 7.

Since we have found the missing digits in both factors, we can now multiply to find the missing digits in the partial products and in the product.

Answer:

$$
\begin{array}{r}
3\,7 \\
\times\, 4\,2 \\
\hline
7\,4 \\
1\,4\,8 \\
\hline
1\,5\,5\,4 \\
\end{array}
$$

Each part of the multiplication cryptarithm that we just discussed was labeled only for the purpose of facilitating our discussion. As you work through other cryptarithms on your own, you will probably find this step unnecessary.

Note that, in some sources, you may find cryptarithms referred to as *alphametics* or *mathematical cryptograms*.

Problems

1. In each of the following cryptarithms, each letter represents a different digit.
   What is the value of each letter?

a.
```
    I
  + M
  ─────
  M E
```

b.
```
  S O N G
+ B I R D
─────────
S I N G S
```

c.
```
  A T
+   A
─────
T E E
```

d.
```
  S E N D
+ M O R E
─────────
M O N E Y
```

e.
```
    A B
  ×   C
  ─────
  A A A
```

f.
```
  A B C
×     C
──────
D B C
```

g.
```
A B C D
×     4
───────
D C B A
```

h.
```
A B C D E F
×         3
───────────
B C D E F A
```

i.
```
    A B
  × C D
  ─────
  C B C
  A B
  ─────
  B E C
```

j.
```
    G O
  × T O
  ─────
  T G O
  G O
  ─────
  F R O
```

k.
```
    N I P
  ×   I N
  ───────
  A N O N
  N I P
  ───────
  C O R N
```

l.
```
        S Z T N
  ×       F Q N
  ─────────────
  X H T X Q
  S Z T N
  H F Q U F
  ─────────────
  H X U E Z F Q
```

m.
```
          I T
  W E ) S E W
        S O
        ─────
          E W
          W E
          ─────
            S
```

n.
```
              O N
  B E T ) T H A T
          T E N
          ─────
            B E T
            B E T
            ─────
```

o.
```
                D B C
  A B C ) B D E A C
          A B C
          ─────
          F A A
          E G C
          ─────
          D D E C
          D D E C
          ─────
```

p. $(HE)^2 = HEE$

q. $(EE)^2 = EYE$

r. $\sqrt{MADAM} = MAM$

2. Reconstruct each of the following multiplications and divisions.

a.

b.
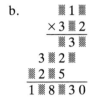

c.
```
      ▨▨5
    ×1 4 6
    4▨▨0
   ▨▨0 0
   ▨▨▨
  ▨▨▨8▨▨
```

d.
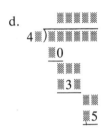

e.
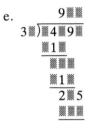

f.
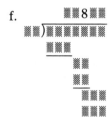

3. Some cryptarithms use both letters of the alphabet and blank boxes as placeholders. Reconstruct each of the following multiplications. What is the value of
each letter?

a.
```
   ▨▨▨
 ×  A▨
 A▨▨B
 ▨AB
 ▨BAB
```

b.
```
    A B C
  × B A C
   ▨▨▨▨
  ▨▨A
 ▨▨▨B
 ▨▨▨▨▨
```

c.
```
    ▨AA▨
  ×  ▨▨▨
  ▨▨A▨▨
 ▨▨▨▨A
 A▨▨▨A
 ▨▨▨▨▨▨
```

4. You will find that some cryptarithms have more
than one solution. In the cryptarithm at the right,
each letter represents a different digit. Find two
different solutions.

```
   S E V E N
 −   N I N E
   E I G H T
```

5. Find a four-digit number such that if 14 is placed at its right, the resulting
number is two times as great as the number formed if 14 is placed at its left.

7.2 Probability Problems
Sure Thing!

Suppose you know that there are ten black and ten navy blue socks in your drawer. The room is dark and you cannot turn on a light. What is the least number of socks that you must take out of your drawer to be certain that you have a pair of the same color?

The solution of a problem such as this is based on the likelihood that something will happen. Mathematically, this is referred to as the **probability that an event will occur.** Although you may be familiar with some probability techniques that are fairly advanced, you can solve this problem using some simple strategies that are within the grasp of even young children. Here is one method that you might use.

Let's use the letter *B* to represent a black sock and the letter *N* to represent a navy blue sock. You know that you have to take at least two socks out of your drawer, so start by considering *how many ways* you could do this. We can list all the possibilities in the following way.

B, B   *B, N*   *N, B*   *N, N*

Here "*B, N*" means that *B* was the first selection and *N* was the second selection. In probability problems the order in which events occur makes a difference, and so "*B, N*" and "*N, B*" are listed as two distinct possibilities. Notice that the two other possibilities, "*B, B*" and "*N, N*" do contain a matched pair. However, only one of these four possibilities can actually happen, so taking only two socks out of your drawer is not sufficient to be *certain* that you'll get a pair of the same color.

How many ways could you take *three* socks out of your drawer? Again, let's make an organized list.

B, B, B   *B, B, N*   *B, N, B*   *N, B, B*
B, N, N   *N, B, N*   *N, N, B*   *N, N, N*

This time there are eight possibilities, and each possibility contains a matched pair of either black or navy blue socks.

Answer: To be certain that you have a pair of the same color, you must take three socks out of your drawer.

Suppose that in the same situation you need to be certain that you have a pair of *navy blue* socks. What is the least number of socks that you must take out of your drawer?

In this case, you could again make listings of what might happen if you take various numbers of socks out of your drawer. However, this process would probably be unnecessarily time-consuming. You may find it a more direct approach to reason through the problem somewhat like this.

Consider the "worst" that could happen: you could take ten socks out of your drawer and all ten might be black. However, at least you would know that there were no more black socks in your drawer. If you then take two *more* socks out of your drawer, you know that you must have a pair of navy blue socks.

Answer: To be certain that you have a pair of navy blue socks, you must take twelve socks out of your drawer.

Problems

1. Suppose you know that there are ten black, ten navy blue, and ten green socks in your drawer. The room is dark and you cannot turn on a light. What is the least number of socks that you must take out of your drawer to be certain that you meet each of the following conditions?

   a. You have a pair of the same color.

   b. You have a pair of black socks.

   c. You have one pair of each color.

2. Suppose you know that there are eight black and ten navy blue socks in your drawer. The room is dark and you cannot turn on a light. What is the least number of socks that you must take out of your drawer to be certain that you meet each of the following conditions?

   a. You have a pair of the same color.

   b. You have a pair of black socks.

   c. You have a pair of navy blue socks.

   d. You have one pair of each color.

3. A complete set of checkers usually consists of twelve black checkers and twelve red checkers. Suppose that a complete set of checkers is placed in a bag. Without looking, how many checkers must you select from the bag to be certain that you have four checkers of the same color?

4. A box contains buttons of five different colors, and there are ten buttons of each color. Each button is the same size as the others. If you are blindfolded, how many buttons must you select from this box to be certain that you have four buttons of the same color?

5. A standard deck of 52 playing cards is placed face-down on a table. How many cards must you draw from the deck to be certain that you have a pair of the same value?

6. How many people must be gathered together to be certain that two people of the group have birthdays that fall in the same month?

7. A certain school has an enrollment of 400 students. Must there be at least two students in this school whose birthdays fall on the same day of the year? Why or why not?

8. What is the least enrollment that a school must have to be certain that there are three students enrolled whose birthdays fall on the same day of the year?

9. How many people must be gathered together to be certain that each of the following sets of conditions is met?

   a. Two of the people have the same first-name initial.

   b. Three of the people have the same last-name initial.

   c. Two of the people have the same first-name initial *and* the same last-name initial.

10. Some biologists claim that the greatest number of hairs that can be on a person's head is one million. Suppose that there are one million bald people in New York City. Show that, if these biologists are correct, there must be at least two people in New York City who have the same number of hairs on their heads.

7.3 Venn Diagram Problems
School Daze

There are 400 students enrolled at Castleton School. Of these students, 85 study French and 50 study Spanish. If 120 students study either French or Spanish, how many students study both French *and* Spanish?

This is an example of a type of problem that can be solved by representing the situation with a **Venn diagram.** In this special kind of diagram, circles are usually used to represent groups of people, animals, or objects that possess certain characteristics. The positioning of the circles in relation to one another represents relationships among these groups. The diagram can then be used to help infer the solution of the problem. These diagrams were named after John Venn (1834–1923), an English mathematician who was among the first to use them extensively.

Let's solve our problem using the Venn diagram at the right. Here circle *F* represents those students who study French and circle *S* represents those students who study Spanish. (Note that the size of each circle is not necessarily related to the number of students in the group it represents.) The rectangle drawn around the circles represents the entire enrollment of Castleton School.

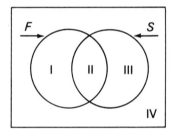

The circles separate the interior of the rectangle into four distinct regions, and these are labeled I, II, III, and IV. Region IV represents those students at Castleton School who study neither French nor Spanish, so for the purposes of this problem we will not be concerned with this region. Region I represents students who study French but not Spanish, while region III represents students who study Spanish but not French. It follows that region II represents those students who study both French and Spanish, and it is the value of this region that we must find.

We can now label our Venn diagram with the data given in the problem: there are 85 students in circle *F* and 50 students in circle *S*. What about regions I, II, and III? If we introduce the variable *n* to represent the number of students in region II, do you see that we can label region I as $85 - n$ and region III as $50 - n$?

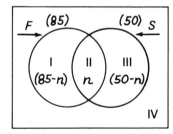

There is one other fact that we have not yet used: the total number of students who study either French or Spanish is 120. In the diagram, this is the same as the total of regions I, II, and III. We can therefore use our labels from the diagram to write a simple equation.

$$
\begin{aligned}
\mathrm{I} \quad + \mathrm{II} + \quad \mathrm{III} \quad &= 120 \\
(85 - n) + n + (50 - n) &= 120 \\
135 - n &= 120 \\
n &= 15
\end{aligned}
$$

Answer: There are 15 students who study both French and Spanish.

Note that the fact that Castleton School has an enrollment of 400 is irrelevant.
Sometimes you need to consider relationships among three or more groups. For example, suppose that we also had information about the group of students who study German at Castleton School. You could picture the relationships among the three groups of students—those who study French, Spanish, and German—with a Venn diagram such as the one below.

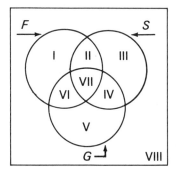

This time the circles separate the interior of the rectangle into eight distinct regions. The meaning of each of these regions is described in the table below. An entry of "Yes" under any language indicates that the students assigned to that region *do* study the language; an entry of "No" indicates that the students assigned to that region do *not* study the language.

Region	French	Spanish	German
I	Yes	No	No
II	Yes	Yes	No
III	No	Yes	No
IV	No	Yes	Yes
V	No	No	Yes
VI	Yes	No	Yes
VII	Yes	Yes	Yes
VIII	No	No	No

Problems

1. There are 30 students in Mrs. Murale's homeroom.

   a. All the students study either French or Spanish. If 21 study French and 14 study Spanish, how many students study both French and Spanish?

   b. All the students study mathematics. The number of students who passed the first math test this year is 24; the number who passed the second math test is 27. If 23 students passed both math tests, how many students *failed* both?

   c. Of the students in the homeroom, 9 had not studied either chemistry or physics, but 14 had studied chemistry. How many students had studied physics but not chemistry?

   d. Of the students in the homeroom, 14 are boys. There are 13 students who play a musical instrument, and 6 of these are boys. How many girls in the homeroom do not play a musical instrument?

2. The following information was obtained in a survey of 120 students.

   66 students study English.
   42 students study history.
   38 students study math.
   19 students study English and history.
   18 students study English and math.
   16 students study history and math.
   8 students study English, history, and math.

   a. How many students study math but neither English nor history?

   b. How many students study English and math but not history?

   c. How many students study none of the three subjects?

3. The members of an English class were assigned books A, B, and C to read during one semester. A poll of the class after two months showed that each student had read at least one of the books. It also showed this additional information.

   10 students had read all three books.
   15 students had read books A and B.
   17 students had read books A and C.
   13 students had read books B and C.
   28 students had read book A.
   21 students had read book B.
   24 students had read book C.

   How many students were in the class?

4. The following information was obtained by studying the orders of the people who dined in a certain restaurant one evening.

   50 people ordered salad.

   40 people ordered soup.

   65 people ordered dessert.

   20 people ordered soup and dessert.

   15 people ordered salad and soup.

   30 people ordered salad and dessert.

   8 people ordered salad, soup, and dessert.

   12 people ordered neither salad, soup, nor dessert.

   a. How many people ordered salad and dessert but not soup?

   b. How many people ordered salad but not dessert?

   c. How people ordered only soup?

   d. How many people were there in all?

5. Thirty people took a trip to Europe to visit either France, England, or Spain. Of this group, 16 visited France, 16 visited England, 11 visited Spain, 5 visited France and Spain, 5 visited only Spain, 8 visited only England, and 3 visited all three countries. How many visited only France?

6. A psychologist ran 50 mice through a maze experiment and reported the following data: 25 mice were male; 25 were previously trained; 20 turned left at the first point where there was a choice; 10 were previously-trained males; 4 males turned left; 15 previously-trained mice turned left; and 3 previously-trained males turned left. How many female mice who were not previously trained did not turn left?

7.4 Whodunits
Who's on First?

Finley, Garber, and Harris are a banker, a computer programmer, and a secretary, but not necessarily in that order. Finley is neither the banker nor the secretary. Harris is not the secretary. What is the occupation of each?

A **whodunit** is a puzzle that involves a group of people or objects and one or more sets of characteristics associated with the people or objects. Each characteristic can be matched one-to-one with each person or object. The problem is to determine this one-to-one matching.

One way to sort through all the information you are given in this whodunit is to make a chart like the one below. Here the letters F, G, and H represent, respectively, the Finley, Garber, and Harris of our problem. The letters B, CP, and S represent their occupations: banker, computer programmer, and secretary, respectively.

Occupations

	B	CP	S
F			
G			
H			

Names

Reread the problem to search for clues. Can you determine that any person is *not* associated with a certain occupation? If so, mark an × on the chart in the appropriate block.

Finley is neither the banker nor the secretary.

	B	CP	S
F	×		×
G			
H			

Harris is not the secretary.

	B	CP	S
F	×		×
G			
H			×

Now look at each row and column of the chart. Does any row or column have only one possible association remaining? If so, mark a ✓ in those blocks.

	B	CP	S
F	X	✓	X
G			✓
H			X

Any row or column of the chart can contain only one ✓, so use ✕s to fill out any rows or columns that now have ✓s.

	B	CP	S
F	X	✓	X
G	X	X	✓
H		X	X

Recalling that each row and column must contain one and only one ✓, mark any remaining blocks.

	B	CP	S
F	X	✓	X
G	X	X	✓
H	✓	X	X

Answer: Finley is the computer programmer, Garber is the secretary, and Harris is the banker.

The problem that we have just discussed involved matching a single set of characteristics to a group of people. How do you proceed if you are given *two* sets of characteristics? Let's consider the same problem, but with some additional information.

Finley, Garber, and Harris are a banker, a computer programmer, and a secretary, but not necessarily in that order. *Their first names are Alex, Bob, and Cynthia.* Finley is neither the banker nor the secretary. Harris is not the secretary, *and Alex is not the banker. Cynthia is older than both Garber and Harris.* What is the complete name and occupation of each?

It is possible to solve this problem by using an expanded form of the chart that we used to solve our original whodunit. As shown below, this chart permits you not only to compare the people with their occupations, but also to compare the people with their first names and to compare their first names with their occupations.

A, B, and C represent the names Alex, Bob, and Cynthia.

The procedure to use with this type of chart is essentially the same as before. Probably the most significant difference is that it is often possible to mark a √ or × in one section of this chart by linking information from the other two sections. Here is an example.

As a result of our previous discussion, we are already able to complete the "Last Names/Occupations" section of this chart. Note that we have already deduced that Harris is the banker. One of the *new* clues is that Alex is *not* the banker. Therefore, we also know that Alex's last name is not Harris, and we can mark the chart in two locations.

	B	CP	S	A	B	C
F	X	✓	X			
G	X	X	✓			
H	✓	X	X	X		
A	X					
B						
C						

Alex's last name is not Harris.

Alex is not the banker.

Now it's your turn. Complete the chart and solve this whodunit.

Answer:

	B	CP	S	A	B	C
F	X	✓	X	X	X	✓
G	X	X	✓	✓	X	X
H	✓	X	X	X	✓	X
A	X	X	✓			
B	✓	X	X			
C	X	✓	X			

Alex Garber is the secretary, Bob Harris is the banker, and Cynthia Finley is the computer programmer.

Charts such as the ones that we have used in this section are an effective strategy to use in solving many whodunits. However, it is important to note that you may not find such charts necessary or even appropriate to solving *all* whodunits that you encounter. There will probably be times when you feel other reasoning processes are more appropriate.

Problems

1. Art, Bill, and Dave play first base, second base, and third base on their school's baseball team, but not necessarily in that order. Art and the third baseman took Dave to the movies yesterday. Art does not play first base. Who's on first?

2. Kate, Linda, and Maya each ate something different for supper yesterday. One ate steak, one ate lamb chops, and one ate chicken. Maya did not have lamb chops or chicken, and Linda did not have lamb chops. What did each person eat for supper?

3. Doctors Pierce, Otis, and Simmons specialize in pediatrics, orthopedics, and surgery. Simmons' specialty is not orthopedics. None of the last names of the doctors begins with the same letter as that doctor's specialty. What is the specialty of each doctor?

4. The last names of Helen, Irving, and Jacqueline are Abrams, Barrow, and Clancy, but not necessarily in that order. Clancy is Jacqueline's uncle. Helen's last name is not Barrow. What are each person's first and last names?

5. Each of Ina, Jill, Louis, and Miguel has a different favorite color among red, blue, green, and orange. No person's name contains the same number of letters as her or his favorite color. Louis and the boy who likes blue live in different parts of town. Red is the favorite color of one of the girls. What is each person's favorite color?

6. A certain family has four pets: a rabbit, a turtle, a dog, and a cat. Two pets are male and two are female. The nicknames of the pets are Star, Mike, Butch, and Pete. The rabbit and the cat recently gave birth. The rabbit is younger than Pete but older than Mike, who is a mother. Pete is older than the dog. Star likes to have his back rubbed. What is the nickname of each pet?

7. Ivanov, Jacobowski, Lebedev, and Malinkov are an architect, composer, dancer, and singer. Ivanov and her husband invited the composer and his wife to dinner. The dancer said that he enjoyed playing chess with Lebedev. The singer complimented Malinkov on her excellent recipe for cabbage soup. What is the occupation of each person, and is that person male or female?

8. The last names of Charles, Dolores, Edward, and Felice are Gold, Hendricks, Insull and Jackson, but not necessarily in that order. Insull is Jackson's grandmother but is not related to Charles. Dolores is an infant and is not related to either Felice or Hendricks. What is the first and last name of each person?

9. Charlotte, Deborah, and Ethan are students at Bayview Elementary School. Their last names are Jones, Knutsen, and Lattimer. Their ages are 10, 11, and 12. Charlotte is younger than both Deborah and Knutsen. Lattimer is older than Knutsen. What are the first name, last name, and age of each student?

10. For a project, Nancy, Oliver, and Peter used a saw, a hammer, and a plane. Each used just one of the tools. Their last names are Ellis, Farelli, and Gross.

    Oliver's last name is not Ellis.

    Gross and the boy who used the hammer live in the same neighborhood.

    Farelli likes to go fishing with her father.

    Nancy did not use the saw.

    What is the first and last name of each student, and what tool did each use?

11. Smith, Robinson, and Jones are a conductor, a porter, and an engineer on a certain train. Also aboard the train are three passengers with the same last names: Mr. Smith, Mr. Robinson, and Mr. Jones.

    Mr. Robinson lives in Detroit.

    The porter lives exactly halfway between Chicago and Detroit.

    Mr. Jones earns exactly $50,000 per year.

    The porter's nearest neighbor, who is one of the three passengers, earns exactly three times as much as the porter.

    Smith usually beats the conductor at tennis.

    The passenger whose last name is the same as the porter's lives in Chicago.

    Who is the engineer?

12. Alice, Betty, and Carolyn went on vacation. One went to Africa, one went to Bali, and one went to China. Only one of the following four statements is true.

    i. Carolyn went to Africa. ii. Carolyn did not go to Bali.

    iii. Alice did not go to Bali. iv. Alice did not go to China.

    Where did each go on vacation?

Solutions to Problems of Part C

Section 1.1
Pages 67-68

1. a. 19   b. 31   c. 226   d. 601

2. a.

number of strokes	1	2	3	4	5
number of parts	3	5	7	9	11

   Notice that, each time a new stroke is drawn, the number of parts increases by 2.

   b. 3, 5, 7, 9, 11, . . .

   c. Yes. One way to state a rule is that each term is one greater than twice its order. You could also state that any given term is the sum of 3, the first term, and a number of 2s that is one less than the order of the given term.

   d. $2 \times 100 + 1 = 200 + 1 = 201$, or

   $3 + 99 \times 2 = 3 + 198 = 201$

   Either way, you obtain the result that the symbol is separated into 201 parts.

   e. 82

3. a. 23, 27, 31

   b. 11, 12, 13

   c. $4\frac{1}{2}$, 5, $5\frac{1}{2}$

   d. 6.5, 6.8, 7.1

4. a. 199 $(4 \times 50 - 1$ or $3 + 49 \times 4)$

   b. 55 $(1 \times 50 + 5$ or $6 + 49 \times 1)$

   c. $26\frac{1}{2}$ $(\frac{1}{2} \times 50 + 1\frac{1}{2}$ or $2 + 49 \times \frac{1}{2})$

   d. 19.7 $(0.3 \times 50 + 4.7$ or $5 + 49 \times 0.3)$

5. Method 1:

Each term of the sequence is three less than five times the order of the term. If we choose n to represent the order of the term, then the term can be represented as $5n - 3$. The given term has a value of 102, so solve the equation $5n - 3 = 102$ to get $n = 21$. Since n represents the order of the term, we have arrived at the fact that 102 is the 21st term of this sequence.

Method 2:

The sequence follows a pattern of adding 5s. Starting at 2, the first term of the sequence, the number of 5s that must be added to arrive at 102 is 20. Therefore, 102 is the 21st term of the sequence.

6. The tenth term of any arithmetic sequence is equal to the first term increased by the constant difference nine times. In this arithmetic sequence, the total of these nine constant differences is $68 - 5 = 63$. Therefore, *each* constant difference is $63 \div 9 = 7$. The first ten terms of the sequence are 5, 12, 19, 26, 33, 40, 47, 54, 61, and 68.

7.

number of wraparounds	1	2	3	4	5
number of pieces	2	4	6	8	10

Organizing some data as in the table above, you see that the number of pieces is always twice the number of wraparounds. Therefore, for 50 wraparounds, the number of pieces formed would be $2 \times 50 = 100$.

8. a. **E**   b. **G**

For both parts **a** and **b**, consider each column to represent an arithmetic sequence whose constant difference is 7 and whose first term is either 1, 2, 3, 4, 5, 6, or 7. You can find the correct column for 999 by dividing by 7: $999 \div 7 = 142$ R5. This gives you the information that 999 is the result of adding 142 sevens to 5. Therefore, 5 is the first term of the appropriate sequence for 999. In part **a**, 5 appears under **E**; in part **b**, 5 appears under **G**.

9. Monday

10. Friday

11. April 10

12.
$$4 + 3 \times (n - 1) = 4 + 3 \times n - 3 \times 1$$
$$= 4 + 3 \times n - 3$$
$$= (3 \times n) + 1$$

1. a.

day	1	2	3	4	5
pay (in cents)	5	15	45	135	405

   b. 5, 15, 45, 135, 405, . . .

   c. Yes. One way to state a rule is that each term is the product of 5 multiplied by 3 raised to an exponent that is one less than order of the term.

   d. $5 \times 3^9 = 5 \times 19{,}683 = 98{,}415$ cents $= \$984.15$.

2. a. 486, 1458, 4374

   b. 9375; 46,875; 234,375

   c. $\dfrac{64}{729}, \dfrac{128}{2187}, \dfrac{256}{6561}$

   d. 0.05, 0.005, 0.0005

3. a. 2×3^{19}

   b. 3×5^{19}

   c. $\dfrac{2}{3} \times \left(\dfrac{2}{3}\right)^{19}$, or $\left(\dfrac{2}{3}\right)^{20}$

   d. $5000 \times (0.1)^{19}$, or $5000 \times \left(\dfrac{1}{10}\right)^{19}$

4. The sequence follows a pattern of multiplying the first term, 4, by a number of 3s. Consider that $8748 \div 4 = 2187$, and $2187 = 3^7$. Then $8748 = 4 \times 3^7$. Since the number of 3s being multiplied would be one less than the order of the given term, 8748 is the eighth term of this sequence.

5. The fifth term of any geometric sequence is equal to the first term multiplied by the constant quotient four times. In this geometric sequence, the product of these four constant quotients is $1250 \div 2 = 625$. Since $625 = 5^4$, the constant quotient is 5. The first five terms of the sequence are 2, 10, 50, 250, and 1250.

6.

number of tears	1	2	3	4	5
number of pieces	2	4	8	16	32

Organizing some data as in the table on the previous page, you see that the number of pieces is always a power of 2. Specifically, the number of pieces is equal to 2 raised to an exponent that equals the number of tears: 1 tear yields $2 = 2^1$ pieces; 2 tears yield $4 = 2^2$ pieces; 3 tears yield $8 = 2^3$ pieces, and so on. Therefore, 20 tears would yield $2^{20} = 1,048,576$ pieces. Since each piece is 0.001 in. thick, the height of the final pile is $1,048,576 \times 0.001 = 1048.576$ in., which is approximately 87 ft, or 29 yd.

7. If each amoeba reproduces itself in three minutes, then every three minutes the volume is doubled. Working backwards, if the jar was filled in three hours, then it was half full only three minutes before. Therefore, it took two hours, fifty-seven minutes for the jar to become half full.

Section 1.3
Pages 73-74

1. a. 78   b. 120   c. 171   d. 210

2.

layer	1	2	3	4	5
number of pumpkins	1	4	9	16	25

Organizing some data as in the table above, you see that the number of pumpkins in each layer is the square of the number of the layer.

a. $12^2 = 144$ b. $15^2 = 225$ c. $50^2 = 2500$ d. $100^2 = 10,000$

3. a. 2   5   9   14   20   27   35   44
$\searrow_{+3}\nearrow\searrow_{+4}\nearrow\searrow_{+5}\nearrow\searrow_{+6}\nearrow\searrow_{+7}\nearrow\searrow_{+8}\nearrow\searrow_{+9}\nearrow$
The next three terms are 27, 35, and 44.

b. 2   5   10   17   26   37   50   65
$\searrow_{+3}\nearrow\searrow_{+5}\nearrow\searrow_{+7}\nearrow\searrow_{+9}\nearrow\searrow_{+11}\nearrow\searrow_{+13}\nearrow\searrow_{+15}\nearrow$
The next three terms are 37, 50, and 65.

c. 3   7   13   21   31   43   57   73
$\searrow_{+4}\nearrow\searrow_{+6}\nearrow\searrow_{+8}\nearrow\searrow_{+10}\nearrow\searrow_{+12}\nearrow\searrow_{+14}\nearrow\searrow_{+16}\nearrow$
The next three terms are 43, 57, and 73.

d. 2   7   16   29   46   67   92   121
$\searrow_{+5}\nearrow\searrow_{+9}\nearrow\searrow_{+13}\nearrow\searrow_{+17}\nearrow\searrow_{+21}\nearrow\searrow_{+25}\nearrow\searrow_{+29}\nearrow$
The next three terms are 67, 92, and 121.

4. a. Each term is one greater than the square of its order.

   b. Each term is one less than the square of its order.

   c. Each term is twice the square of its order.

   d. Each term is the sum of its order and the square of its order.

5. a. $12^2 + 1 = 144 + 1 = 145$

   b. $12^2 - 1 = 144 - 1 = 143$

   c. $2 \times 12^2 = 2 \times 144 = 288$

   d. $12^2 + 12 = 144 + 12 = 156$

6. a. 1   5   12   22   35   51   70   92   117   145
       +4 +7 +10 +13 +16 +19 +22 +25 +28

   1, 5, 12, 22, 35, 51, 70, 92, 117, and 145

   b. 1   6   15   28   45   66   91   120   153   190
       +5 +9 +13 +17 +21 +25 +29 +33 +37

   1, 6, 15, 28, 45, 66, 91, 120, 153, and 190

   c. 2   6   12   20   30   42   56   72   90   110
       +4 +6 +8 +10 +12 +14 +16 +18 +20

   2, 6, 12, 20, 30, 42, 56, 72, 90, and 110

Section 1.4
Pages 76-78

1. a. 12, 42

   The numbers are the multiples of 3 with the order of their digits reversed.

   b. 96, 1

   The numbers are formed by adding 4 to the previous number, then reversing the order of the digits in this sum.

   c. 89, 145

   The numbers are formed by adding the squares of the digits of the previous number.

   d. 14, 11

   The pattern is: subtract 3, add 4; subtract 3, add 6; subtract 3, add 8; subtract 3, add 10; and so on.

2. a. Each letter is the first letter of the name of a counting number, in order: *One, Two, Three, Four, Five, Six, Seven.* The next letter would be *E*.

   b. Each symbol is a numeral for a counting number and its mirror image along a vertical line at its left:

   $$\text{ᘔ, ᘔ, 8, ᘔ...}$$

   The next symbol would be 5 and its mirror image: ᘔ

3. a. Beginning with the third term of the sequence, each term is the sum of the two preceding terms.

   b. 21, 34, 55

   c.

Consecutive Terms	Square of Middle Term	Product of Outer Terms
1, 1, 2	1	2
1, 2, 3	4	3
2, 3, 5	9	10
3, 5, 8	25	24
5, 8, 13	64	65

   Organizing some data as in the table above, you see that the product of the outer terms is one greater or one less than the square of the middle term. If the *order* of the middle term is an even number, then the product of the outer terms is one greater than the square of the middle term; otherwise, the product of the outer terms is one less.

   d.

Consecutive Terms	Product of Middle Terms	Product of Outer Terms
1, 1, 2, 3	2	3
1, 2, 3, 5	6	5
2, 3, 5, 8	15	16
3, 5, 8, 13	40	39

   Organizing some data as in the table above, you see that the products differ by one. If the *order* of the first term is an odd number, then the product of the outer terms is one greater than the product of the middle terms; otherwise, the outer product is one less.

4.

leaf	2	3	4	5	6	7	8	9
distance from previous leaf	$\frac{1}{2}$	$\frac{2}{3}$	$\frac{3}{5}$	$\frac{5}{8}$	$\frac{8}{13}$	$\frac{13}{21}$	$\frac{21}{34}$	$\frac{34}{55}$

The numerators and denominators of the fractions follow the progression of the Fibonacci sequence. The 9th leaf will sprout $\frac{34}{55}$ of the way around the stalk from the 8th leaf.

5. Draw a diagram following a portion of the male bee's ancestry, then record the data in a table.

Generation of Ancestors

generation of ancestors	1	2	3	4	5	6	7	8	9	10
number of ancestors	1	2	3	5	8	13	21	34	55	89

The ancestry of the male bee follows the Fibonacci sequence of numbers. The male bee has two 2nd generation ancestors, three 3rd generation ancestors, five 4th generation ancestors, eight 5th generation ancestors, and eighty-nine 10th generation ancestors.

6. a. Each entry in the interior of the array is the sum of the two closest entries above it.

b. 1, 7, 21, 35, 35, 21, 7, 1

c. 1, 1, 1;   7, 8, 9;   21, 28, 36;   35, 56, 84

7. a. The number of different routes to each position is shown on this grid.

$$
\begin{array}{l}
\quad\ B\,(1)\ \ D\,(1)\ \ G\,(1)\ \ L\,(1) \\
A\,(1)\ \ E\,(2)\ \ J\,(3)\ \ N\,(4) \\
C\,(1)\ \ H\,(3)\ \ O\,(6) \\
F\,(1)\ \ M\,(4) \\
K\,(1)\qquad\qquad\qquad Z
\end{array}
$$

b. Note that, when viewed diagonally, the numbers on the grid above are the numbers of the Pascal triangle. Continue the pattern across the grid, as shown below.

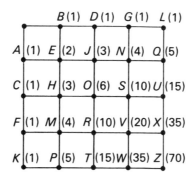

There are 70 different routes to location Z.

8. a. Proceeding clockwise, the number in each link is the sum of the numbers in the two preceding links, providing that the sum is less than 10. If the sum is 10 or greater, the number in the new link is just the ones' digit of the sum.

b. Proceeding clockwise from the 2, 2, 4 sequence at the top of the bracelet, the numbers in the twenty links are as follows:

2, 2, 4, 6, 0, 6, 6, 2, 8, 0, 8, 8, 6, 4, 0, 4, 4, 8, 2, 0

c. Proceeding clockwise from the *1, 1, 2* sequence that is given, the numbers in the sixty links are as follows:

1, 1, 2, 3, 5, 8, 3, 1, 4, 5, 9, 4, 3, 7, 0,
7, 7, 4, 1, 5, 6, 1, 7, 8, 5, 3, 8, 1, 9, 0,
9, 9, 8, 7, 5, 2, 7, 9, 6, 5, 1, 6, 7, 3, 0,
3, 3, 6, 9, 5, 4, 9, 3, 2, 5, 7, 2, 9, 1, 0

If you proceed beyond the sixtieth number, the sequence of numbers will begin repeating at the *1, 1, 2* sequence with which you started.

Section 1.5
Pages 79-81

1. a. There are 5 pairs of numbers that each have the sum 11.
   The sum of all 5 pairs is $5 \times 11 = 55$.

   b. There are 25 pairs of numbers that each have the sum 51.
   The sum of all 25 pairs is $25 \times 51 = 1275$.

   c.

   There are 37 pairs of numbers that each have the sum 76, but there is also the number 38 that cannot be paired with another number. Therefore, the sum of all the numbers is $37 \times 76 + 38 = 2812 + 38 = 2850$.

   d. There are 5 pairs of numbers that each have the sum 15.
   The sum of all 5 pairs is $5 \times 15 = 75$.

   e. There are 43 pairs of numbers that each have the sum 95.
   The sum of all 43 pairs is $43 \times 95 = 4085$.

   f. This problem is similar to problem 1c above. In this case, there are 20 pairs of numbers that each have the sum 70, but there is also the number 35 that cannot be paired with another number. Therefore, the sum of all the numbers is $20 \times 70 + 35 = 1400 + 35 = 1435$.

2. $1¢ + 2¢ + 3¢ + \ldots + 183¢ + \ldots + 363¢ + 364¢ + 365¢ =$ 66,795¢ or $667.95

3. The numbers of pins in the forty rows would be the first forty counting numbers. Therefore, the total number of pins in the arrangement is
1 + 2 + 3 + . . . + 38 + 39 + 40 = 820.

4. The sum of all the numbers on the clock face is 1 + 2 + 3 + . . . + 10 + 11 + 12 = 78. If the two lines that you draw do not intersect, they will separate the clock face into 3 regions. Therefore, the sum of the numbers in each region would have to be 78 ÷ 3 = 26. The following placement of the lines will give you the desired result.

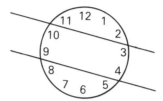

Note that, if you tried to draw two lines so that they intersected within the clock face, the lines would separate the clock face into 4 regions. But 78 ÷ 4 = $19\frac{1}{2}$, so it would be impossible for the numbers in the 4 regions to have the same sum.

5. Answers may vary. One possible answer is given.
   a. 1, 2, 3
      (1 + 2 + 3 = 6)
   b. 1, 2, 3, 4, 5, 6, 7, 8, 9, 10, 11, 12
      (1 + 2 + 3 + . . . + 10 + 11 + 12 = 78)
   c. 0, 1, 2, 3, 4, 5, 6, 7, 8
      (1 + 2 + 3 + . . . + 6 + 7 + 8 = 36)
   d. 1, 2, 3, 4, 5, 6, 7, 8, 12

6. a. The numbers can be paired so that there are 25 pairs of numbers, each having the sum 100. The sum of all 25 pairs is 25 × 100 = 2500.

   b. The numbers can be paired so that there are 12 pairs of numbers, each having the sum 98. There is also the number 49, which cannot be paired with another number. The sum of all the numbers is
      12 × 98 + 49 = 1176 + 49 = 1225.

   c. The numbers can be paired so that there are 19 pairs of numbers, each having the sum 150. The sum of all 19 pairs is 19 × 150 = 2850.

d. The numbers can be paired so that there are 16 pairs of numbers, each having the sum 100. There is also the number 50, which cannot be paired with another number. The sum of all the numbers is $16 \times 100 + 50 = 1650$.

8. There are many possible answers.

Case 1: Place 1 in the center circle. Four arrangements of the other numbers are possible.

one diagonal	other diagonal
2, 3, 8, 9	4, 5, 6, 7
2, 4, 7, 9	3, 5, 6, 8
2, 5, 6, 9	3, 4, 7, 8
2, 5, 7, 8	3, 4, 6, 9

Case 2: Place 3 in the center circle. Three arrangements of the other numbers are possible.

one diagonal	other diagonal
1, 4, 7, 9	2, 5, 6, 8
1, 5, 6, 9	2, 4, 7, 8
1, 5, 7, 8	2, 4, 6, 9

Case 3: Place 5 in the center circle. Four arrangements of the other numbers are possible.

one diagonal	other diagonal
1, 2, 8, 9	3, 4, 6, 7
1, 3, 7, 9	2, 4, 6, 8
1, 4, 6, 9	2, 3, 7, 8
1, 4, 7, 8	2, 3, 6, 9

Case 4: Place 7 in the center circle. Three arrangements of the other numbers are possible.

one diagonal	other diagonal
1, 3, 6, 9	2, 4, 5, 8
1, 4, 6, 8	2, 3, 5, 9
1, 4, 5, 9	2, 3, 6, 8

Case 5: Place 9 in the center circle. Four arrangements of the other numbers are possible.

one diagonal	other diagonal
1, 2, 7, 8	3, 4, 5, 6
1, 3, 6, 8	2, 4, 5, 7
1, 4, 5, 8	2, 3, 6, 7
1, 4, 6, 7	2, 3, 5, 8

Note that an even number cannot be placed in the center circle, since that would leave five odd numbers to be distributed along the diagonals. No matter how you did this, one diagonal would have to have an odd sum while the other diagonal would have an even sum.

9.

	Day	Number of People Told	Total	
(1)	Sunday	1	1	$(1 = 2^1 - 1)$
(2)	Monday	2	$1 + 2 = 3$	$(3 = 2^2 - 1)$
(3)	Tuesday	4	$1 + 2 + 4 = 7$	$(7 = 2^3 - 1)$
(4)	Wednesday	8	$1 + 2 + 4 + 8 = 15$	$(15 = 2^4 - 1)$
(5)	Thursday	16	$1 + 2 + 4 + 8 + 16 = 31$	$(31 = 2^5 - 1)$

If we assign the counting numbers to the days as shown in the table above, on day n the total number of people who know the secret is $2^n - 1$. The following Sunday would be day 8 of this progression, and so the total number of people who would know the secret by the end of the day is $2^8 - 1 = 256 - 1 = 255$.

10. a.
$$S = \frac{1}{2} + \frac{1}{4} + \frac{1}{8} + \frac{1}{16} + \frac{1}{32} + \cdots$$
$$\frac{1}{2}S = \quad \frac{1}{4} + \frac{1}{8} + \frac{1}{16} + \frac{1}{32} + \cdots$$
$$S - \frac{1}{2}S = \frac{1}{2}$$
$$\frac{1}{2}S = \frac{1}{2}$$
$$S = 1$$

b.
$$S = 1 + \frac{1}{5} + \frac{1}{25} + \frac{1}{125} + \frac{1}{625} + \cdots$$
$$\frac{1}{5}S = \quad \frac{1}{5} + \frac{1}{25} + \frac{1}{125} + \frac{1}{625} + \cdots$$
$$S - \frac{1}{5}S = 1$$
$$\frac{4}{5}S = 1$$
$$S = \frac{5}{4}$$

c. 　$S = 3 + \frac{3}{4} + \frac{3}{16} + \frac{3}{64} + \frac{3}{256} + \ldots$

$$\frac{1}{4}S = \quad \frac{3}{4} + \frac{3}{16} + \frac{3}{64} + \frac{3}{256} + \ldots$$

$$S - \frac{1}{4}S = 3$$

$$\frac{3}{4}S = 3$$

$$S = 4$$

d. 　$S = 0.5 + 0.05 + 0.005 + 0.0005 + 0.00005 + \ldots$

$$0.1S = \quad\quad 0.05 + 0.005 + 0.0005 + 0.00005 + \ldots$$

$$S - 0.1S = 0.5$$

$$0.9S = 0.5$$

$$S = \frac{5}{9}$$

e. 　$S = 0.27 + 0.0027 + 0.000027 + \ldots$

$$0.01S = \quad\quad 0.0027 + 0.000027 + \ldots$$

$$S - 0.01S = 0.27$$

$$0.99S = 0.27$$

$$S = \frac{27}{99} = \frac{3}{11}$$

Section 2.1
Page 84

1. The lockers that would be open are those numbered with the perfect-square numbers from 1 to 200:
1, 4, 9, 16, 25, 36, 49, 64, 81, 100, 121, 144, 169, and 196.

2. Examining the perfect-square numbers near 1000, we find that $31^2 = 961$, which is less than 1000; and $32^2 = 1024$, which is greater than 1000. Therefore, the numbers of the lockers that would be open are 1^2, 2^2, 3^2, . . . , 31^2. Clearly, 31 lockers would be open.

3. For 4 students, 7 lockers would be open:
   lockers 1, 4, 5, 6, 7, 8, and 11.

   For 6 students, 7 lockers would be open:
   lockers 1, 4, 7, 8, 10, 11, and 12.

   For 10 students, 5 lockers would be open:
   lockers 1, 4, 9, 11, and 12.

4. The lockers that would be open are those that were changed by an odd
   number of students. Therefore, the lockers that would be open are those
   whose numbers have an odd number of factors among the numbers 1, 2, 3,
   and 4. There are 29 such numbers: 1, 4, 5, 6, 7, 8, 11, 13, 16, 17, 18, 19, 20,
   23, 25, 28, 29, 30, 31, 32, 35, 37, 40, 41, 42, 43, 44, 47, and 49. Therefore, 29
   lockers would be open.

5. 1, 2, 3, 4, 6, 9, 12, 18, 36
   $1 \times 36 = 36$; $2 \times 18 = 36$; $3 \times 12 = 36$; $4 \times 9 = 36$
   6 cannot be paired with another factor.

6. 1×90, 2×45, 3×30, 5×18, 6×15, 9×10

7. $1 \times 1 \times 24$, $1 \times 2 \times 12$, $1 \times 3 \times 8$, $1 \times 4 \times 6$, $2 \times 2 \times 6$, $2 \times 3 \times 4$

8. a. six $(700 \times 80{,}000 = 56{,}000{,}000)$

   b. five $(500 \times 600 = 300{,}000)$

   c. six $(800 \times 30 \times 4000 = 96{,}000{,}000)$

   d. six $(5 \times 10^1 \times 10^2 \times 10^3 = 5 \times 10 \times 100 \times 1000 = 5{,}000{,}000)$

9. $1{,}000{,}000 = \quad 1000 \quad \times \quad 1000$
   $\qquad\qquad\quad = 8 \times 125 \times 8 \times 125$
   $\qquad\qquad\quad = 8 \times 8 \times 125 \times 125$
   $\qquad\qquad\quad = 64 \times 15{,}625$

10. Look for all number pairs whose product contains one or more terminal zeros.
    Also consider that 10 or 20 as a factor will produce a terminal zero.

    a. one $(5 \times 2 = 1\underline{0})$

    b. two $(5 \times 2 = 1\underline{0}; 1\underline{0})$

    c. three $(5 \times 2 = 1\underline{0}; 1\underline{0}; 4 \times 15 = 6\underline{0})$

    d. six $(5 \times 2 = 1\underline{0}; 1\underline{0}; 4 \times 15 = 6\underline{0}; 2\underline{0}; 8 \times 25 = 2\underline{00})$

11. Make a table that lists all the ways that 72 can be expressed as the product of three whole numbers. Include in the table the sum of each combination of whole numbers.

Numbers	Sum
1, 1, 72	74
1, 2, 36	39
1, 3, 24	28
1, 4, 18	23
1, 6, 12	19
1, 8, 9	18
2, 2, 18	22
2, 3, 12	17
2, 4, 9	15
2, 6, 6	14
3, 3, 8	14
3, 4, 6	13

Since the census worker knew the house number, he or she would know the children's ages in every case *except* if the house number was 14, because there are two combinations of possible ages that have a sum of 14. Therefore, this must be the source of the census worker's confusion; the ages of the children could be 2, 6, and 6 or 3, 3, and 8. The additional information that there is an oldest child eliminates 2, 6, and 6 as possible ages for the children. Therefore, the children's ages are 3, 3, and 8.

Section 2.2
Page 86

1. a. Since 29 is prime, it has exactly 2 factors.
   Locker 29 will be changed 2 times.

   b. Since $81 = 3^4$, the number of factors of 81 is $4 + 1 = 5$.
   Locker 81 will be changed 5 times.

   c. Since $100 = 2^2 \times 5^2$, the number of factors of 100 is
   $(2 + 1) \times (2 + 1) = 3 \times 3 = 9$.
   Locker 100 will be changed 9 times.

d. Since $360 = 2^3 \times 3^2 \times 5^1$, the number of factors of 360 is
$(3 + 1) \times (2 + 1) \times (1 + 1) = 4 \times 3 \times 2 = 24$.
Locker 360 will be changed 24 times.

2. Since $600 = 2^3 \times 3^1 \times 5^2$, the number of factors of 600 is
$(3 + 1) \times (1 + 1) \times (2 + 1) = 4 \times 2 \times 3 = 24$.
Therefore, 600 has 24 factors.

3. $900 = 2^2 \times 3^2 \times 5^2$.
The number of factors of 900 is
$(2 + 1) \times (2 + 1) \times (2 + 1) = 3 \times 3 \times 3 = 27$.
They can be listed in the following way.

$1 \times 1 \times 1 = 1$	$1 \times 3^1 \times 1 = 3$	$1 \times 3^2 \times 1 = 9$
$1 \times 1 \times 5^1 = 5$	$1 \times 3^1 \times 5^1 = 15$	$1 \times 3^2 \times 5^1 = 45$
$1 \times 1 \times 5^2 = 25$	$1 \times 3^1 \times 5^2 = 75$	$1 \times 3^2 \times 5^2 = 225$
$2^1 \times 1 \times 1 = 2$	$2^1 \times 3^1 \times 1 = 6$	$2^1 \times 3^2 \times 1 = 18$
$2^1 \times 1 \times 5^1 = 10$	$2^1 \times 3^1 \times 5^1 = 30$	$2^1 \times 3^2 \times 5^1 = 90$
$2^1 \times 1 \times 5^2 = 50$	$2^1 \times 3^1 \times 5^2 = 150$	$2^1 \times 3^2 \times 5^2 = 450$
$2^2 \times 1 \times 1 = 4$	$2^2 \times 3^1 \times 1 = 12$	$2^2 \times 3^2 \times 1 = 36$
$2^2 \times 1 \times 5^1 = 20$	$2^2 \times 3^1 \times 5^1 = 60$	$2^2 \times 3^2 \times 5^1 = 180$
$2^2 \times 1 \times 5^2 = 100$	$2^2 \times 3^1 \times 5^2 = 300$	$2^2 \times 3^2 \times 5^2 = 900$

4. The lockers that will be changed exactly two times have these numbers:
2, 3, 5, 7, 11, 13, 17, 19, 23, 29, 31, 37, 41, 43, and 47.
Each of these locker numbers is a prime number.

5. Find the largest prime number less than 1000: 999 is divisible by 9; 998 is divisible by 2; 997 is prime. Locker 997 has the largest number of those lockers that are changed exactly two times.

6. 11, 11;   17, 71;   37, 73;   79, 97

7. a. $6 = 3 + 3$
   $10 = 3 + 7$ or $5 + 5$
   $28 = 5 + 23$ or $11 + 17$
   $96 = 7 + 89$; $13 + 83$; $17 + 79$; $23 + 73$; $29 + 67$; $37 + 59$;   or $43 + 53$

b. 9 = 2 + 2 + 5 or 3 + 3 + 3

21 = 2 + 2 + 17;   3 + 5 + 13;   3 + 7 + 11;   5 + 5 + 11;   or 7 + 7 + 7

45 = 2 + 2 + 41;   3 + 5 + 37;   3 + 11 + 31;   3 + 13 + 29;   3 + 19 + 23;
       5 + 11 + 29;   5 + 17 + 23;   7 + 7 + 31;   7 + 19 + 19;   11 + 11 + 23;
       11 + 17 + 17;   or 13 + 13 + 19

61 = 3 + 5 + 53;   3 + 11 + 47;   3 + 17 + 41;   3 + 29 + 29;   5 + 13 + 43;
       5 + 19 + 37;   7 + 7 + 47;   7 + 11 + 43;   7 + 13 + 41;   7 + 17 + 37;
       7 + 23 + 31;   11 + 13 + 37;   11 + 19 + 31;   13 + 17 + 31;
       13 + 19 + 29;   or 19 + 19 + 23

Section 2.3
Page 89

1. Find the greatest common factor of each pair of numbers of checkers.

   a. 6   b. 28   c. 12   d. 1

2. a. 18   b. 19   c. 37 (Apply Euclid's algorithm as shown below.)

$$
\begin{array}{r} 3 \\ 629\overline{)2257} \\ 1887 \\ \hline 370 \end{array}
\qquad
\begin{array}{r} 1 \\ 370\overline{)629} \\ 370 \\ \hline 259 \end{array}
\qquad
\begin{array}{r} 1 \\ 259\overline{)370} \\ 259 \\ \hline 111 \end{array}
\qquad
\begin{array}{r} 2 \\ 111\overline{)259} \\ 222 \\ \hline 37 \end{array}
\qquad
\begin{array}{r} 3 \\ 37\overline{)111} \\ 111 \\ \hline 0 \end{array}
$$

3. a. $\dfrac{54}{72} = \dfrac{54 \div 18}{72 \div 18} = \dfrac{3}{4}$

   b.
$$
\begin{array}{r} 3 \\ 119\overline{)391} \\ 357 \\ \hline 34 \end{array}
\qquad
\begin{array}{r} 3 \\ 34\overline{)119} \\ 102 \\ \hline 17 \end{array}
\qquad
\begin{array}{r} 2 \\ 17\overline{)34} \\ 34 \\ \hline 0 \end{array}
$$

   $\dfrac{119}{391} = \dfrac{119 \div 17}{391 \div 17} = \dfrac{7}{23}$

   c.
$$
\begin{array}{r} 1 \\ 1921\overline{)2599} \\ 1921 \\ \hline 678 \end{array}
\qquad
\begin{array}{r} 2 \\ 678\overline{)1921} \\ 1356 \\ \hline 565 \end{array}
\qquad
\begin{array}{r} 1 \\ 565\overline{)678} \\ 565 \\ \hline 113 \end{array}
\qquad
\begin{array}{r} 5 \\ 113\overline{)565} \\ 565 \\ \hline 0 \end{array}
$$

   $\dfrac{1921}{2599} = \dfrac{1921 \div 113}{2599 \div 113} = \dfrac{17}{23}$

4. The greatest common factor of 96, 72, and 48 is 24; therefore, the greatest number of discussion groups would be 24. Each discussion group will have 4 students from the United States, 3 students from Canada, and 2 students from Mexico.

5. a. 27 and 64 are relatively prime.

   b. 112 and 175 are not relatively prime, since 7 is a common factor.

   c. 18, 35, and 75 are not relatively prime since 5 is a common factor of 35 and 75.

   d. 13, 45, and 56 are relatively prime.

6. a. 2 tiles by 3 tiles:
   The line crosses 4 tiles.

   4 tiles by 6 tiles:
   The line crosses 8 tiles.

   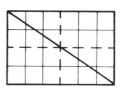

   6 tiles by 9 tiles:
   The line crosses 12 tiles.

   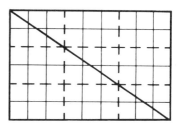

   8 tiles by 12 tiles:
   The line crosses 16 tiles.

   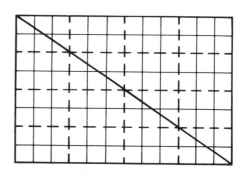

b. 56 tiles

c. Add the dimensions, then subtract the GCF of the dimensions from this sum. The result is the number of tiles crossed by the diagonal line.

d. $54 + 96 = 150$
   The GCF of 54 and 96 is 6.
   $150 - 6 = 144$.
   The diagonal line will cross 144 tiles.

Section 2.4
Pages 90-91

1. The number of members in the flag squad would have to be a multiple of 5 that is 1 less than a common multiple of 2, 3, and 4. The common multiples of 2, 3, and 4 can be listed as 12, 24, 36, 48, 60, 72, . . . Therefore, consider the numbers that are 1 less: 11, 23, 35, 47, 59, 71, . . . The first of these that is a multiple of 5 is 35, so the least number of members in the flag squad is 35.

2. When the total number of people to be seated at the tables for 8 is subtracted from the total number of 79 people, the difference must be a multiple of 5. This will only occur if the ones' digit of the number of people seated at the tables for 8 is 4. Thus the only possibilities are that there are 3 or 8 tables for 8 people.

   Case 1: 3 tables of 8 people
           $3 \times 8 = 24; 79 - 24 = 55; 55 \div 5 = 11$
           There would be 11 tables of 5, for a total of $11 + 3 = 14$ tables.

   Case 2: 8 tables of 8 people
           $8 \times 8 = 64; 79 - 64 = 15; 15 \div 5 = 3$
           There would be 3 tables of 5, for a total of $3 + 8 = 11$ tables.

   Only the second case satisfies the condition that less than one dozen tables will be used. Therefore, there will be 3 tables of 5 people and 8 tables of 8 people.

3. The number must be 1 greater than a common multiple of 2, 3, 4, and 5. The common multiples of 2, 3, 4, and 5 are 60, 120, 180, 240, . . .
   Therefore, consider the numbers that are 1 greater: 61, 121, 181, 241, . . .
   The least number that satisfies the conditions of the problem is 61.

4. If 1 is added to the unknown number, then the result will be a common multiple of 2, 3, 4, and 5. The common multiples of 2, 3, 4, and 5 can be listed as 60, 120, 180, 240 . . . The least of these is 60, but 60 is 1 greater than the unknown number. Therefore, the least number that satisfies the conditions of the problem is $60 - 1 = 59$.

5. Make a table of the results for some simpler problems.

number	3^1	3^2	3^3	3^4	3^5	3^6	3^7
remainder when divided by 5	3	4	2	1	3	4	2

From the table, you see that, as the exponent of 3 is constantly increased by 1, the remainders follow a cycle of repeating the numbers 3, 4, 2, and 1. Continuing this pattern, the 10th number would be 4. Therefore, the remainder when 3^{10} is divided by 5 is 4.

6. a. Consider not the total of 25 appetizers, but the 24 appetizers that were taken before the tray last reached Helen.

Case 1: If the number of people seated at the table is odd, it takes two passes of the tray around the table before it reaches Helen again. On each of these two passes of the tray, each person seated at the table takes exactly one appetizer. Therefore, 24 would have to be a multiple of the number of people at the table.

Case 2: If the number of people seated at the table is even, the tray reaches Helen each time it is passed around the table. However, each time the tray is passed around the table, only half the people seated at the table take an appetizer. Therefore, 24 would have to be a multiple of *half* the number of people at the table.

The number 24 is a multiple of 1, 2, 3, 4, 6, 8, 12, and 24. Combining the above two cases, then, it is possible that the number of people at the table is 2, 3, 4, 6, 8, 12, 16, 24, or 48. (The number 1 is eliminated because it could not meet the condition that every *other* person takes an appetizer.)

b. Consider the $50 - 1 = 49$ appetizers that were taken before the tray last reached Helen, and follow the reasoning of part **a**. Since 49 is a multiple of 1, 7, and 49, the possible numbers of people are 2, 7, 14, 49, and 98. However, we need to also consider the additional information that Helen took a total of 8 appetizers.

Case 1: If the number of people seated around the table is even, then the tray had to pass around the table $8 - 1 = 7$ times. On each of these passes, though, only half the people took an appetizer. The only even number of people that satisfies these conditions is 14.
($7 \times (\frac{1}{2}$ of $14) = 7 \times 7 = 49$)

Case 2: If the number of people seated around the table is odd, then the tray passed around the table $(8 - 1) \times 2 = 14$ times. On each 2 of these passes, each person takes one appetizer. The only odd number of people that satisfies these conditions is 7.
($14 \div 2 \times 7 = 7 \times 7 = 49$)

There are either 7 or 14 people seated at the table.

Section 2.5
Page 93

1. a. 30   b. 216   c. 756

2. Find the least common multiple of 4, 5, and 6.
   The least number of dancers that the producer must hire is 60.

3. Find the least common multiple of 6, 7, and 8.
   The least number of scouts in the troop is 168.

4. Find the least common multiple of 9, 10, 11, and 12.
   The least number of coins in the collection is 1980.

5. $16 \times 20 = 320$ $18 \times 48 = 864$
   GCF of 16 and 20 = 4   GCF of 18 and 48 = 6
   LCM of 16 and 20 = 80   LCM of 18 and 48 = 144
   GCF $\times$ LCM = 320   GCF $\times$ LCM = 864

   a. The product of two numbers is equal to the product of their GCF and LCM.

   b. To find the LCM, divide the product of the numbers by their GCF.

   c. $36 \times 60 = 2160$
      $2160 \div 12 = 180$
      The LCM of 36 and 60 is 180.

Section 3.1
Pages 95-96

1. a. There are two cases to consider.

    Case 1: The ones' digit is 5. Every set of ten consecutive whole numbers contains one number whose ones' digit is 5. Since 500 page numbers contain 50 such sets, there are 50 different page numbers whose ones' digit is 5.

    Case 2: The ones' digit is 0. These numbers will satisfy the conditions of the problem only if they have a 5 in the tens' or hundreds' places. There are 6 such numbers: 50, 150, 250, 350, 450, and 500.

    Considering both cases, there are 50 + 6 = 56 page numbers that contain the digit 5 and are also divisible by 5.

    b. The digit 5 cannot be in the ones' place, since the number would be divisible by 5. The only number with the digit 5 in the hundreds' place is 500, and this is divisible by 5. Therefore, consider only those numbers that contain the digit 5 in the tens' place. The following page numbers satisfy the conditions of the problem.

    51, 52, 53, 54, 56, 57, 58, 59
    151, 152, 153, 154, 156, 157, 158, 159
    251, 252, 253, 254, 256, 257, 258, 259
    351, 352, 353, 354, 356, 357, 358, 359
    451, 452, 453, 454, 456, 457, 458, 459

    Count the entries in the list. There are 40 page numbers that contain the digit 5 but are not divisible by 5.

    c. Consider only those numbers whose ones' digit is 0. The following numbers satisfy the conditions of the problem.

    10, 20, 30, 40, 60, 70, 80, 90
    100, 110, 120, 130, 140, 160, 170, 180, 190
    200, 210, 220, 230, 240, 260, 270, 280, 290
    300, 310, 320, 330, 340, 360, 370, 380, 390
    400, 410, 420, 430, 440, 460, 470, 480, 490

    Count the entries in the list. There are 44 page numbers that do not contain the digit 5 but are divisible by 5.

2. a. even   b. even   c. odd   d. even
   e. odd   f. odd   g. even

3. a. even b. odd c. even d. even
   e. odd f. even g. even

4. a.

+	E	O
E	E	O
O	O	E

b.

×	E	O
E	E	E
O	E	O

5. a. 5: 21, 23, 25, 27, 29

   b. 10: 21, 23, 25, 27, 29
           121, 123, 125, 127, 129

   c. 60: 21, 23, 25, 27, 29   241, 243, 245, 247, 249
           121, 123, 125, 127, 129   251, 253, 255, 257, 259
           201, 203, 205, 207, 209   261, 263, 265, 267, 269
           211, 213, 215, 217, 219   271, 273, 275, 277, 279
           221, 223, 225, 227, 229   281, 283, 285, 287, 289
           231, 233, 235, 237, 239   291, 293, 295, 297, 299

6. a. A number is divisible by 1000 if it has 3 terminal zeros.

   b. A number is divisible by 10,000 if it has 4 terminal zeros.

   c. A number is divisible by 10^n if it has n terminal zeros.

Section 3.2
Page 97

1. a. Yes: $56 + 21 = 7 \times 8 + 7 \times 3$

   b. No: 42 is divisible by 7, but 65 is not.

   c. Yes: $210 - 49 = 7 \times 30 - 7 \times 7$

   d. No: 770 is divisible by 7, but 540 is not.

2. a. Yes: $98 = 70 + 28 = 7 \times 10 + 7 \times 4$

   b. Yes: $154 = 140 + 14 = 7 \times 20 + 7 \times 2$

c. Yes: $133 = 140 - 7 = 7 \times 20 - 7 \times 1$

d. Yes: $693 = 700 - 7 = 7 \times 100 - 7 \times 1$

3. a. Yes: $253 = 220 + 33 = 11 \times 20 + 11 \times 3$

   b. No: $784 = 770 + 14$

   $770 = 11 \times 70$, but 14 is not divisible by 11.

   c. Yes: $6589 = 6600 - 11 = 11 \times 600 - 11 \times 1$

   d. No: $8777 = 8800 - 23$

   $8800 = 11 \times 800$, but 23 is not divisible by 11.

4. No. The person will be 62 in the year whose number is $1945 + 62$. 1945 is divisible by 5, but 62 is not divisible by 5. Therefore, the sum $1945 + 62$ is not divisible by 5.

5. No. The divisibility principle for sums and differences states, in effect, that if one of two addends is divisible by a given number, the sum is divisible by the given number only if the second addend is also divisible by the given number. The principle does not address a case in which neither addend is divisible by the given number.

6. Any whole number greater than 10 can be written as the sum of its ones' digit and a multiple of 10. Any multiple of 10 is divisible by 5. Therefore, according to the divisibility principle for sums and differences, if the ones' digit is divisible by 5, the sum is divisible by 5. The only ones' digits that are divisible by 5 are 0 and 5.

Example: $147 = 140 + 7$

   140 is divisible by 5, but 7 is not divisible by 5.

   Therefore $140 + 7 = 147$ is not divisible by 5.

7. A number is divisible by 25 if the number formed by its last two digits is divisible by 25. Therefore, a number is divisible by 25 if its last two digits are 00, 25, 50, or 75. This test works because any whole number greater than 100 can be written as the sum of a multiple of 100 and the number formed by its last two digits. Any multiple of 100 is divisible by 25. Therefore, according to the divisibility principle for sums and differences, if the number formed by the last two digits is divisible by 25, the sum is divisible by 25.

Example: $675 = 600 + 75$

   600 is divisible by 25, and 75 is divisible by 25.

   Therefore $600 + 75 = 675$ is divisible by 25.

8. A number is divisible by 125 if the number formed by its last three digits is divisible by 125. Therefore, a number is divisible by 125 if its last three digits are 000, 125, 250, 375, 500, 625, 750, or 875. This test works because any whole number greater than 1000 can be written as the sum of a multiple of 1000 and the number formed by its last three digits. Any multiple of 1000 is divisible by 125. Therefore, according to the divisibility principle for sums and differences, if the number formed by the last three digits is divisible by 125, the sum is divisible by 125.

Example: 3425 = 3000 + 425
               3000 is divisible by 125, but 425 is not divisible by 125.
               Therefore, 3000 + 425 = 3425 is not divisible by 125.

Section 3.3
Page 99

1. Test just the last four digits for divisibility by 16 (2^4).

   a. Yes   b. Yes   c. No

2. a. Following the pattern from the table, since $32 = 2^5$, a number is divisible by 32 if the number formed by its last 5 digits is divisible by 32.

   b. Test just the last five digits for divisibility by 32.

     100,032: Yes
     2,306,420: No
     8,732,128: Yes

3. The Olympic games are held every four years, in those years whose numbers are divisible by 4. Since 1952 is divisible by 4, the Olympic games were held in Helsinki in that year.

4. The relationship between ounces and pounds is 16 oz = 1 lb. Therefore, test just the last 4 digits of 2,197,216 for divisibility by 16. Since 7216 is divisible by 16, there will be no pure silver left over.

5. For divisibility by 4:

   a. 1, 3, 5, 7, or 9   b. any replacement   c. no replacement

   For divisibility by 8:

   a. 3 or 7   b. 1, 3, 5, 7, or 9   c. no replacement

6. To be divisible by 16, the number must also be divisible by 4. Therefore, the candidates for the missing digit are 1, 3, 5, 7, and 9. Of these, only 1 and 9 will make the number divisible by 16.

7. No. If the number is to be divisible by 4, the number must be even. Therefore, the digit in the ones' place must be 4. But neither 14, 54, or 74 is divisible by 4. Since the number formed by the last two digits must be divisible by 4, it is impossible for this number to be divisible by 4.

8. Either 6 or 8 must be in the ones' place. Test the following combinations: 876, 786, 678, 768. Only 768 is divisible by 8.

9. Of the two-digit numbers that can be formed from 1, 2, 3, and 4, only 12, 24, and 32 are divisible by 4. Therefore, the last two digits of the four-digit number must be 12, 24, or 32. The numbers that satisfy the conditions of the problem can be listed as follows.

3412   1324   1432
4312   3124   4132

10. If the page number is divisible by 8, it is also divisible by 4. Therefore, consider only those page numbers whose last two digits are 12, 32, 52, 72, or 92. The following page numbers satisfy the conditions of the problem.

112	32	152	72	192
312	232	352	272	392
512	432	552	472	592
712	632	752	672	792
912	832	952	872	992

There are 25 page numbers that contain the digit 2 in the ones' place and are divisible by 8.

Section 3.4
Page 101

1. a. Sum of the digits = 26 + ▒ , so ▒ = 1.

   b. Sum of the digits = 19 + ▒ , so ▒ = 8.

   c. Sum of the digits = 21 + ▒ , so ▒ = 6.

2. a. ▒ = 1, 4, or 7   b. ▒ = 2, 5, or 8   c. ▒ = 0, 3, 6, or 9

3. The sum of the two replacement digits must be either 4 or 13. There are 11 possible pairs of replacements, resulting in the following numbers.

054	459
153	558
252	657
351	756
450	855
	954

4. The sum of the replacement digits must be either 1, 4, 7, 10, 13, or 16. There are 33 possible pairs of replacements, resulting in the following numbers.

051	054	057	159	459	759
150	153	156	258	558	858
	252	255	357	657	957
	351	354	456	756	
	450	453	555	855	
		552	654	954	
		651	753		
		750	852		
			951		

5. The sum of the digits must be 9. The tens' digit of the product is always one less than the number multiplying 9, and the ones' digit is simply the difference between 9 and the tens' digit.

6. a.

$51	$685	$40,752	$382,861
− 15	− 658	− 40,572	− 328,861
$36	$ 27	$ 180	$ 54,000

  b. Yes

  c. A possible source of error is a reversal of two digits when a figure is entered into the ledger.

7. Examples:

6281	472	94	87,654,321
−1826	−274	−49	−12,345,678
4455	198	45	75,308,643

If one number contains the same digits as another, but in reverse order, the difference of the two numbers will be divisible by 9. (In fact, the same is true if one number contains the same digits as another, but in any order.)

8. No. No matter how the digits are arranged, the sum $1 + 2 + 3 + \ldots + 7 + 8 + 9$ is equal to 45. Thus, no matter how the digits are arranged, the number will be divisible by both 3 and 9. Therefore the number cannot be prime.

Section 3.5
Page 104

1. a. $8 + 6 = 14; 1 + 2 = 3; 14 - 3 = 11$
      1826 is divisible by 11.

   b. $2 + 9 = 11; 7 + 5 = 12; 12 - 11 = 1$
      7259 is not divisible by 11.

   c. $8 + 9 + 7 = 24; 2 + 0 = 2; 24 - 2 = 22$
      82,907 is divisible by 11.

   d. $1 + 2 + 9 + 3 = 15; 7 + 4 + 4 = 15; 15 - 15 = 0$
      1,724,943 is divisible by 11.

2. a. $(9 + ▥) - 3 = 6 + ▥; 6 + 5 = 11$, so $▥ = 5$

   b. $(7 + 9) - (3 + ▥) = 13 - ▥; 13 - 2 = 11$, so $▥ = 2$

   c. $(9 + 2) - (3 + ▥ + 1) = 7 - ▥; 7 - 7 = 0$, so $▥ = 7$

   d. $(▥ + 8 + 9) - (0 + 1) = ▥ + 16; 6 + 16 = 22$, so $▥ = 6$

3. The sum of the replacement digits must be either 5 or 16. There are 9 possible pairs of replacements, resulting in the following numbers.

055	759
154	858
253	957
352	
451	
550	

4. The digits must be arranged so that 1 and 4 are paired as either odd-place or even-place digits, and 7 and 9 are paired as either odd-place or even-place digits. There are 8 possible combinations.

1749	4719	7194	9174
1947	4917	7491	9471

5. 1243   Notice that each of the digits 1, 2, 3, and 4 appear
   1342   twice in each column. Therefore, the sum of the
   2431   digits in each column is 20, and the sum of the eight
   2134   numbers is 22,220.
   3124
   3421
   4213
   4312

6. Since the sum of the digits is 28, the number will be divisible by 11 only if the sum of the odd-place digits is 14 and the sum of the even-place digits is 14, for then the difference between the two sums will be $14 - 14 = 0$. (Note that there is no set of numbers that have a sum of 28 and a difference of 11.) The combinations of digits that will satisfy these conditions are listed in this table.

odd-place digits	2, 3, 4, 5	1, 3, 4, 6	1, 2, 5, 6	1, 2, 4, 7
even-place digits	1, 6, 7	2, 5, 7	3, 4, 7	3, 5, 6

It is possible to write 144 different numbers using *each* of the above sets of odd-place and even-place digits. Therefore, there are a total of $4 \times 144 = 576$ different numbers that contain the digits 1, 2, 3, 4, 5, 6, and 7 and that are divisible by 11. Some examples are 2,136,475; 5,621,473; and 3,741,265.

7. Try the number 149▧. Then $(1 + 9) - (4 + ▧) = 6 - ▧$. Since $6 - 6 = 0$, ▧ $= 6$. The greatest number of students who can play football is 1496.

Section 3.6
Page 105

1. a. No.

    5824 is divisible by 4, but it is not divisible by 3.

    Therefore, 5824 is not divisible by 12.

  b. Yes.

    7416 is divisible by 4, and it is divisible by 3.

    Therefore, 7416 is divisible by 12.

  c. No.

    12,054 is divisible by 3, but it is not divisible by 4.

Therefore, 12,054 is not divisible by 12.

d. Yes.

428,676 is divisible by 4, and it is divisible by 3.

Therefore, 428,676 is divisible by 12.

2. Yes. The number 9762 is divisible both by 2 and by 3. Therefore, it is divisible by 6, and the 9762 eggs can be packed in cartons that each contain 6 eggs with none left over.

3. a. Yes.

972 is divisible by 2, and it is divisible by 9.

Therefore, 972 is divisible by 18.

b. Yes.

8946 is divisible by 2, and it is divisible by 9.

Therefore, 972 is divisible by 18.

c. No.

9081 is divisible by 9, but it is not divisible by 2.

Therefore, 9081 is not divisible by 18.

d. No.

15,018 is divisible by 2, but it is not divisible by 9.

Therefore, 15,018 is not divisible by 18.

4. A number is divisible by 15 if it is divisible both by 3 and by 5. Therefore, a number is divisible by 15 if the sum of its digits is divisible by 3 *and* if its ones' digit is 0 or 5.

5. a. 4230, 8235

(The resulting number must be divisible both by 5 and by 9.)

b. 3312

(The resulting number must be divisible both by 8 and by 9.)

c. 5472, 1476

(The resulting number must be divisible both by 4 and by 9.)

d. 8470, 2475

(The resulting number must be divisible both by 5 and by 11.)

6. 198, 297, 396, 495, 594, 693, 792, 891, 990

(The numbers must be divisible both by 9 and by 11.)

Section 3.7
Page 107

1. a. $180{,}124 = 180{,}180 - 56$
      $56 = 7 \times 8$
      180,124 is divisible by 7, but not by 11 or 13.

   b. $621{,}595 = 621{,}621 - 26$
      $26 = 13 \times 2$
      621,595 is divisible by 13, but not by 7 or 11.

   c. $236{,}346 = 236{,}236 + 110$
      $110 = 11 \times 10$
      236,346 is divisible by 11, but not by 7 or 13.

   d. $430{,}445 = 430{,}430 + 15$
      $15 = 3 \times 5$
      430,445 is not divisible by 7, 11, or 13.

   e. $583{,}660 = 583{,}583 + 77$
      $77 = 7 \times 11$
      583,660 is divisible by 7 and by 11, but not by 13.

   f. $900{,}869 = 900{,}000 - 31$
      31 is prime.
      900,869 is not divisible by 7, 11, or 13.

   g. $98{,}126 = 98{,}098 + 28$
      $28 = 7 \times 4$
      98,126 is divisible by 7, but not by 11 or 13.

   h. $63{,}078 = 63{,}063 + 15$
      $15 = 3 \times 5$
      63,078 is not divisible by 7, 11, or 13.

   i. $52{,}143 = 52{,}052 + 91$
      $91 = 7 \times 13$
      52,143 is divisible by 7 and by 13, but not by 11.

2. Since $2002 = 2 \times 1001$, and $1001 = 7 \times 11 \times 13$, $2002 = 2 \times 7 \times 11 \times 13$.

3. The numbers 2, 3, 5, 7, 11, and 13 are the six least prime numbers, so their product is the required number. $2 \times 3 \times 5 = 30$, and $7 \times 11 \times 13 = 1001$, so

their combined product is $30 \times 1001 = 30{,}030$. The least number that has six different prime factors is 30,030.

4. a. $340 - 060 + 270 = 550$; $550 = 11 \times 50$

   270,060,340 is divisible by 11, but not by 7 or by 13.

   b. $134 - 515 + 600 = 219$; $219 = 3 \times 73$

   600,515,314 is not divisible by 7, 11, or 13.

   c. $531 - 482 + 29 = 78$; $78 = 13 \times 6$

   29,482,531 is divisible by 13, but not by 7 or by 11.

5. Apply the divisibility test discussed in problem 4 above.

   $738 - 811 + 125 = 52$; $52 = 13 \times 4$

   $125,811,738 is divisible by 13, so the departments can receive equal amounts.

Section 4.1
Pages 109-110

1. a. first denominator: $\frac{1}{2} \times (3 + 1) = \frac{1}{2} \times 4 = 2$

   second denominator: $3 \times 2 = 6$

   $\frac{2}{3} = \frac{1}{2} + \frac{1}{6}$

   b. first denominator: $\frac{1}{2} \times (9 + 1) = \frac{1}{2} \times 10 = 5$

   second denominator: $9 \times 5 = 45$

   $\frac{2}{9} = \frac{1}{5} + \frac{1}{45}$

   c. first denominator: $\frac{1}{2} \times (15 + 1) = \frac{1}{2} \times 16 = 8$

   second denominator: $15 \times 8 = 120$

   $\frac{2}{15} = \frac{1}{8} + \frac{1}{120}$

   d. first denominator: $\frac{1}{2} \times (25 + 1) = \frac{1}{2} \times 26 = 13$

   second denominator: $25 \times 13 = 325$

   $\frac{2}{25} = \frac{1}{13} + \frac{1}{325}$

2. a. $\dfrac{1}{4} = \dfrac{1}{(4+1)} + \dfrac{1}{4 \times (4+1)} = \dfrac{1}{5} + \dfrac{1}{4 \times 5} = \dfrac{1}{5} + \dfrac{1}{20}$

b. $\dfrac{1}{7} = \dfrac{1}{(7+1)} + \dfrac{1}{7 \times (7+1)} = \dfrac{1}{8} + \dfrac{1}{7 \times 8} = \dfrac{1}{8} + \dfrac{1}{56}$

c. $\dfrac{1}{10} = \dfrac{1}{(10+1)} + \dfrac{1}{10 \times (10+1)} = \dfrac{1}{11} + \dfrac{1}{10 \times 11} = \dfrac{1}{11} + \dfrac{1}{110}$

d. $\dfrac{1}{11} = \dfrac{1}{(11+1)} + \dfrac{1}{11 \times (11+1)} = \dfrac{1}{12} + \dfrac{1}{11 \times 12} = \dfrac{1}{12} + \dfrac{1}{132}$

3. $\dfrac{1}{3} = \dfrac{1}{4} + \dfrac{1}{12}$

$\dfrac{1}{3} = \dfrac{1}{5} + \dfrac{1}{20} + \dfrac{1}{13} + \dfrac{1}{156}$

4. $\dfrac{1}{2} = \dfrac{1}{3} + \dfrac{1}{6}$

$\dfrac{1}{2} = \dfrac{1}{4} + \dfrac{1}{12} + \dfrac{1}{6}$

or

$\dfrac{1}{2} = \dfrac{1}{3} + \dfrac{1}{6}$

$\dfrac{1}{2} = \dfrac{1}{3} + \dfrac{1}{7} + \dfrac{1}{42}$

5. a. $\dfrac{1}{2} - \dfrac{1}{3} = \dfrac{1}{2 \times 3} = \dfrac{1}{6}$

b. $\dfrac{1}{4} - \dfrac{1}{5} = \dfrac{1}{4 \times 5} = \dfrac{1}{20}$

c. $\dfrac{1}{7} - \dfrac{1}{8} = \dfrac{1}{7 \times 8} = \dfrac{1}{56}$

d. $\dfrac{1}{9} - \dfrac{1}{10} = \dfrac{1}{9 \times 10} = \dfrac{1}{90}$

6. $\dfrac{1}{12} = \dfrac{1}{3 \times 4} = \dfrac{1}{3} - \dfrac{1}{4}$

7. a. As discussed in problem 5, each of the addends can be rewritten as the difference of consecutive unit fractions.

$\dfrac{1}{1 \times 2} + \dfrac{1}{2 \times 3} + \ldots + \dfrac{1}{9 \times 10}$

$= \left(\dfrac{1}{1} - \dfrac{1}{2}\right) + \left(\dfrac{1}{2} - \dfrac{1}{3}\right) + \ldots + \left(\dfrac{1}{9} - \dfrac{1}{10}\right)$

$= \dfrac{1}{1} - \dfrac{\cancel{1}}{\cancel{2}} + \dfrac{\cancel{1}}{\cancel{2}} - \dfrac{\cancel{1}}{\cancel{3}} + \dfrac{\cancel{1}}{\cancel{3}} + \ldots - \dfrac{\cancel{1}}{\cancel{9}} + \dfrac{\cancel{1}}{\cancel{9}} - \dfrac{1}{10}$

$= \dfrac{1}{1} - \dfrac{1}{10} = 1 - \dfrac{1}{10} = \dfrac{9}{10}$

b. Consider the following.

$$\frac{1}{1 \times 2} + \frac{1}{2 \times 3} = \frac{3}{1 \times 2 \times 3} + \frac{1}{1 \times 2 \times 3} = \frac{4}{1 \times 2 \times 3} = \frac{\cancel{2} \times 2}{1 \times \cancel{2} \times 3} = \frac{2}{1 \times 3} = 2\left(\frac{1}{1 \times 3}\right)$$

$$\frac{1}{3 \times 4} + \frac{1}{4 \times 5} = \frac{5}{3 \times 4 \times 5} + \frac{3}{3 \times 4 \times 5} = \frac{8}{3 \times 4 \times 5} = \frac{2 \times \cancel{4}}{3 \times \cancel{4} \times 5} = \frac{2}{3 \times 5} = 2\left(\frac{1}{3 \times 5}\right)$$

. . .

$$\frac{1}{9 \times 10} + \frac{1}{10 \times 11} = \frac{11}{9 \times 10 \times 11} + \frac{9}{9 \times 10 \times 11} = \frac{20}{9 \times 10 \times 11} = \frac{2 \times \cancel{10}}{9 \times \cancel{10} \times 11} = \frac{2}{9 \times 11}$$

$$= 2\left(\frac{1}{9 \times 11}\right)$$

Therefore, we can rewrite the given expression as follows.

$$\frac{1}{1 \times 3} \quad + \quad \frac{1}{3 \times 5} \quad + \ldots + \quad \frac{1}{9 \times 11}$$

$$= \frac{1}{2}\left(\frac{1}{1 \times 2} + \frac{1}{2 \times 3}\right) + \frac{1}{2}\left(\frac{1}{3 \times 4} + \frac{1}{4 \times 5}\right) + \ldots + \frac{1}{2}\left(\frac{1}{9 \times 10} + \frac{1}{10 \times 11}\right)$$

$$= \frac{1}{2}\left(\frac{1}{1 \times 2} + \frac{1}{2 \times 3} + \frac{1}{3 \times 4} + \frac{1}{4 \times 5} + \ldots + \frac{1}{9 \times 10} + \frac{1}{10 \times 11}\right)$$

$$= \frac{1}{2}\left(\frac{1}{1} - \frac{1}{2} + \frac{1}{2} - \frac{1}{3} + \frac{1}{3} - \frac{1}{4} + \frac{1}{4} - \frac{1}{5} + \ldots + \frac{1}{9} - \frac{1}{10} + \frac{1}{10} - \frac{1}{11}\right)$$

$$= \frac{1}{2}\left(\frac{1}{1} - \frac{1}{11}\right) = \frac{1}{2}\left(1 - \frac{1}{11}\right) = \frac{1}{2}\left(\frac{10}{11}\right) = \frac{10}{22} = \frac{5}{11}$$

8. a. $\frac{1}{12} + \frac{1}{12}, \quad \frac{1}{7} + \frac{1}{42}, \quad \frac{1}{10} + \frac{1}{15}, \quad \frac{1}{8} + \frac{1}{24}, \quad \frac{1}{9} + \frac{1}{18}$

   b. $\frac{1}{20} + \frac{1}{20}, \quad \frac{1}{11} + \frac{1}{110}, \quad \frac{1}{14} + \frac{1}{35}, \quad \frac{1}{12} + \frac{1}{60}, \quad \frac{1}{15} + \frac{1}{30}$

   c. $\frac{1}{8} + \frac{1}{8}, \quad \frac{1}{5} + \frac{1}{20}, \quad \frac{1}{6} + \frac{1}{12}$

   d. $\frac{1}{24} + \frac{1}{24}, \quad \frac{1}{13} + \frac{1}{156}, \quad \frac{1}{16} + \frac{1}{48}, \quad \frac{1}{14} + \frac{1}{84}, \quad \frac{1}{18} + \frac{1}{36}, \quad \frac{1}{21} + \frac{1}{28}, \quad \frac{1}{15} + \frac{1}{60}$

9. Answers may vary. One possible solution is given.

   a. $\frac{3}{4} = \frac{2}{4} + \frac{1}{4} = \frac{1}{2} + \frac{1}{4}$

   b. $\frac{5}{6} = \frac{3}{6} + \frac{2}{6} = \frac{1}{2} + \frac{1}{3}$

   c. $\frac{3}{5} = \frac{18}{30} = \frac{15}{30} + \frac{3}{30} = \frac{1}{2} + \frac{1}{10}$

   d. $\frac{2}{7} = \frac{8}{28} = \frac{7}{28} + \frac{1}{28} = \frac{1}{4} + \frac{1}{28}$

Section 4.2
Pages 111-112

1. a. $\frac{15}{16}$ b. $\frac{20}{9}$ c. $\frac{16}{27}$ d. $\frac{3}{8}$

2. a. $\frac{16}{15}$ b. $\frac{9}{20}$ c. $\frac{27}{16}$ d. $\frac{3}{2}$

3. a. 2 b. $\frac{5}{3}$ c. $\frac{4}{9}$ d. $\frac{10}{37}$

4. 3

5. $\frac{3}{8}$

6. a. $\frac{3}{10}$ b. $\frac{5}{7}$ c. $\frac{5}{6}$ d. $\frac{3}{5}$

7. a. $\dfrac{\frac{1}{2}+\frac{1}{3}}{\frac{1}{2}-\frac{1}{3}} = \dfrac{\frac{5}{6}}{\frac{1}{6}} = \dfrac{\frac{5}{6}\times\frac{6}{1}}{\frac{1}{6}\times\frac{6}{1}} = \dfrac{\frac{30}{6}}{1} = \dfrac{30}{6} = 5$

   b. $\dfrac{\frac{1}{2}+\frac{1}{3}}{3} = \dfrac{\frac{5}{6}}{3} = \dfrac{\frac{5}{6}\times\frac{1}{3}}{3\times\frac{1}{3}} = \dfrac{\frac{5}{18}}{1} = \dfrac{5}{18}$

   c. $\dfrac{\frac{1}{2}-\frac{1}{3}}{4} = \dfrac{\frac{1}{6}}{4} = \dfrac{\frac{1}{6}\times\frac{1}{4}}{4\times\frac{1}{4}} = \dfrac{\frac{1}{24}}{1} = \dfrac{1}{24}$

8. $\frac{1}{5} \,\#\, \frac{1}{7} = \dfrac{\frac{1}{5}+\frac{1}{7}}{2} = \dfrac{\frac{12}{35}}{2} = \dfrac{\frac{12}{35}\times\frac{1}{2}}{2\times\frac{1}{2}} = \dfrac{\frac{12}{70}}{1} = \dfrac{12}{70} = \dfrac{6}{35}$

   $\frac{1}{3} \,\#\, \left(\frac{1}{5}\,\#\,\frac{1}{7}\right) = \frac{1}{3}\,\#\,\frac{6}{35} = \dfrac{\frac{1}{3}+\frac{6}{35}}{2} = \dfrac{\frac{53}{105}}{2} = \dfrac{\frac{53}{105}\times\frac{1}{2}}{2\times\frac{1}{2}} = \dfrac{\frac{53}{210}}{1} = \dfrac{53}{210}$

Section 4.3
Page 113

1. a. $\cfrac{1}{3+\cfrac{1}{3+\cfrac{1}{3+\frac{1}{3}}}} = \cfrac{1}{3+\cfrac{1}{3+\frac{1}{\frac{10}{3}}}} = \cfrac{1}{3+\cfrac{1}{3+\frac{3}{10}}} = \cfrac{1}{3+\frac{1}{\frac{33}{10}}} = \cfrac{1}{\frac{33}{10}} = \frac{10}{33}$

   b. $\cfrac{1}{1+\cfrac{1}{1+\cfrac{1}{1+\frac{1}{3}}}} = \cfrac{1}{1+\cfrac{1}{1+\frac{1}{\frac{4}{3}}}} = \cfrac{1}{1+\cfrac{1}{1+\frac{3}{4}}} = \cfrac{1}{1+\cfrac{1}{\frac{7}{4}}} = \cfrac{1}{1+\frac{4}{7}} = \cfrac{1}{\frac{11}{7}} = \frac{7}{11}$

   c. $2 + \cfrac{1}{1+\frac{1}{2}} = 2 + \cfrac{1}{\frac{3}{2}} = 2 + \frac{2}{3} = \frac{8}{3}$

   d. $1 + \cfrac{1}{1+\cfrac{1}{2+\frac{1}{3}}} = 1 + \cfrac{1}{1+\cfrac{1}{\frac{7}{3}}} = 1 + \cfrac{1}{1+\frac{3}{7}} = 1 + \cfrac{1}{\frac{10}{7}} = 1 + \frac{7}{10} = \frac{17}{10}$

2. a. $\frac{3}{7} = \cfrac{1}{\frac{7}{3}} = \cfrac{1}{2+\frac{1}{3}}$

   b. $\frac{13}{30} = \cfrac{1}{\frac{30}{13}} = \cfrac{1}{2+\frac{4}{13}} = \cfrac{1}{2+\cfrac{1}{\frac{13}{4}}} = \cfrac{1}{2+\cfrac{1}{3+\frac{1}{4}}}$

   c. $\frac{8}{13} = \cfrac{1}{\frac{13}{8}} = \cfrac{1}{1+\frac{5}{8}} = \cfrac{1}{1+\cfrac{1}{\frac{8}{5}}} = \cfrac{1}{1+\cfrac{1}{1+\frac{3}{5}}} = \cfrac{1}{1+\cfrac{1}{1+\cfrac{1}{\frac{5}{3}}}} = \cfrac{1}{1+\cfrac{1}{1+\cfrac{1}{1+\frac{2}{3}}}} = \cfrac{1}{1+\cfrac{1}{1+\cfrac{1}{1+\cfrac{1}{\frac{3}{2}}}}}$

   $= \cfrac{1}{1+\cfrac{1}{1+\cfrac{1}{1+\cfrac{1}{1+\frac{1}{2}}}}}$

   d. $\frac{14}{3} = 4 + \frac{2}{3} = 4 + \cfrac{1}{\frac{3}{2}} = 4 + \cfrac{1}{1+\frac{1}{2}}$

Section 4.4
Page 115

1. a. If $\frac{3}{5}$ of the number is 21, then $\frac{1}{5}$ of the number is $21 \div 3 = 7$, and $\frac{5}{5}$ of the number is $5 \times 7 = 35$.
   The number is 35.

   b. If $\frac{2}{7}$ of the number is 14, then $\frac{1}{7}$ of the number is $14 \div 2 = 7$, and $\frac{7}{7}$ of the number is $7 \times 7 = 49$.
   The number is 49.

   c. If the product of $1\frac{1}{2}$ and the number is 12, then $\frac{3}{2}$ of the number is 12. If $\frac{3}{2}$ of the number is 12, then $\frac{1}{2}$ of the number is $12 \div 3 = 4$, and $\frac{2}{2}$ of the number is $2 \times 4 = 8$.
   The number is 8.

   d. Think of the double of the number as double $\frac{4}{4}$, or $\frac{8}{4}$. Then 56 is added to $\frac{1}{4}$ of the number to produce $\frac{8}{4}$ of the number. Thus, 56 must be $\frac{8}{4} - \frac{1}{4} = \frac{7}{4}$ of the number. If 56 is $\frac{7}{4}$ of the number, then $\frac{1}{4}$ of the number is $56 \div 7 = 8$, and $\frac{4}{4}$ of the number is $4 \times 8 = 32$.
   The number is 32.

   e. Think of the triple of the number as triple $\frac{2}{2}$, or $\frac{6}{2}$. Then 6 is added to $\frac{5}{2}$ of the number to produce $\frac{6}{2}$ of the number. Thus, 6 must be $\frac{6}{2} - \frac{5}{2} = \frac{1}{2}$ of the number. If 6 is $\frac{1}{2}$ of the number, then $\frac{2}{2}$ of the number is $2 \times 6 = 12$.
   The number is 12.

   f. Think of $3\frac{1}{4}$ times the number as $\frac{13}{4}$ times the number. Then 15 is added to $\frac{13}{4}$ of the number to produce 4 times the number or $\frac{16}{4}$ of the number. Thus, 15 must be $\frac{16}{4} - \frac{13}{4} = \frac{3}{4}$ of the number. If 15 is $\frac{3}{4}$ of the number, then $\frac{1}{4}$ of the number is $15 \div 3 = 5$, and $\frac{1}{4}$ of the number is $4 \times 5 = 20$.
   The number is 20.

2. If Dave spent $\frac{3}{5}$ of his money, then $\frac{2}{5}$ of his money was left. If \$12 is $\frac{2}{5}$ of his money, then $\frac{1}{5}$ of his money is $\$12 \div 2 = \$6$, and $\frac{5}{5}$ of his money is $5 \times \$6 = \$30$. Therefore, Dave originally had \$30.

3. If Anne spent $\frac{1}{3}$ of her money, then $\frac{2}{3}$ of her money was left. Therefore, she lost $\frac{1}{2}$ of $\frac{2}{3}$ of her money, which is equivalent to $\frac{1}{3}$ of her money. The 10¢ which she had left is the remaining $\frac{1}{3}$ of her money. If 10¢ is $\frac{1}{3}$ of her money, then $\frac{3}{3}$ of her money is $3 \times 10¢ = 30¢$. Therefore, Anne originally had 30¢.

4. Rewrite the two given fractions as equivalent fractions with a common denominator: $\frac{1}{6} = \frac{5}{30}$ and $\frac{1}{5} = \frac{6}{30}$. Inserting *two* fractions in an arithmetic sequence between the two given fractions can be accomplished by separating

the difference between the two fractions into *three* equal parts. Therefore, multiply each of the equivalent fractions by $\frac{3}{3}$: $\frac{5}{30} = \frac{15}{90}$ and $\frac{6}{30} = \frac{18}{90}$. This gives two fractions, $\frac{16}{90}$ and $\frac{17}{90}$, between the two given fractions. The completed arithmetic sequence is $\frac{15}{90}, \frac{16}{90}, \frac{17}{90}, \frac{18}{90}$; or, in lowest terms, $\frac{1}{6}, \frac{8}{45}, \frac{17}{90}, \frac{1}{5}$.

5. Rewrite the two given fractions as equivalent fractions with a common denominator: $\frac{1}{3} = \frac{2}{6}$ and $\frac{1}{2} = \frac{3}{6}$. Inserting *three* fractions in an arithmetic sequence between the two given fractions can be accomplished by separating the difference between the two fractions into *four* equal parts. Therefore, multiply each of the equivalent fractions by $\frac{4}{4}$: $\frac{2}{6} = \frac{8}{24}$ and $\frac{3}{6} = \frac{12}{24}$. This gives three fractions, $\frac{9}{24}, \frac{10}{24}$, and $\frac{11}{24}$, between the two given fractions. The completed arithmetic sequence is $\frac{8}{24}, \frac{9}{24}, \frac{10}{24}, \frac{11}{24}, \frac{12}{24}$; or, in lowest terms, $\frac{1}{3}, \frac{3}{8}, \frac{5}{12}, \frac{11}{24}, \frac{1}{2}$.

6. The sum of the fractions in the farmer's will was not 1, but only $\frac{17}{18}$ $\left(\frac{1}{2} + \frac{1}{3} + \frac{1}{9} = \frac{9}{18} + \frac{6}{18} + \frac{2}{18} = \frac{17}{18}\right)$. With the addition of the eighteenth cow, the children were able to take $\frac{1}{2}, \frac{1}{3}$, and $\frac{1}{9}$ of the total, but this was still only $\frac{17}{18}$ of 18 cows, or 17 cows.

Section 5.1
Page 120

1. a. $6^2 = 36$ b. $5^2 = 25$ c. $4^2 = 16$
   d. $3^2 = 9$ e. $2^2 = 4$ f. $1^2 = 1$

2. a. $6^2 + 5^2 + 4^2 + 3^2 + 2^2 + 1^2 = 91$
   b. $7^2 + (6^2 + 5^2 + 4^2 + 3^2 + 2^2 + 1^2) = 49 + 91 = 140$
   c. $9^2 + 8^2 + (7^2 + 6^2 + 5^2 + 4^2 + 3^2 + 2^2 + 1^2) = 81 + 64 + 140 = 285$
   d. $10^2 + (9^2 + 8^2 + 7^2 + 6^2 + 5^2 + 4^2 + 3^2 + 2^2 + 1^2) = 100 + 285 = 385$

3.

Size of Square	a	b	c	d
1 × 1	12	12	8	16
2 × 2	6	5	5	—
3 × 3	2	—	4	1
4 × 4	—	—	1	4
5 × 5	—	—	—	1
Total	20	17	18	22

a. 20   b. 17   c. 18   d. 22

4. a. 1   b. 3   c. 6

   d. 10   e. 15   f. 21

The pattern is that the total number of rectangles is the sum of all the counting numbers from 1 to the number of squares in the figure.

Example: □□□□ $1 + 2 + 3 + 4 = 10$

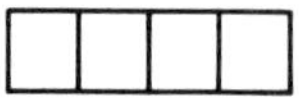

5.

Size of Rectangle	a	b	c	d
1 × 1	5	5	4	6
1 × 2	4	4	4	7
1 × 3	2	2	—	2
1 × 4	1	—	—	—
2 × 2	—	—	1	2
2 × 3	—	—	—	1
Total	12	11	9	18

a. 12   b. 11   c. 9   d. 18

Section 5.2
Page 123

Type of Triangle	Listing by Letter	Number
1-part	b, c, d	3
2-part	a-b, b-c, c-d, d-a	4
3-part	—	0
4-part	a-b-c-d	1

1. a. (label for table above)

The total number of triangles is $3 + 4 + 1 = 8$.

b.

Type of Triangle	Listing by Letter	Number
1-part	a, b, c, d	4
2-part	c-d, b-d	2
3-part	a-d-c, a-d-b	2

The total number of triangles is 4 + 2 + 2 = 8.

c.

Type of Triangle	Listing by Letter	Number
1-part	a, b, c, d, e	5
2-part	—	0
3-part	a-f-c, a-f-d, b-f-e, b-f-d, c-f-e	5

The total number of triangles is 5 + 5 = 10.

d.

Type of Triangle	Listing by Letter	Number
1-part	a, b, c, d, e, f, g, h, i, j	10
2-part	a-b, b-c, c-d, d-e, e-f, f-g, g-h, h-i, i-j, j-a	10
3-part	a-b-c, c-d-e, e-f-g, g-h-i, i-j-a, j-k-d, j-k-f, b-k-h, b-k-f, d-k-h	10
4-part	—	0
5-part	b-k-f-g-h, d-k-h-i-j, f-k-j-a-b, h-k-b-c-d, j-k-d-e-f	5

The total number of triangles is 10 + 10 + 10 + 5 = 35.

2. a. 1   b. 3   c. 6   d. 10   e. 15   f. 21

The pattern is that the total number of triangles is the sum of all the counting numbers from 1 to the number of small triangles in the figure.

Example:  $1 + 2 + 3 = 6$

3. They are the same. The total number of triangles in these figures can be counted using the same pattern as used in counting the total number of rectangles in the figures on page 120.

4. a. 5   b. 13   c. 27   d. 48

Section 5.3
Pages 125-126

1. a. 2   b. 4   c. 11   d. 16

2.

Number of Straight Cuts	Greatest Number of Pieces of Pie	
0	1	
1	2	+ 1
2	4	+ 2
3	7	+ 3
4	11	+ 4
5	16	+ 5

3. a. The difference between successive numbers in the right-hand column increases by one from line-to-line. That is, the first cut adds 1 to the previous number of pieces, the second cut adds 2 to the previous number of pieces, the third cut adds 3 to the previous number of pieces, the fourth cut adds 4 to the previous number of pieces, and the fifth cut adds 5 to the previous number of pieces.

   b. Add three more entries to the table in problem 2.
   $16 + 6 = 22; 22 + 7 = 29; 29 + 8 = 37$
   For 8 straight cuts, the greatest number of pieces of pie is 37.

4. The greatest number of pieces is 7, which is the same as if the pie were round.

5. a. 7

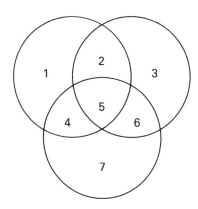

b. Four intersecting circles:

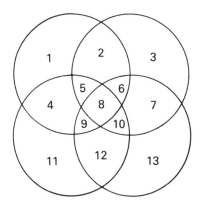

Five intersecting circles:

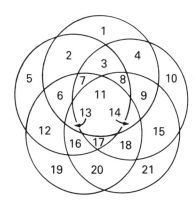

Number of Intersecting Circles	Greatest Number of Regions Formed
1	1
2	3
3	7
4	13
5	21

$\big\}$ + 2
$\big\}$ + 4
$\big\}$ + 6
$\big\}$ + 8

c. Add three more entries to the table above.
21 + 10 = 31; 31 + 12 = 43; 43 + 14 = 57
The greatest number of regions formed when 8 circles intersect is 57.

6. Cut the wheel of cheese along the dashed lines.

Section 5.4
Page 129

1. a. Method 1: make a table.

width	3	4	5	6	7
length	6	8	10	12	14
Perimeter	18	24	30	36	42

Method 2: write and solve an equation.

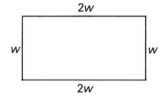

$$w + 2w + w + 2w = 42$$
$$6w = 42$$
$$\frac{6w}{6} = \frac{42}{6}$$
$$w = 7$$

The width is 7 m and the length is 14 m.

b. Method 1: make a table.

width	5	6	7	8	9
length	8	9	10	11	12
Perimeter	26	30	34	38	42

Method 2: write and solve an equation.

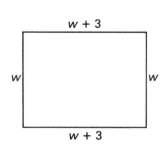

$$w + (w + 3) + w + (w + 3) = 42$$
$$4w + 6 = 42$$
$$4w + 6 - 6 = 42 - 6$$
$$4w = 36$$
$$\frac{4w}{4} = \frac{36}{4}$$
$$w = 9$$

The width is 9 m and the length is 12 m.

c. Method 1: make a table.

width	4	5	6	7	8
length	5	7	9	11	13
Perimeter	18	24	30	36	42

Method 2: write and solve an equation.

$$w + (2w - 3) + w + (2w - 3) = 42$$
$$6w - 6 = 42$$
$$6w - 6 + 6 = 42 + 6$$
$$6w = 48$$
$$\frac{6w}{6} = \frac{48}{6}$$
$$w = 8$$

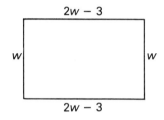

The width is 8 m and the length is 13 m.

d. Method 1: make a table.

width	6	5	4	3
length	30	25	20	15
Perimeter	72	60	48	36

The perimeter 42 is halfway between 48 and 36, so try a width that is halfway between 4 and 3, or $3\frac{1}{2}$. If the width is $3\frac{1}{2}$, the length is $5 \times 3\frac{1}{2} = 17\frac{1}{2}$, and the perimeter is $3\frac{1}{2} + 17\frac{1}{2} + 3\frac{1}{2} + 17\frac{1}{2} = 42$.

Method 2: write and solve an equation.

$$l + \tfrac{1}{5}l + l + \tfrac{1}{5}l = 42$$
$$\tfrac{12}{5}l = 42$$
$$\tfrac{12}{5}l \times \tfrac{5}{12} = 42 \times \tfrac{5}{12}$$
$$l = \tfrac{210}{12} = 17\tfrac{6}{12} = 17\tfrac{1}{2}$$

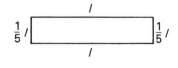

The length is $17\frac{1}{2}$ m and the width is $3\frac{1}{2}$ m.

2. a. If the perimeter is 10, the sum of the length and width is 5.
There are 2 different rectangles.

l	4	3
w	1	2

If the perimeter is 12, the sum of the length and width is 6.
There are 3 different rectangles.

l	5	4	3
w	1	2	3

If the perimeter is 14, the sum of the length and width is 7.
There are 3 different rectangles.

l	6	5	4
w	1	2	3

If the perimeter is 16, the sum of the length and width is 8.
There are 4 different rectangles.

l	7	6	5	4
w	1	2	3	4

If the perimeter is 24, the sum of the length and width is 12.
There are 6 different rectangles.

l	11	10	9	8	7	6
w	1	2	3	4	5	6

b. If the given perimeter is a multiple of 4, the number of rectangles with different shapes that have the given perimeter is $\frac{1}{4}$ of the perimeter. If the given perimeter is an even number that is *not* a multiple of 4, subtract 2 from the given perimeter; the number of rectangles is then $\frac{1}{4}$ of the result.

c. No. If the length is represented by l and the width is represented by w, the perimeter is represented by $2l + 2w$. Since each of the quantities $2l$ and $2w$ are even numbers, their sum is an even number. Therefore, the perimeter has to have an even-number measure.

3. Let a, b, and c represent the lengths of the sides of the triangle. Make a table of all combinations of three whole-number measures that have a sum of 10.

a	1	1	1	1	2	2	2	3
b	1	2	3	4	2	3	4	3
c	8	7	6	5	6	5	4	4

Since the sum of the lengths of any two sides of a triangle must be greater than the length of the third side, all but the last two combinations in the table have to be eliminated. Therefore, there are only *two* different triangles that have a perimeter of 10: $a = 2$, $b = 4$, $c = 4$ and $a = 3$, $b = 3$, $c = 4$.

4. The perimeter of the figure whose perimeter is 30 is the sum of the lengths of 10 individual sides of squares. Therefore, the length of just *one* of these sides is $30 \div 10 = 3$.

   a. $12 \times 3 = 36$ b. $12 \times 3 = 36$ c. $12 \times 3 = 36$ d. $14 \times 3 = 42$

5. a. If the perimeter of *PQRS* is 1, then the length of a side of *PQRS* is $\frac{1}{4}$, and the perimeter of the shaded region in the diagram at the right is $4 \times \frac{1}{8} = \frac{1}{2}$.

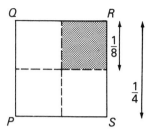

b. If the length of one side of *PQRS* is represented by *l*, then the perimeter of the shaded region in the diagram at the right is $l + \frac{1}{2}l + l + \frac{1}{2}l$.

$$l + \frac{1}{2}l + l + \frac{1}{2}l = 24$$
$$3l = 24$$
$$\frac{3l}{3} = \frac{24}{3}$$
$$l = 8$$

The perimeter of *PQRS* is $4 \times l = 4 \times 8 = 32$.

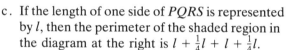

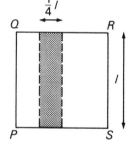

c. If the length of one side of *PQRS* is represented by *l*, then the perimeter of the shaded region in the diagram at the right is $l + \frac{1}{4}l + l + \frac{1}{4}l$.

$$l + \frac{1}{4}l + l + \frac{1}{4}l = 15$$
$$\frac{5}{2}l = 15$$
$$\frac{5}{2}l \times \frac{2}{5} = 15 \times \frac{2}{5}$$
$$l = 6$$

The perimeter of *PQRS* is $4 \times l = 4 \times 6 = 24$.

Section 5.5
Page 131

1. a. $C = 2\pi r$
   $$\approx 2 \times \frac{22}{7} \times 42$$
   $$\approx 264$$

   The wheel travels approximately 264 cm in one turn.

   b. 5.5 km = 550,000 cm
   $$550,000 \div 264 = 2083\frac{1}{3}$$

   The wheel turns approximately 2083 times.

2. Let C represent the *circumference* of the wheel.
   Then $240 \times C$ represents the distance the wheel travels in 240 turns.

   Since 1 mile = 5280 feet:
   $$240 \times C = 5280$$
   $$C = \frac{5280}{240} = 22$$

   Since $C = 2\pi r$:
   $$2\pi r = 22$$
   $$2 \times \frac{22}{7} \times r \approx 22$$
   $$\frac{44}{7} \times r \approx 22$$
   $$\frac{44}{7} \times r \times \frac{7}{44} \approx 22 \times \frac{7}{44}$$
   $$r \approx \frac{7}{2}, \text{ or } 3\frac{1}{2}$$

   The radius of the wheel is approximately $3\frac{1}{2}$ ft.

3. Note that the two semicircles at the ends have a combined circumference equal to the circumference of one complete circle with diameter equal to 70 yd.

   Since $C = \pi \times d$:
   $$C \approx \frac{22}{7} \times 70$$
   $$C \approx 220$$

   This circumference, together with the two 100-yd lengths, constitutes the distance around the track. Therefore, the distance around the track is approximately $220 + 100 + 100 = 420$ yd.

4. a. Counterclockwise

   b. Clockwise

   c. When Gear A makes 3 complete turns, $3 \times 40 = 120$ teeth pass the point of contact with Gear B. Since Gear B has 20 teeth, it will make $120 \div 20 = 6$ complete turns.

   d. Follow the logic employed in part **c**. Since Gear C has 30 teeth, it will make $120 \div 30 = 4$ complete turns.

5. Let the circumference of the inner circle $= 2\pi r$. Since the width of the shaded ring is equal to r, the radius of the outer circle is $2r$, and its circumference is $2\pi \times 2r$, or $4\pi r$. The ratio of the circumferences is then $2\pi r$ to $4\pi r$, or 1 to 2.

6. In one revolution, the tip of the hour hand travels a path that is equal in length to the circumference of a circle of radius 4 in.

$$C = 2\pi r$$
$$C \approx 2 \times 3.14 \times 4$$
$$C \approx 25.12$$

In one revolution, the tip of the hour hand travels approximately 25.12 in. The hour hand makes 2 revolutions in a 24-hour period. Therefore, in a 24-hour period, the tip of the hour hand travels *approximately* 2×25.12 in., which is approximately 50 in.

In one revolution, the tip of the minute hand travels a path that is equal in length to the circumference of a circle of radius 6 in.

$$C = 2\pi r$$
$$C \approx 2 \times 3.14 \times 6$$
$$C \approx 37.68$$

In one revolution, the tip of the minute hand travels approximately 37.68 in. The minute hand makes 24 revolutions in a 24-hour period. Therefore, in a 24-hour period, the tip of the minute hand travels approximately 24×37.68 in., which is approximately 904 in.

7.

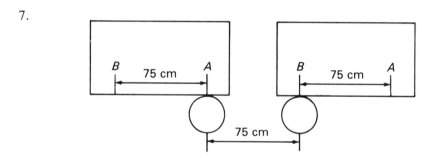

Suppose that A is the original point of contact between one cylinder and the crate, and B is the point of contact after one complete turn of this cylinder. Then the distance that the cylinder moves along the crate in one complete turn is equal to the circumference of the cylinder, or 75 cm. However, drawing a diagram such as the one above, note that the cylinder also advances an additional 75 cm along the ground. Each point, A and B, has traveled a total distance of $75 + 75 = 150$ cm. Therefore, the entire crate moves 150 cm for each complete turn of the cylinders.

Section 5.6
Pages 133-134

1. a. The largest rectangular garden that can be enclosed will always be a square with the given perimeter.

   One carton:
   > Perimeter = 1 × 24 = 24 ft
   > One side = 24 ÷ 4 = 6 ft
   > Area = 6 × 6 = 36 ft^2

   Two cartons:
   > Perimeter = 2 × 24 = 48 ft
   > One side = 48 ÷ 4 = 12 ft
   > Area = 12 × 12 = 144 ft^2

   Three cartons:
   > Perimeter = 3 × 24 = 72 ft
   > One side = 72 ÷ 4 = 18 ft
   > Area = 18 × 18 = 324 ft^2

   b. For a given number of cartons, the area of the largest rectangular garden that can be enclosed is 36 times the *square* of the given number of cartons.

   c. A 32 ft^2 garden can have one of these sets of dimensions: 32 ft × 1 ft; 16 ft × 2 ft; or 8 ft × 4 ft. The least of the perimeters is for the 8 ft × 4 ft garden: 8 + 4 + 8 + 4 = 24 ft. Therefore, one carton is the least number needed.

   A 128 ft^2 garden can have one of these sets of dimensions: 128 ft × 1 ft; 64 ft × 2 ft; 32 ft × 4 ft; or 16 ft × 8 ft. The least of the perimeters is for the 16 ft × 8 ft garden: 16 + 8 + 16 + 8 = 48. Therefore, two cartons is the least number needed.

2. Draw and label a diagram of the pool and the walk as shown at the right. The area of the walk is equal to the difference between the areas of the outer and inner rectangles in the diagram.

   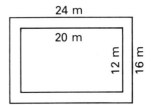

   Outer rectangle: A = l × w = 16 × 24 = 384 m^2

   Inner rectangle: A = l × w = 12 × 20 = 240 m^2

   Difference: 384 − 240 = 144 m^2

   The area of the concrete walk is 144 m^2.

3. a. Separate the floor into three rectangular regions, as shown at the right. The total area of the floor is the sum of the areas of the three rectangular regions.

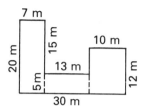

Area = 7 × 20 + 13 × 5 + 10 × 12
    = 140 + 65 + 120 = 325 m²

b. Separate the floor into five rectangular regions, as shown at the right. The total area of the floor is the sum of the areas of the five rectangular regions.

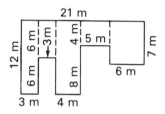

Area
= 3 × 12 + 3 × 6 + 4 × 12 + 5 × 4 + 7 × 6
=   36   + 18 +   48   + 20 + 42
= 164 m²

4. Area of bottom: 3 × 5 = 15 ft²
Area of front and back: 2 × (2 × 3) = 12 ft²
Area of left and right: 2 × (2 × 5) = 20 ft²

The total area of the plywood needed will be
15 + 12 + 20 = 47 ft²

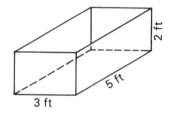

5. a. If the area of *PQRS* is 1, then the length of a side of *PQRS* is 1. The area of the shaded region in the diagram at the right is then
$\frac{1}{2} \times \frac{1}{2} = \frac{1}{4}$.

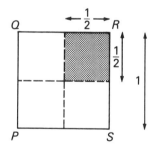

b. If the area of *PQRS* is 16, then the length of a side of *PQRS* is 4. The area of the shaded region in the diagram at the right is then
4 × 3 = 12.

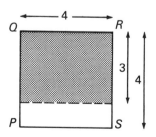

c. The length of the new figure is twice its width. Therefore, if the perimeter of the new figure is 24, its length must be 8 and its width must be 4. The area of the shaded region in the diagram at the right is then 8 × 4 = 32.

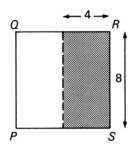

6. If the four triangular lawn areas are moved together, as shown in the diagram at the right, they form a square with sides that measure 12 ft. The total lawn area is therefore
12 ft × 12 ft = 144 ft².

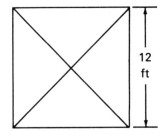

7. Draw segments *EG* and *FH*, intersecting at point *O*. Note that the area of triangle *OEF* is half the area of square *OEBF*. Since the sides of square *ABCD* measure 2, a side of square *OEBF* measures 1, and the area of square *OEBF* is 1 × 1 = 1. Therefore, the area of triangle *OEF* is $\frac{1}{2}$ of 1, or $\frac{1}{2}$. Since square *EFGH* is formed by triangle *OEF* and three triangles congruent to it, the area of square *EFGH* is 4 × $\frac{1}{2}$ = 2.

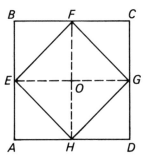

8. Let *s* represent the length of a side of the square. Then its perimeter is 4 × *s*, and its length is *s* × *s*. According to the conditions of the problem, then, *s* × *s* = 4 × *s*. The only number that makes this a true statement is *s* = 4. Therefore, the length of a side of the square must be 4.

9. No. Let *s* represent the length of a side of the original square. Then the area of the original square is *s* × *s*, or *s*². If the measure of the side of the square is now doubled, 2*s* represents the length of a side of the new square. Then the area of the new square is 2*s* × 2*s*, or 4*s*². If the measure of each side of a square is doubled, the area is four times as great.

10. $A: \frac{1}{4}$ square unit $\qquad E: \frac{1}{16}$ square unit

    $B: \frac{1}{4}$ square unit $\qquad F: \frac{1}{8}$ square unit

    $C: \frac{1}{16}$ square unit $\qquad G: \frac{1}{8}$ square unit

    $D: \frac{1}{8}$ square unit

Section 5.7
Pages 136-137

1. The area of the piece of tin that is cut from the square piece of tin is equal to one fourth of the area of a circle that has a radius of 30 cm. Therefore, we have the following.

    Area of square = 30 cm × 30 cm = 900 cm²

    Area of tin that is cut = $\frac{1}{4} \times \pi \times (30 \text{ cm})^2$

                           $\approx \frac{1}{4} \times 3.14 \times 900 \text{ cm}^2$

                           $\approx 706.5 \text{ cm}^2$

    Area of scraps $\approx 900 \text{ cm}^2 - 706.5 \text{ cm}^2$

                   $\approx \qquad 193.5 \text{ cm}^2$

2. a. From the placement of the disks in the given figure, we see that each circle has a diameter of 2 ft and a radius of 1 ft. Therefore, the area of the disks that are cut from the rectangular piece of tin is equal to eight times the area of a circle that has a radius of 1 ft. We then have the following.

    Area of rectangle = 8 ft × 4 ft = 32 ft²

    Area of disks = $8 \times \pi \times (1 \text{ ft})^2$

                   $\approx 8 \times 3.14 \times 1 \text{ ft}^2$

                   $\approx 25.12 \text{ ft}^2$

    Area of scraps $\approx 32 \text{ ft}^2 - 25.12 \text{ ft}^2$

                  $\approx \qquad 6.88 \text{ ft}^2$

    b. 1-ft diameter: 4 × 8 = 32

       2-ft radius: 1 × 2 = 2

       6-in. diameter: 8 × 16 = 128

       8-in. radius: 3 × 6 = 18

c. 1-ft diameter: $\approx 32 \text{ ft}^2 - 32 \times \pi \times \left(\frac{1}{2} \text{ ft}\right)^2$
$\approx 32 \text{ ft}^2 - 32 \times 3.14 \times \frac{1}{4} \text{ ft}^2$
$\approx 32 \text{ ft}^2 - 25.12 \text{ ft}^2$
$\approx 6.88 \text{ ft}^2$

2-ft radius: $\approx 32 \text{ ft}^2 - 2 \times \pi \times (2 \text{ ft})^2$
$\approx 32 \text{ ft}^2 - 2 \times 3.14 \times 4 \text{ ft}^2$
$\approx 32 \text{ ft}^2 - 25.12 \text{ ft}^2$
$\approx 6.88 \text{ ft}^2$

6-in. diameter: $\approx 32 \text{ ft}^2 - 128 \times \pi \times \left(\frac{1}{4} \text{ ft}\right)^2$
$\approx 32 \text{ ft}^2 - 128 \times 3.14 \times \frac{1}{16} \text{ ft}^2$
$\approx 32 \text{ ft}^2 - 25.12 \text{ ft}^2$
$\approx 6.88 \text{ ft}^2$

8-in. radius: $\approx 32 \text{ ft}^2 - 18 \times \pi \times \left(\frac{2}{3} \text{ ft}\right)^2$
$\approx 32 \text{ ft}^2 - 18 \times 3.14 \times \frac{4}{9} \text{ ft}^2$
$\approx 32 \text{ ft}^2 - 25.12 \text{ ft}^2$
$\approx 6.88 \text{ ft}^2$

3. Consider the situation as pictured in the diagram at the right. The shaded region represents the piece of paper remaining after all scraps have been discarded. The dashed lines separate the original piece of paper into four square regions; clearly, one half of each of these four regions has been discarded. Therefore, one half of the entire square has been discarded.

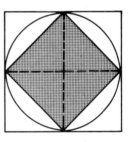

4. Note that 1.26 m = 126 cm.

Area of rectangle = 126 cm $\times$ 84 cm = 10,584 cm^2

Area of semicircle = $\frac{1}{2}$ (Area of circle)

$= \frac{1}{2} \times \pi \times (42 \text{ cm})^2$

$\approx \frac{1}{2} \times \frac{22}{7} \times 1764 \text{ cm}^2$

$\approx 2772 \text{ cm}^2$

Area of window = Area of rectangle + Area of semicircle

$\approx \quad 10,584 \text{ cm}^2 \quad + \quad 2772 \text{ cm}^2$

$\approx \qquad\qquad 13,356 \text{ cm}^2$

$\approx \qquad\qquad 1.34 \text{ m}^2$

5. Note that the radius of the outer circle is equal to the width of the ring plus the radius of the inner circle, or 10 cm + 5 cm = 15 cm.

Area of ring = Area of outer circle − Area of inner circle

$$
\begin{aligned}
&= & \pi \times 15^2 \quad &- & \pi \times 5^2 \\
&= & 225\,\pi \quad &- & 25\,\pi \\
&= & & 200\,\pi & \\
&\approx & 200 \times 3.14 \quad &\text{or} \quad 628 \text{ square units}
\end{aligned}
$$

6. Note that the two semicircles at the ends have a combined area equal to the area of one complete circle with diameter equal to 400 yd, or radius equal to 200 yd.

$$
\begin{aligned}
\text{Area of shaded region} &= \text{Area of square } + \text{ Area of circle} \\
&= 400 \text{ yd} \times 400 \text{ yd} + \pi \times (200 \text{ yd})^2 \\
&\approx 160{,}000 \text{ yd}^2 + 3.14 \times 40{,}000 \text{ yd}^2 \\
&\approx 160{,}000 \text{ yd}^2 + 125{,}600 \text{ yd}^2 \\
&\approx 285{,}600 \text{ yd}^2
\end{aligned}
$$

7. Note that the area of the shaded region is equal to the area of the large circle minus the area of the two small circles. Let r represent the radius of one of the small circles. Then $2r$ represents the radius of the large circle, and we have the following.

Area of large circle = $\pi \times (2r)^2 = 4\pi r^2$

Area of two small circles = $2 \times (\pi \times r^2) = 2\pi r^2$

Area of shaded region = $4\pi r^2 - 2\pi r^2 = 2\pi r^2$

The ratio of the area of the shaded region to the area of the large circle is $2\pi r^2$ to $4\pi r^2$, or 1 to 2.

8. a. Using a diagram such as the one at the right, note that the goat is able to graze on a piece of land that is shaped like $\frac{3}{4}$ of a circle with a radius equal to the length of the rope, which is 28 ft. Therefore, we have the following.

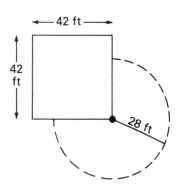

$$
\begin{aligned}
\text{Grazing area} &= \tfrac{3}{4} \times \pi r^2 \\
&\approx \tfrac{3}{4} \times \tfrac{22}{7} \times (28 \text{ ft})^2 \\
&\approx \tfrac{3}{4} \times \tfrac{22}{7} \times 784 \text{ ft}^2 \\
&\approx 1848 \text{ ft}^2
\end{aligned}
$$

The goat can graze on approximately 1848 ft² of land.

b. As in part **a**, the goat is able to graze on a piece
    of land that is shaped like $\frac{3}{4}$ of a circle with a
    radius equal to the length of the rope, which is
    56 ft. This time, though, a diagram helps to see
    that the goat can also graze on *two* smaller
    pieces of land that are in the shape of $\frac{1}{4}$ of a
    circle with a radius equal to 14 ft, the difference
    between the length of the rope and the length of
    a side of the barn. Therefore, we have the
    following.

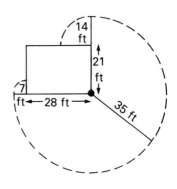

Large grazing area $= \frac{3}{4} \times \pi \times (56 \text{ ft})^2$

$\approx \frac{3}{4} \times \frac{22}{7} \times 3136 \text{ ft}^2$

$\approx 7392 \text{ ft}^2$

Small grazing areas $= 2 \times \frac{1}{4} \times \pi \times (14 \text{ ft})^2$

$\approx 2 \times \frac{1}{4} \times \frac{22}{7} \times 196 \text{ ft}^2$

$\approx 308 \text{ ft}^2$

Total grazing area $\approx 7392 \text{ ft}^2 + 308 \text{ ft}^2$

$\approx \quad\quad 7700 \text{ ft}^2$

The goat can graze on approximately 7700 ft²
of land.

9. Using a diagram and the reasoning employed in
    problem 8, we see that the grazing area can be
    separated into three distinct parts: $\frac{3}{4}$ of a circle with
    radius 35 ft, $\frac{1}{4}$ of a circle with radius 14 ft, and $\frac{1}{4}$ of a
    circle with radius 7 ft. Therefore, we have the
    following.

Grazing area $= \frac{3}{4} \times \pi \times (35 \text{ ft})^2 + \frac{1}{4} \times \pi \times (14 \text{ ft})^2 + \frac{1}{4} \times \pi + (7 \text{ ft})^2$

$\approx \frac{3}{4} \times \frac{22}{7} \times 1225 \text{ ft}^2 + \frac{1}{4} \times \frac{22}{7} \times 196 \text{ ft}^2 + \frac{1}{4} \times \frac{22}{7} + 49 \text{ ft}^2$

$\approx \quad 2887.5 \text{ ft}^2 \quad + \quad\quad 154 \text{ ft}^2 \quad + \quad\quad 38.5 \text{ ft}^2$

$\approx \quad\quad\quad\quad\quad\quad 3080 \text{ ft}^2$

The goat can graze on approximately 3080 ft² of land.

Section 5.8
Page 140

1. a. Five

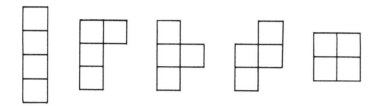

   b. If the length of the side of one of the squares measures 1 unit, then the perimeter of each of the first four tetrominoes above is 10, while the perimeter of the last tetromino is 8. Therefore, the square tetromino has the least perimeter.

2. a. One

   b. One

   c. Three

   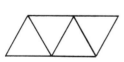 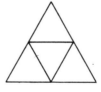 

3. Five

4. a.

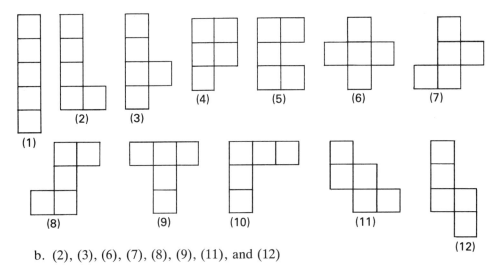

(1) (2) (3) (4) (5) (6) (7)

(8) (9) (10) (11) (12)

b. (2), (3), (6), (7), (8), (9), (11), and (12)

c. The following are three possible arrangements.

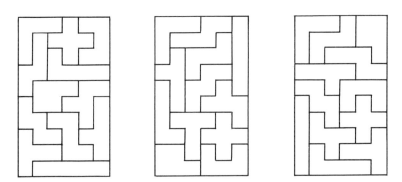

5. No. Each domino covers exactly two squares. The 3 by 3 grid contains 9 squares, and 9 ÷ 2 is not a whole number.

6. A checkerboard has 64 squares, usually 32 black squares and 32 colored squares in the alternating arrangement pictured on page 116. Note that each pair of diagonally opposite corner squares is of the same color. If two diagonally opposite corner squares are removed, the numbers of black and colored squares remaining will not be equal to each other. However, given its shape, each domino has to cover one black and one colored square. Furthermore, any whole number of dominoes must cover equal numbers of black and colored squares. Therefore, it is impossible for a whole number of dominoes to cover this board without overlapping.

Section 6.1
Page 143

1. The trains are separating at the rate of $95 + 105 = 200$ km/h.

   a. At the end of $2\frac{1}{2}$ h, the trains will be $2\frac{1}{2} \times 200 = 500$ km apart.

   b. For the trains to be 350 km apart, the amount of time needed will be $350 \div 200 = 1\frac{3}{4}$ h, or 1 h 45 min.

2. The trains are separating at the rate of $108 - 72 = 36$ km/h.

   a. At 1:05 P.M., the trains will have been traveling for 3 h 5 min, or $3\frac{1}{12}$ h. Therefore, they will be $3\frac{1}{12} \times 36 = 111$ km apart.

   b. For the trains to be 270 km apart, the amount of time needed will be $270 \div 36 = 7\frac{1}{2}$ h, or 7 h 30 min. This will occur at 5:30 P.M. of the same day.

3. Helen and Kenji are approaching each other at the rate of $6 + 8 = 14$ mi/h. If they meet in $\frac{1}{2}$ h, their distance apart when they started was $\frac{1}{2} \times 14 = 7$ mi.

4. The distance between the father and son is decreasing at the rate of $72 - 48 = 24$ km/h. Since they were 48 km apart when the son left home, it will take $48 \div 24 = 2$ h for the son to overtake his father.

5. Given the presence of the current, in this river Lisa can row downstream at the rate of $3 + 1 = 4$ mi/h and upstream at the rate of $3 - 1 = 2$ mi/h. Therefore, the 8-mi trip downstream will require $8 \div 4 = 2$ h, and the 8-mi trip upstream will require $8 \div 2 = 4$ h. The entire trip takes a total of $2 + 4 = 6$ h.

6. If the trains are 270 km apart and pass each other in 3 h, they were approaching each other at the rate of $270 \div 3 = 90$ km/h. However, 90 km/h is the *sum* of their two rates. Suppose that x represents the rate of the freight train. Then $2x$ represents the rate of the passenger train, and we have the following.

$$x + 2x = 90$$
$$3x = 90$$
$$\frac{3x}{3} = \frac{90}{3}$$
$$x = 30$$

   The rate of the freight train is 30 km/h, and the rate of the passenger train is $2 \times 30 = 60$ km/h.

7. Draw a diagram such as the following.

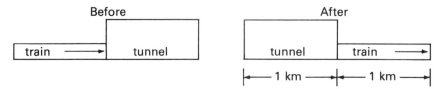

Before   After

train → | tunnel   tunnel | train →

|← 1 km →|← 1 km →|

From the diagram, we see that the train must travel a distance of 2 km to clear the tunnel. The train is traveling at the rate of 30 km/h, which is the same as 30 km per 60 min or 1 km per 2 min. Therefore, it takes the train $2 \times 2 = 4$ min to travel 2 km and clear the tunnel.

8. The freight train is passing Leo at a rate equal to the *combined* rates of the passenger and freight trains, or $40 + 20 = 60$ mi/h. The rate of 60 mi/h is the same as 60 mi per 3600 seconds. Since 15 seconds is $\frac{1}{240}$ of 3600 seconds, the length of the freight train is $\frac{1}{240}$ of 60 mi, or $\frac{1}{4}$ mi.

9. After the front parts of the trains meet, each train must travel the length of the other train before the rear parts meet and pass. Since each train is $\frac{1}{12}$ mi long, each train must then travel $\frac{1}{12}$ mi. Each train is traveling at the rate of 50 mi/h, which is the same as 50 mi per 3600 seconds, or 1 mi per 72 seconds. To travel $\frac{1}{12}$ mi, then, each train requires $\frac{1}{12} \times 72 = 6$ seconds. Therefore, the rear parts of the trains will pass each other 6 seconds after the front parts meet.

10. The trains are approaching each other at the rate of $55 + 65 = 120$ km/h. Since they only need to travel a combined distance of 60 km, they will meet in $\frac{1}{2}$ h. Although the bee reverses its direction frequently, it is flying at a constant rate of 80 km/h. Therefore, in $\frac{1}{2}$ h the bee will have flown $\frac{1}{2}$ of 80 km, or 40 km.

Section 6.2
Page 145

1. a.

Page Numbers	Number of Digits
1-9	$9 \times 1 = 9$
10-99	$90 \times 2 = 180$
100-375	$276 \times 3 = 828$
Total	1017

The printer will need a total of 1017 pieces of type.

b. Ones' place: 38

   Tens' place: 40

   Hundreds' place: 76

   The total number of 3s that the printer will need is 38 + 40 + 76 = 154.

c. Ones' place: 38

   Tens' place: 40

   Hundreds' place: 0

   The total number of 4s that the printer will need is 38 + 40 + 0 = 78.

d. Ones' place: 37

   Tens' place: 30

   Hundreds' place: 0

   The total number of 8s that the printer will need is 37 + 30 + 0 = 67.

2. From the solution to problem **1a**, we already know that pages 1 through 99 require 9 + 180 = 189 pieces of type. Then the remaining pages of this book must require 402 − 189 = 213 pieces of type. Since each page following page 99 requires 3 pieces of type (until page 1000 is reached), there must be 213 ÷ 3 = 71 remaining pages, beginning with page 100. The next 71 pages would be numbered 101, 102, 103, . . . , 170. Therefore, this book contains 170 pages.

3. Begin by finding two perfect-square numbers that bound the product. For example, $30^2 = 900$ and $40^2 = 1600$. We now know that the two page numbers are between 30 and 40. Since the ones' digit of the product is 0, one of the page numbers has to be 35. Since 35 is a right-hand page, the facing page is a left-hand page, and its number is 34.

4. Method 1: write and solve an equation.

   Since the pages would be numbered consecutively, they can be represented by n, $n + 1$, $n + 2$, $n + 3$, $n + 4$, and $n + 5$. We then have the following.

   $$n + (n + 1) + (n + 2) + (n + 3) + (n + 4) + (n + 5) = 513$$
   $$6n + 15 = 513$$
   $$6n + 15 - 15 = 513 - 15$$
   $$6n = 498$$
   $$\frac{6n}{6} = \frac{498}{6}$$
   $$n = 83$$

   The first page number is 83, followed by 84, 85, 86, 87, and 88.

Method 2: use deduction.

Since the pages would be numbered with six consecutive counting numbers, we know that the average of the six page numbers is $513 \div 6 = 85.5$. Therefore, the middle two page numbers are 85 and 86, and the other page numbers are the two numbers immediately preceding 85 and the two numbers immediately following 86. The complete set of page numbers is then 83, 84, 85, 86, 87, and 88.

Section 6.3
Pages 147-148

1. Working alone, the adult can do $\frac{1}{3}$ of the job in one hour and the child can do $\frac{1}{7}$ of the job in one hour. Working together, the adult and child can do $\frac{1}{3} + \frac{1}{7} = \frac{10}{21}$ of the job in one hour. Since $\frac{10}{21}$ of the job requires one hour, $\frac{1}{21}$ of the job requires $\frac{1}{10}$ of one hour, or 6 min. The entire job will then require $21 \times 6 = 126$ min, or two hours six minutes.

2. Working alone, the old-model machine can stamp $\frac{1}{4}$ of the parts in one hour and the new-model machine can stamp $\frac{1}{2}$ of the parts in one hour. (Notice that the exact number of parts is extraneous information.) Working together, the two machines can stamp $\frac{1}{4} + \frac{1}{2} = \frac{3}{4}$ of the parts in one hour. Since $\frac{3}{4}$ of the parts require one hour, $\frac{1}{4}$ of the parts require $\frac{1}{3}$ of one hour, or 20 min. To stamp all the parts then, the two machines will need $4 \times 20 = 80$ min, or one hour twenty minutes.

3. Working alone, Laura can do $\frac{1}{3}$ of the job in one day, Eric can do $\frac{1}{4}$ of the job in one day, and Connie can do $\frac{1}{4}$ of the job in one day. Working together, all three can do $\frac{1}{3} + \frac{1}{4} + \frac{1}{4} = \frac{5}{6}$ of the job in one day. Since $\frac{5}{6}$ of the job requires one day, $\frac{1}{6}$ of the job requires $\frac{1}{5}$ of a day. The entire job will then require $6 \times \frac{1}{5} = 1\frac{1}{5}$ days.

4. In one minute, water from the faucet will fill $\frac{1}{3}$ of the tub and the open drain will empty $\frac{1}{4}$ of the tub. When both the faucet and drain are open, $\frac{1}{3} - \frac{1}{4} = \frac{1}{12}$ of the tub will be filled in one minute. Therefore, it will take 12 min for the tub to fill completely.

5. Working alone, it would take one worker $9 \times 8 = 72$ days to pave the stretch of road. Therefore, it would take 12 workers $72 \div 12 = 6$ days to do the job working together.

6. The number of individual daily rations that were purchased is $6 \times 15 = 90$. Therefore, a group of 9 scouts will consume the rations in $90 \div 9 = 10$ days.

7. Working alone, it would take one machine $4 \times 6 = 24$ min to make the copies. Therefore, 3 machines working together would require $24 \div 3 = 8$ min to make the copies.

8. Working alone, the faster computer can do $\frac{1}{20}$ of the payroll in one minute. Therefore, in $13\frac{1}{3}$ min the faster computer can do $13\frac{1}{3} \times \frac{1}{20} = \frac{2}{3}$ of the payroll. Thus, in $13\frac{1}{3}$ min, the *slower* computer can do $\frac{1}{3}$ of the payroll. To do the entire payroll, then, the slower computer requires $3 \times 13\frac{1}{3} = 40$ min.

Section 6.4
Page 149

1. a. As discussed on page 148, the clock must gain a total of 720 min before it again shows the correct time. Since it gains 3 min every hour, it will gain 720 min in $720 \div 3 = 240$ h, which is ten days.

   b. This clock needs to *lose* a total of 720 min before it again shows the correct time. Since it loses 2 min every hour, it will lose 720 min in $720 \div 2 = 360$ h, which is fifteen days.

   c. This clock must gain a total of 720 min $= 43{,}200$ s before it again shows the correct time. Since it gains 2 s every 3 h, it gains $\frac{2}{3}$ s every hour. Thus it will gain 43,200 s in $43{,}200 \div \frac{2}{3} = 64{,}800$ h, which is 2700 days.

2. The complete clock face is associated with the 360° of a circle, and each of the 12 hour-intervals around the clock is associated with $360 \div 12 = 30°$. Therefore, the hands of a clock will form an angle that measures 60° at any time when exactly two of these hour-intervals lie between them. The only hours at which this occurs are 2 o'clock and 10 o'clock.

3. a. The hands of a clock lie directly opposite each other 11 times in each twelve-hour interval, or 22 times each day.

   b. The hands of a clock are perpendicular to each other 22 times in each twelve-hour interval, or 44 times each day.

4. In the course of one hour, the hour hand of the clock touches just *five* of the sixty minute-marks. Therefore, the hour hand points exactly at one of the minute-marks every one fifth of an hour, or every twelve minutes: 1:00, 1:12, 1:24, 1:36, 1:48, 2:00, 2:12, 2:24, and so on through the day. Examining these times, though, we see that: at 1:00 there are 4 minute-marks between the hour and minute hands; at 1:12 there are 5 minute-marks between the hour and minute hands; at 1:24 there are 16 minute-marks between the hour and minute

hands; and so on. The only times when the hour and minute hands point exactly to adjacent minute-marks are 2:12 and 9:48. Therefore, Larry looked at the clock at either 2:12 A.M., 9:48 A.M., 2:12 P.M., or 9:48 P.M.

5. Method 1: use deduction.

Since the time that had elapsed since noon was equal to half the time that remained until midnight, note that the time that had elapsed since noon was also one third of the total time from noon until midnight. Therefore, the time that had elapsed since noon was one third of twelve hours, or four hours. The time was 4:00 P.M.

Method 2: write and solve an equation.

Using the variable t to represent the amount of time that had elapsed since noon, the expression $12 - t$ represents the amount of time that remains until midnight. The information given in the problem can then be translated into the following equation.

$$t = \tfrac{1}{2}(12 - t)$$
$$t = 6 - \tfrac{1}{2}t$$
$$t + \tfrac{1}{2}t = 6 - \tfrac{1}{2}t + \tfrac{1}{2}t$$
$$\tfrac{3}{2}t = 6$$
$$\tfrac{3}{2}t \times \tfrac{2}{3} = 6 \times \tfrac{2}{3}$$
$$t = 4$$

The amount of time that had elapsed since noon was 4 h, and the time was 4:00 P.M.

6. In each twelve-hour interval, there is a 2 in the hour display constantly during the 2nd and 12th hours. This is a total of four hours each day, for $4 \times 60 = 240$ min.

For the remaining twenty hours of the day, there is a 2 in the tens' place of the minute display for ten minutes of every hour (from :20 to :29). This is a total of $20 \times 10 = 200$ min.

For the remaining fifty minutes of each of the twenty hours, there is a 2 in the minute display once every ten minutes (:02, :12, :22, :32, :42, and :52), or five minutes every hour. This is a total of $20 \times 5 = 100$ min.

Therefore, there is at least one 2 in the display of the clock for $240 + 200 + 100 = 540$ min of the day.

7. Sixty actual minutes take only $60 - 6 = 54$ min of time on the slow clock. Then one minute of time on the slow clock takes $\frac{60}{54} = 1\tfrac{1}{9}$ actual min. The slow clock takes 90 of its minutes in going from 10:30 A.M. to 12:00. The *actual* time for this period is $90 \times 1\tfrac{1}{9} = 100$ min, or 1 h 40 min. Therefore, when the slow clock first shows 12:00, the correct time will be 12:10 P.M.

Section 6.5
Pages 153-154

1. If we continue with the group of five people discussed on pages 150-151, then the presence of a sixth person requires 5 new handshakes, for a total of 10 + 5 = 15 handshakes.

2.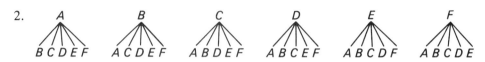

   The tree diagram displays a total of $6 \times 5 = 30$ connections, but each handshake has been counted twice. Therefore, there are $30 \div 2 = 15$ distinct handshakes.

3.

Number of People	Number of Handshakes
2	1
3	3
4	6
5	10
6	15
7	21
8	28

4. The entries in the "Number of Handshakes" column form a pattern of increasing differences, as discussed in Section 1.3. Add two entries to the table in problem 3 to find the number of handshakes that would be exchanged by 10 people.

   1   3   6   10   15   21   28   36   45
   ↘+2↗↘+3↗↘+4↗↘+5↗↘+6↗↘+7↗↘+8↗↘+9↗

   If each person shakes hands with each of the others exactly once, ten people would exchange 45 handshakes.

5. Consider the logic employed in the tree diagram. If the variable n represents the number of people, then each person shakes hands $(n - 1)$ times. However, the expression $n \times (n - 1)$ counts each handshake twice, so the total number of handshakes exchanged is $n \times (n - 1) \div 2$. Therefore, we are looking for two consecutive numbers whose product is 240, since $240 \div 2 = 120$, the given number

of handshakes. Since $10^2 = 100$ and $20^2 = 400$, the numbers are between 10 and 20. Since the ones' digit of 240 is 0, one of the numbers must be 15; $240 \div 15 = 16$, so the other number is 16. There are 16 people in the group.

6. $20 \times 19 \div 2 = 280 \div 2 = 190$
   There will be 190 games played altogether.

7. Since these problems are examples of the same mathematical model as used in the handshake problem, the answers here are the same as for the numbers of handshakes exchanged by 6, 7, 8, and 10 people.

   a. 15   b. 21   c. 28   d. 45

8. Although the five points lie on the same line, the number of segments that can be named is the same as if the points did *not* lie on the same line. There are 10 segments, and they can be listed as follows.

   $\overline{AB}$ $\overline{AC}$ $\overline{AD}$ $\overline{AE}$

   $\overline{BC}$ $\overline{BD}$ $\overline{BE}$

   $\overline{CD}$ $\overline{CE}$

   $\overline{DE}$

9. The total number of sides *and* diagonals will be the same as the total number of line segments that can be drawn connecting 10 points that do not lie on a straight line. As discussed in problem **7d**, this number is 45. Ten of these segments form the 10 sides of the decagon, so the number of diagonals must be $45 - 10 = 35$.

10. The solution of this problem can be related to the solution of the handshake problem in the following manner. Clearly the figure in part **a** contains just one rectangle, so consider the figure in part **b**. Each of the 3 vertical segments of the figure can be assigned a letter as follows.

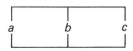

    Note that each pair of these vertical segments determines one rectangle. Therefore, all the rectangles in the figure may be listed as follows.

    a, b   *a, c*

    b, c

The total number of rectangles is 3, the same as the number of handshakes exchanged among 3 people. The figures in parts **c** through **f** can be related similarly to the numbers of handshakes exchanged among 4, 5, 6, and 7 people.

a. 1   b. 3   c. 6   d. 10   e. 15   f. 21

11. The solution of this problem can be related to the solution of problem 10 in the following manner. Consider the figure in part **a**. Note that the first column of the figure is similar to the figure in part **b** of problem 10, so the first column alone contains 3 rectangles. But each rectangle in the first column also marks a *row* of 3 rectangles, as shown below.

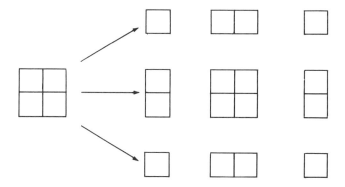

Since there are 3 rows of 3 rectangles, the entire figure contains $3 \times 3 = 9$ rectangles. Following the same reasoning, the figures in parts **b**, **c**, and **d** can be related, respectively, to the figures in parts **c**, **d**, and **e** of problem 10.

a. $3 \times 3 = 9$ b. $6 \times 6 = 36$ c. $10 \times 10 = 100$ d. $15 \times 15 = 225$

12. Follow the reasoning employed in problem 11. The total number of rectangles on a standard 8 by 8 checkerboard is $36 \times 36 = 1296$.

Section 7.1
Pages 157-158

1. a.
$$\begin{array}{r} 9 \\ + \ 1 \\ \hline 10 \end{array}$$
b.
$$\begin{array}{r} 1673 \\ + \ 9058 \\ \hline 10731 \end{array}$$
or
$$\begin{array}{r} 1453 \\ + \ 9078 \\ \hline 10531 \end{array}$$
c.
$$\begin{array}{r} 91 \\ + \ 9 \\ \hline 100 \end{array}$$

d.
$$\begin{array}{r} 9567 \\ + \ 1085 \\ \hline 10652 \end{array}$$
e.
$$\begin{array}{r} 37 \\ \times \ 9 \\ \hline 333 \end{array}$$
f.
$$\begin{array}{r} 125 \\ \times \ 5 \\ \hline 625 \end{array}$$
or
$$\begin{array}{r} 175 \\ \times \ 5 \\ \hline 875 \end{array}$$

g.
```
  2178
×    4
 8712
```

h.
```
  142857
×      3
 428571
```
or
```
  285714
×      3
 857142
```

i.
```
   57
×  13
  171
   57
  741
```

j.
```
   25
×  15
  125
   25
  375
```

k.
```
   513
×   15
  2565
   513
  7695
```

l.
```
   7029
×   519
  63261
   7029
  35145
 3648051
```

m.
```
       21
  45)954
     90
     54
     45
      9
```

n.
```
        31
  247)7657
      741
      247
      247
```

o.
```
         135
  235)31725
      235
      822
      705
     1175
     1175
```

p. $(10)^2 = 100$ q. $(11)^2 = 121$ r. $\sqrt{10201} = 101$

2. a.
```
    78
×   45
   390
   312
  3510
```

b.
```
    415
×   382
    830
   3320
   1245
 158530
```

c.
```
    725
×   146
   4350
   2900
    725
 105850
```

d.
```
        20301
  45)913545
     90
     135
     135
       45
       45
```

e.
```
         997
  35)34895
     315
     339
     315
     245
     245
```

f.
```
          90809
  12)1089708
     108
       97
       96
      108
      108
```

3. a.
```
    364
×    27
   2548
    728
   9828
```

b.
```
    286
×   826
   1716
    572
   2288
 236236
```

c.
```
     8662
×     834
    34648
    25986
    69296
  7224108
```

4.
```
   21514
−   4641
   16873
```

```
   54146
−   6764
   47382
```

5. If you choose A, B, C, and D to represent the digits of the unknown number, then the problem can be represented by the following cryptarithm.

$$
\begin{array}{r}
14ABCD \\
\times \quad\quad 2 \\
\hline
ABCD14
\end{array}
$$

Solving the cryptarithm, we obtain the following.

$$
\begin{array}{r}
142857 \\
\times \quad\quad 2 \\
\hline
285714
\end{array}
$$

Therefore, the four-digit number is 2857.

Section 7.2
Pages 160-161

1. Follow the reasoning employed in the discussion on pages 159-160.
   a. 4   b. 22   c. 22

2. Follow the reasoning employed in the discussion on pages 159-160.
   a. 3   b. 12   c. 10   d. 12

3. It is not sufficient to select 4 checkers, since then there is a possibility that you have selected 3 of one color and 1 of the other color. It is also not sufficient to select 5 checkers, since there is a possibility that you have selected 3 of one color and 2 of the other color. Nor is it sufficient to select 6 checkers, since there is still a possibility that you have selected 3 of one color and 3 of the other. However, with the selection of 7 checkers, every possible combination that you could select contains at least 4 checkers of one color. Therefore, to be certain that you have 4 checkers of one color, you must select 7 checkers from the bag.

4. If you select 15 buttons, there is still a possibility that you have selected 3 buttons of each of the 5 colors. However, if you add just one more button to the number you select, then you are certain that you have selected at least 4 buttons of one color. Therefore, you need to select 16 buttons.

5. A standard deck of 52 playing cards contains 4 cards of each of 13 face-values. If you select 13 cards, there is a possibility that each card has a different value. However, if you select one more card, you are then certain that you have at least one pair of the same value. Therefore, you need to select 14 cards.

6. If 12 people are gathered together, there is a possibility that each has a birthday that falls in a different month of the year. However, if one more person is added to the group, then there must be at least 2 people of the group who have birthdays that fall in the same month. Therefore, 13 people must be gathered together.

7. There are 366 possible birthdays. If the school had an enrollment of 366 students, there is a possibility that each has a birthday that falls on a different day of the year. The addition of a 367th student would then guarantee that at least 2 students had birthdays that match. Since this school has 400 students, it is certain that at least two of these students have birthdays that fall on the same day of the year.

8. Suppose that the school had an enrollment of $2 \times 366 = 732$ students. Then there is a possibility that each of the 366 possible birthdays is shared by exactly 2 students. However, if one more student were added to this enrollment, then one birthday would have to be shared by 3 students. Therefore, a school must have an enrollment of 733 students to be certain that there are three students enrolled whose birthdays fall on the same day of the year.

9. a. There are 26 possible first-name initials. Then if 26 people are gathered together, there is a possibility that each has a different first-name initial. However, if one person were added to this group, then one first-name initial would have to be shared by 2 people. Therefore, 27 people must be gathered together.

   b. Suppose that $2 \times 26 = 52$ people are gathered together. Then there is a possibility that each of the 26 possible last-name initials is shared by exactly 2 people. However, if one more person were now added to this group, then one last-name initial must be shared by 3 people. Therefore, 53 people must be gathered together.

   c. There are $26 \times 26 = 676$ possible combinations of first-name and last-name initials. If 676 people were gathered together, there is a possibility that each has a different combination. However, if one more person were added to the group, then one combination must be shared by 2 people. Therefore, 677 people must be gathered together.

10. There are more than 7 million people in New York City. If we subtract the 1 million bald people, then more than 6 million people have hair on their heads. Consider just 1 million of these people. If the biologists are correct, there is a possibility that each of these 1 million people has a different number of hairs on her or his head. With the addition of just one person to this 1 million, two people must have the same number of hairs on their heads. Therefore, since there are more than 6 million people in New York City who have hair on their heads, at least two of these people must have the same number of hairs on their heads.

Section 7.3
Pages 164-165

1. a. Use a Venn diagram such as the one at the right. Circle F represents those students who study French, circle S represents those students who study Spanish, and n represents the number of students who study both French and Spanish. Label the diagram with the given information, then write and solve an equation.

$$
\begin{aligned}
\text{I} \quad + \text{II} + \quad \text{III} \quad &= 30 \\
(21 - n) + n + (14 - n) &= 30 \\
35 - n &= 30 \\
n &= 5
\end{aligned}
$$

There are 5 students who study both French and Spanish.

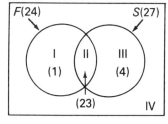

b. Use a Venn diagram such as the one at the right. Here circle F represents those students who passed the first math test and circle S represents those students who passed the second math test. Region IV of the diagram then represents those who failed both tests. Since 23 students passed both tests, the value of region II is 23. Since circle F represents 24 students, the value of region I is $24 - 23 = 1$. Since circle S represents 27 students, the value of region III is $27 - 23 = 4$. So I + II + III = 1 + 23 + 4 = 28, and the value of region IV is $30 - 28 = 2$.

There are 2 students who failed both tests.

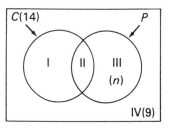

c. Use a Venn diagram such as the one at the right. Here circle C represents those students who had studied chemistry and circle P represents those students who had studied physics. Region III then represents those students who had studied physics but not chemistry. Label the diagram with the given information, then write and solve an equation. (Note that, since circle C represents 14 students, the value of regions I and II together is 14.)

$$I + II + III = 30 - 9$$
$$I + II + III = 21$$
$$14 \quad + \ n = 21$$
$$n = 7$$

There are 7 students who studied physics but not chemistry.

d. Use a Venn diagram such as the one at the right. (This is only one of many diagrams that can be drawn to represent this situation.) Here circle M represents those students who study a musical instrument, and a vertical line separates both the rectangle and the circle into separate regions that represent boys and girls. Region IV then represents those girls who do not play a musical instrument. Let n represent the number of girls in this region. Label the diagram, then write and solve an equation.

$B(14)$ $G(16)$ $M(13)$ I   II   (6) $(16 - n)$ III   IV(n)

$$I + \quad II \quad = 13$$
$$6 + (16 - n) = 13$$
$$22 - n = 13$$
$$n = 9$$

There are 9 girls who do not play a musical instrument.

2. Use a Venn diagram such as the one at the right. Here circle E represents those students who study English, circle H represents those students who study history, and circle M represents those students who study math. Label the diagram with the given information.

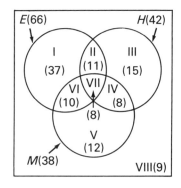

To find the values of regions II, IV, and VI, consider the following simple equations.

II + VII = 19	IV + VII = 16	VI + VII = 18
II + 8 = 19	IV + 8 = 16	VI + 8 = 18
II = 11	IV = 8	VI = 10

Similarly, to find the values of regions I, III, and V, consider these equations.

$$I + II + VII + VI = 66 \qquad III + IV + VII + II = 42$$
$$I + 11 + 8 + 10 = 66 \qquad III + 8 + 8 + 11 = 42$$
$$I + 29 = 66 \qquad\qquad III + 27 = 42$$
$$I = 37 \qquad\qquad\qquad III = 15$$

$$V + VI + VII + IV = 38$$
$$V + 10 + 8 + 8 = 38$$
$$V + 26 = 38$$
$$V = 12$$

Finally, to find the value of region VIII, solve one more simple equation.

$$I + II + III + IV + V + VI + VII + VIII = 120$$
$$37 + 11 + 15 + 8 + 12 + 10 + 8 + VIII = 120$$
$$101 + VIII = 120$$
$$VIII = 19$$

a. This is the value of region V.
   There are 12 students who study math but neither English nor history.

b. This is the value of region VI.
   There are 10 students who study English and math but not history.

c. This is the value of region VIII.
   There are 19 students who study none of the three subjects.

3. Use a Venn diagram such as the one at the right. Here circles A, B, and C represent those students who had read books A, B, and C, respectively. Label the diagram with the given information, using the method employed in problem 2 to find the values of regions II, IV, VI, I, III, and V. Then the number of students in the class, n, is equal to the sum of the values of regions I through VII.

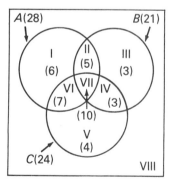

$$n = I + II + III + IV + V + VI + VII$$
$$n = 6 + 5 + 3 + 3 + 4 + 7 + 10$$
$$n = 38$$

There were 38 students in the class.

4. Use a Venn diagram such as the one at the right. Here circle *Sa* represents those people who ordered salad, circle *So* represents those people who ordered soup, and circle *D* represents those people who ordered dessert. Label the diagram with the given information, using the method discussed in problem 2 to find the values of regions II, IV, VI, I, III, and V.

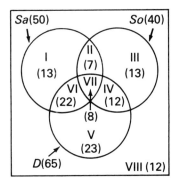

a. This is the value of region VI.
   There are 22 people who ordered salad and dessert but not soup.

b. This is the combined values of regions I and II, or 13 + 7 = 20.
   There are 20 people who ordered salad but not dessert.

c. This is the value of region III.
   There are 13 people who ordered only soup.

d. The total number of people, *n*, is equal to the sum of the values of all the regions I through VIII.

$$n = \text{I} + \text{II} + \text{III} + \text{IV} + \text{V} + \text{VI} + \text{VII} + \text{VIII}$$
$$n = 13 + 7 + 13 + 12 + 23 + 22 + 8 + 12$$
$$n = 110$$

   There were 110 people in all.

5. Use a Venn diagram such as the one at the right. Here circles *F*, *E*, and *S* represent those people who visited France, England, and Spain, respectively. Label the diagram with the given information, using the reasoning employed in problem 2 to label the value of region VI as 2. To find the values of the remaining regions, I, II, and IV, study the diagram and consider the following.

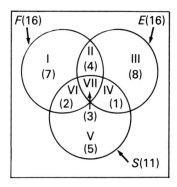

$$\begin{array}{ll}
\text{IV} + \text{V} + \text{VI} + \text{VII} = 11 & \text{II} + \text{III} + \text{IV} + \text{VII} = 16 \\
\text{IV} + 5 + 2 + 3 = 11 & \text{II} + 8 + 1 + 3 = 16 \\
\text{IV} + 10 = 11 & \text{II} + 12 = 16 \\
\text{IV} = 1 & \text{II} = 4
\end{array}$$

$$I + II + VII + VI = 16$$
$$I + 4 + 3 + 2 = 16$$
$$I + 9 = 16$$
$$I = 7$$

The number of people who visited only France is the value of region I, so 7 people visited only France.

6. Use a Venn diagram such as the one at the right. Here, the left half of the rectangle represents males (M), the right half of the rectangle represents females (F), circle L represents those mice who turned left, and circle T represents those mice who were previously trained. Region IV represents those female mice who were not previously trained and who did not turn left. Using the given information and the reasoning processes discussed in problems 2 through 5, we can label the diagram as shown. Then to find the value of region IV, write and solve a simple equation.

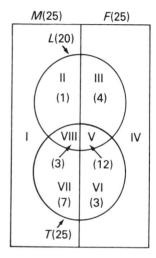

$$IV + III + V + VI = 25$$
$$IV + 4 + 12 + 3 = 25$$
$$IV + 19 = 25$$
$$IV = 6$$

There are 6 female mice who were not previously trained who did not turn left.

Section 7.4
Pages 170-171

1. Stage 1:

	1st	2nd	3rd
A	✕		✕
B			
D			✕

Stage 2:

	1st	2nd	3rd
A	✕	✓	✕
B			✓
D			✕

Stage 3:

	1st	2nd	3rd
A	✕	✓	✕
B	✕	✕	✓
D	✓	✕	✕

Dave plays first base.

2. Stage 1:

	S	L	C
K			
L		✕	
M		✕	✕

Stage 2:

	S	L	C
K		✓	
L		✕	
M	✓	✕	✕

Stage 3:

	S	L	C
K	✕	✓	✕
L	✕	✕	✓
M	✓	✕	✕

Kate had lamb chops, Linda had chicken, and Maya had steak.

3. Stage 1:

Specialties

	P	O	S
P	✕		
O		✕	
S		✕	✕

Stage 2:

	P	O	S
P	✕	✓	
O		✕	
S	✓	✕	✕

Stage 3:

	P	O	S
P	✕	✓	✕
O	✕	✕	✓
S	✓	✕	✕

Pierce's specialty is orthopedics, Otis's specialty is surgery, and Simmons's specialty is pediatrics.

4. Note that two of the first names are female and one is male. This is important in Stage 1, where the information that Clancy is Jacqueline's uncle indicates that Clancy is male and is therefore neither Jacqueline *nor* Helen. Also enter the information that Helen's last name is not Barrow.

Stage 1:

		A	B	C
(f)	H		✕	✕
(m)	I			
(f)	J			✕

Stage 2:

		A	B	C
(f)	H	✓	✕	✕
(m)	I			✓
(f)	J			✕

Stage 3:

		A	B	C
(f)	H	✓	✕	✕
(m)	I	✕	✕	✓
(f)	J	✕	✓	✕

The names are Helen Abrams, Irving Clancy, and Jacqueline Barrow.

5. Note that two of the first names are female and two are male. Therefore, the information that a boy likes blue means that, in Stage 1, we can enter the information that neither Ina nor Jill likes blue. Since one of the girls likes red, we can also enter the information that neither Louis nor Miguel likes red.

Furthermore, the statement that no person's name contains the same number of letters as her or his favorite color indicates that Ina does not like red, Jill does not like blue, Louis does not like green, and Miguel does not like orange.

Stage 1:

		R	B	G	O
(f)	I	×	×		
(f)	J		×		
(m)	L	×	×	×	
(m)	M	×			×

Stage 2:

	R	B	G	O
I	×	×		
J	√	×		
L	×	×	×	√
M	×	√		×

Stage 3:

	R	B	G	O
I	×	×	√	×
J	√	×	×	×
L	×	×	×	√
M	×	√	×	×

Ina's favorite color is green, Jill's favorite color is red, Louis's favorite color is orange, and Miguel's favorite color is blue.

6. Note that the information that the rabbit and cat recently gave birth identifies the rabbit and cat as the females and the turtle and dog as the males. Therefore, the information that Mike is a mother allows us to deduce in Stage 1 that Mike is neither the turtle nor dog. The information that Star likes to have *his* back rubbed indicates that Star is male, and therefore is neither the rabbit nor cat. Other statements also allow us to deduce that the rabbit is neither Pete nor Mike, and that Pete is not the dog.

Stage 1:

		S	M	B	P
(f)	R	×	×		×
(m)	T		×		
(m)	D		×		×
(f)	C	×			

Stage 2:

	S	M	B	P
R	×	×	√	×
T		×		
D		×		×
C	×	√		

Stage 3:

	S	M	B	P
R	×	×	√	×
T	×	×	×	√
D	√	×	×	×
C	×	√	×	×

The rabbit is Butch, the turtle is Pete, the dog is Star, and the cat is Mike.

7. Note that the word "her" is used in referring to both Ivanov and Malinkov, so both are female. "His" is used in referring to the composer, and "he" is used in referring to the dancer, so both are male. Therefore, we can immediately deduce that neither Ivanov nor Malinkov is the composer or the dancer. Other statements allow us to further deduce that Lebedev is not the dancer and that Malinkov is not the singer.

Stage 1:

	A	C	D	S
(f) I		×	×	
J				
L			×	
(f) M		×	×	×

Stage 2:

	A	C	D	S
I		×	×	
J			√	
L			×	
M	√	×	×	×

Stage 3:

	A	C	D	S
I	×	×	×	√
J	×	×	√	×
L	×	√	×	×
M	√	×	×	×

Ivanov is a female singer, Jacobowski is a male dancer, Lebedev is a male composer, and Malinkov is a female architect.

8. Note that two of the first names are female and two are male. Therefore, since Insull is a grandmother, Insull is neither Charles nor Edward. Dolores is an infant, so Dolores cannot be a grandmother; therefore, Dolores cannot be Insull. Also note that Dolores is not Hendricks.

Stage 1:

	G	H	I	J
(m) C			×	
(f) D		×	×	
(m) E			×	
(f) F				

Stage 2:

	G	H	I	J
C			×	
D		×	×	
E			×	
F			√	

Felice Insull is Jackson's grandmother. But statements in the problem indicate that she is related to neither Charles nor Dolores. Therefore, Jackson's first name must be Edward.

Stage 3:

	G	H	I	J
C			×	
D		×	×	
E			×	√
F			√	

Stage 4:

	G	H	I	J
C	×	√	×	×
D	√	×	×	×
E	×	×	×	√
F	×	×	√	×

The names are Charles Hendricks, Dolores Gold, Edward Jackson, and Felice Insull.

9. In making a chart for the solution of this problem, note the following. Since Charlotte is younger than both Deborah and Knutsen, Charlotte must be 10 years old. We know that Charlotte is not Knutsen, so Knutsen must be either 11 or 12 years old. Since Lattimer is older than Knutsen, Lattimer must be 12 years old, while Knutsen is 11 years old. Also note that Deborah cannot be Knutsen. The completed chart is shown below.

	J	K	L	10	11	12
C	√	×	×	√	×	×
D	×	×	√	×	×	√
E	×	√	×	×	√	×
10	√	×	×			
11	×	√	×			
12	×	×	√			

Charlotte Jones is 10 years old, Deborah Lattimer is 12 years old, and Ethan Knutsen is 11 years old.

10. In making a chart for the solution of this problem, note the following. According to the first names, two of the students are male and one is female. The third statement indicates that Farelli is female, so Nancy's last name is Farelli. Nancy did not use the hammer or the saw, so she used the plane. Oliver's last name is not Ellis, so it must be Gross. Then Peter's last name is Ellis. Oliver Gross did not use the hammer, so he must have used the saw while Peter Ellis used the hammer. The completed chart is shown below.

	S	H	P	E	F	G
N	×	×	√	×	√	×
O	√	×	×	×	×	√
P	×	√	×	√	×	×
E	×	√	×			
F	×	×	√			
G	√	×	×			

Nancy Farelli used the plane, Oliver Gross used the saw, and Peter Ellis used the hammer.

11. Mr. Jones is not the porter's nearest neighbor because his earnings of $50,000 cannot be exactly three times as much as the porter's earnings. Since Mr. Robinson lives in Detroit, Mr. Smith must be the porter's nearest neighbor, and Mr. Jones lives in Chicago. This tells us that the porter's last name is Jones. Since Smith is not the conductor, it follows that Smith is the engineer.

12. Examining the given statements, notice that, if ii and iii were *both* false, then both Alice and Carolyn would have gone to Bali. However, this contradicts the given information that each of the three women went to different places. Therefore, either ii or iii must be true. But notice that iii and iv cannot both be false, since then Alice would have gone to both Bali and China. Therefore, iii must be true, and the other statements are false. Since ii is false, Carolyn went to Bali. Since iv is false, Alice went to China. It then follows that Betty went to Africa.

Resource Problems

Foreword

How to Use the Resource Problems

The one hundred problems presented on the following pages were written by the author for use in *Mathematical Olympiads for Elementary Schools* (MOES). These Olympiads are interschool mathematical competitions instituted by the author and held five times during each school year. Students from participating schools compete as a team, with up to thirty-five students on each team. After the fifth competition, MOES presents awards to teams and individuals for outstanding achievement.

Since these problems were originally designed for use in MOES competitions, they are separated into twenty sets each containing five problems. Should you want to conduct similar olympiads with your students, you will find that each of these problem sets is probably suitable for use in one olympiad competition.

There are many ways that you can organize your own olympiads. For example, divide all the students in one class into teams to compete in olympiads among themselves. If other teachers in your school or school system are interested, work with them to sponsor a competition among several classes. Form each class into a single team, or use a test or other selection processes to choose a smaller team of students to represent each class. If a number of classes or schools are involved, the same set of problems should be administered to all teams on the same day and, if possible, at the same time.

To use the resource problems for an olympiad competition, copy an entire problem set onto a master sheet to be duplicated. After that, separate the duplicated sheets of problems into strips of individual problems. This procedure allows students to work on just one problem at a time; students get time between problems to relax, easing some of the tension of competition. A recommended time limit for each problem is provided in parentheses immediately following the problem.

As an alternative, distribute the entire sheet of five problems at once. The advantage of this method is that each student can use the total time allotted for a problem set as needed.

The use of these problems is not restricted to organized olympiad competitions. You may simply wish to use the problems with your class as a resource that supplements your textbook, and some problems might also serve as a source of enrichment material for your more advanced students. You may even find yourself drawn to the challenge of solving some or all of the problems for your own enjoyment.

Experience has shown that these problems have a broad range of appeal, from third graders on up to teachers, administrators, and parents. Now it is your turn to explore their possibilities. Have fun!

Set 1

1. If today is Tuesday, what day of the week will it be 100 days from now? (*Time:* 4 minutes)

2. I have 4 three-cent stamps and 3 five-cent stamps. Using one or more of these stamps, how many different amounts of postage can I make? (*Time:* 5 minutes)

3. Find the sum of the counting numbers from 1 to 25 inclusive. In other words, if $S = 1 + 2 + 3 + \ldots + 24 + 25$, find the value of S. (*Time:* 5 minutes)

4. In a stationery store, pencils cost one amount and pens cost a different amount. The total cost of 2 pencils and 3 pens is 78¢. The total cost of 3 pencils and 2 pens is 72¢. What is the cost of 1 pencil? (*Time:* 5 minutes)

5. A work crew of 3 persons requires 3 weeks and 3 days to do a certain job. How long would it take a work crew of 4 persons to do the same job if they work at the same rate? (*Time:* 5 minutes)

Set 2

1. Jeremy bought a record collection for $10, sold it for $15, bought it back for $20, and finally sold it for $25. How much money did Jeremy make or lose? (*Time:* 5 minutes)

2. I have a collection of 30 coins that consists of nickels and quarters. If the total face value of the coins is $4.10, how many of each kind of coin do I have? (*Time:* 5 minutes)

3. What is the greatest number of 2-in. by 3-in. rectangular cards that can be cut from a rectangular sheet that measures 2 ft by 3 ft? (*Time:* 5 minutes)

4. In three bowling games, Alice scored 139, 143, and 144. What score will she need in a fourth game in order to have an average score of 145 for all four games? (*Time:* 5 minutes)

5. A certain book has 500 pages numbered 1, 2, 3, and so on. How many times does the digit 1 appear in the page numbers? (*Time:* 5 minutes)

Set 3

1. A bag of marbles can be divided in equal shares among 2, 3, 4, 5, or 6 friends. What is the least number of marbles that the bag could contain? (*Time:* 5 minutes)

2. A motorist made a 60-mile trip driving at an average speed of 20 miles per hour. On the return trip, the motorist drove at an average speed of 30 miles per hour. What was the motorist's average speed for the entire trip? (*Time:* 5 minutes)

3. The four-digit number $3AA1$ is divisible by 9. Find the value of A. (*Time:* 5 minutes)

4. Express the following sum as a simple fraction in lowest terms.

$$\frac{1}{1 \times 2} + \frac{1}{2 \times 3} + \frac{1}{3 \times 4} + \frac{1}{4 \times 5} + \frac{1}{5 \times 6}$$

   (*Time:* 5 minutes)

5. If you start at 1 and count by 3s you obtain the following sequence.

$$1, 4, 7, 10, 13, \ldots$$

   What is the 100th number in this sequence? (*Time:* 5 minutes)

Set 4

1. A 100-lb block of cheese is cut into smaller blocks that each weigh $1\frac{1}{4}$ lb. Each small block is then sold for $3.75. What is the total selling price for all the small blocks of cheese? (*Time:* 5 minutes)

2. In the multiplication at the right, A and B represent two different digits. Find the values of A and B. (*Time:* 5 minutes)

$$\begin{array}{r} A\,B \\ \times\ B\,A \\ \hline 1\,1\,4 \\ 3\,0\,4 \\ \hline 3\,1\,5\,4 \end{array}$$

3. Suppose that, for any numbers P and Q, $P \# Q$ means $\frac{P+Q}{2}$. What is the value of $3 \# (6 \# 8)$? (*Time:* 5 minutes)

4. If A and B are different whole numbers, what values of A and B make this a true statement?

$$\frac{1}{3} = \frac{1}{A} + \frac{1}{B}$$

(*Time:* 5 minutes)

5. In the figure at the right, segment MN separates a rectangle into 2 regions. What is the greatest number of regions into which the rectangle could be separated by 4 segments? (*Time:* 5 minutes)

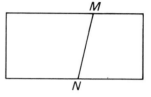

Set 5

1. The numbers 2, 4, 6, 8, 10, 12, . . . are consecutive even numbers. If the sum of five consecutive even numbers is 320, what is the least of the five numbers? (*Time:* 5 minutes)

2. Amy can mow a lawn that measures 600 square yards in $1\frac{1}{2}$ hours. At this rate, how many minutes would it take her to mow a lawn that measures 600 square feet? (*Time:* 5 minutes)

3. Express the following as a simple fraction in lowest terms.

$$\cfrac{1}{2 + \cfrac{1}{2 + \cfrac{1}{2 + \cfrac{1}{2}}}}$$

(*Time:* 5 minutes)

4. List all the two-digit numbers that divide 109 with a remainder of 4. (*Time:* 5 minutes)

5. A dealer packages marbles in two different box sizes. One size holds 5 marbles and the other size holds 12 marbles. This morning the dealer packaged exactly 99 marbles and used more than 10 boxes. How many boxes of each size were used?
(*Time:* 5 minutes)

Set 6

1. Suppose that X and Y are two different numbers selected from the first fifty counting numbers (1 to 50 inclusive). What is the greatest possible value of the following expression?

$$\frac{X + Y}{X - Y}$$

   (*Time:* 3 minutes)

2. A chime clock strikes 1 chime at one o'clock, 2 chimes at two o'clock, 3 chimes at three o'clock, and so on. What is the total number of chimes that the clock will strike in a twelve-hour period? (*Time:* 5 minutes)

3. The average capacity of a set of five containers is 13 liters. A container with a capacity of 7 liters is added to the set of five. What is the average capacity of the set of six containers? (*Time:* 4 minutes)

4. Suppose that you have 100 pennies, 100 nickels, and 100 dimes. Using at least one coin of each type, select 21 coins that have a total value of exactly $1.00. How many coins of each type did you select? (*Time:* 6 minutes)

5. Of a group of 30 high-school students, 8 study French, 12 study Spanish, and 3 study both French and Spanish. How many students of the group study neither French nor Spanish? (*Time:* 5 minutes)

Set 7

1. The **palimage** of a counting number is the number that is formed by the same digits, but in reverse order. For example, 659 and 956 are palimages; so are 1327 and 7231. Add 354 and its palimage. Call this sum X. Add X and its palimage. Call this sum Y. Add Y and its palimage. Call this sum Z. What is the value of Z? (*Time:* 4 minutes)

2. If the counting numbers are arranged in columns as shown at the right, under which letter will the number 1000 appear? (*Time:* 4 minutes)

A	B	C	D	E	F	G
1	2	3	4	5	6	7
8	9	10	11	12	13	14
15	16	17	..	..	..	..
..	..	..	..	..	..	..

3. Dale has these seven coins in his pocket: 2 pennies, 2 nickels, 2 dimes, and 1 quarter. He takes out two coins, records the sum of their values, then returns them to his pocket with the other coins. He continues this same process, taking out two coins, recording the sum of their values, then returning the coins to his pocket. What is the greatest number of different sums that he can record? (*Time:* 5 minutes)

4. A group of twelve people purchases supplies for a ten-day camping trip with the understanding that each of the twelve will get equal daily shares of the supplies. Then they are joined by three more people, but the group makes no further purchases. How many days will the supplies now last if the size of the original daily share for each person is not changed? (*Time:* 4 minutes)

5. The figure at the right is formed by eleven squares of the same size. If the area of the figure is 176 cm², what is its perimeter? (*Time:* 5 minutes)

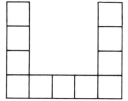

Set 8

1. A bag contains 500 beads of the same size. There are 5 different colors of beads and 100 beads of each color. If you are blindfolded, what is the least number of beads that you must pick before you can be sure that you have picked 5 beads of the same color? (*Time:* 4 minutes)

2. If 20 is added to one third of a number, the result is the double of the number. What is the number? (*Time:* 5 minutes)

3. Each of the small boxes in the figure at the right is a square. What is the total number of different squares that can be traced using the lines of the figure? (*Time:* 5 minutes)

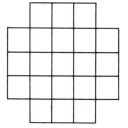

4. Danny spent two thirds of his money. Then he lost two thirds of the money that was left. Four dollars remained. How much money did Danny have in the beginning? (*Time:* 5 minutes)

5. If a counting number ends in zeros, the zeros are called **terminal zeros.** For example, 520,000 has four terminal zeros while 502,000 has just three terminal zeros. Let *P* be the product of all the counting numbers from 1 through 20 ($P = 1 \times 2 \times 3 \times 4 \times \ldots \times 20$). How many terminal zeros will *P* have when it is written in standard form? (*Time:* 5 minutes)

Set 9

1. It is possible to make the figure at the right a magic square by replacing the letters with numbers so that the sum of the three numbers in each row, column, and major diagonal is the same. What values of *A*, *B*, *C*, *D*, and *E* will make this a magic square? (*Time:* 5 minutes)

15	A	35
50	B	C
25	D	E

2. If you start at 2 and count by 3s until you reach 449, you obtain the sequence 2, 5, 8, . . . , 449. You can see that 2 is the first number of the sequence, 5 is the second number, 8 is the third number, and so on. We say that 449 is the *n*th number. What is the value of *n*? (*Time:* 3 minutes)

3. You know that the perimeter of a certain rectangle measures 22 in. If its length and width each measure a whole number of inches, how many different areas (in square inches) are possible for this rectangle? (*Time:* 5 minutes)

4. Sam drives from his home at an average speed of 30 miles per hour to a shopping center that is 20 miles from his home. On the return trip he encounters heavy traffic and drives at an average speed of only 12 miles per hour. How long does it take Sam to drive to and from the shopping center? (*Time:* 5 minutes)

5. In the division at the right, the boxes represent missing digits, and *A* and *B* represent the digits of the quotient. What are the values of *A* and *B*? (*Time:* 5 minutes)

Set 10

1. In the addition at the right, each letter represents a different digit. What are the values of H, E, and A? (*Time:* 3 minutes)

$$\begin{array}{r} H\ E \\ H\ E \\ H\ E \\ +H\ E \\ \hline A\ H \end{array}$$

2. The product of two whole numbers is 144. If the difference of the numbers is 10, what is their sum? (*Time:* 5 minutes)

3. Find whole numbers A and B so that the following is true.

$$\frac{A}{11} + \frac{B}{3} = \frac{31}{33}$$

(*Time:* 5 minutes)

4. The XYZ club collected a total of $1.21 from its members, with each member contributing the same amount. If each member paid for her or his share with 3 coins, how many nickels were contributed? (*Time:* 5 minutes)

5. During one school year, Nancy was given 25¢ for each math test she passed and was fined 50¢ for each math test she failed. By the end of the school year, Nancy passed 7 times as many math tests as she failed and she had a total of $3.75. How many tests did she fail? (*Time:* 5 minutes)

Set 11

1. Julius Caesar wrote the Roman numerals I, II, III, IV, and V in a special order from left to right. He wrote I before III but after IV. He wrote II after IV but before I. He wrote V after II but before III. If V was *not* the third numeral, in what order did he write these five numerals from left to right? (*Time:* 5 minutes)

2. In the multiplication at the right, each box represents a missing digit. What is the product? (*Time:* 5 minutes)

3. Glen, Harry, and Kim each have a different favorite sport among tennis, baseball, and soccer. Glen does not like baseball or soccer. Harry does not like baseball. Name the favorite sport of each person. (*Time:* 4 minutes)

4. An acute angle is an angle whose measure is between 0° and 90°. How many different acute angles can be traced using the rays in the figure at the right? (*Time:* 4 minutes)

5. Suppose that 13 plums weigh as much as 2 apples and 1 pear. Furthermore, 4 plums and 1 apple weigh as much as 1 pear. How many plums weigh as much as 1 pear? (*Time:* 5 minutes)

Set 12

1. Arrange the digits 1, 1, 2, 2, 3, and 3 as a six-digit number in which the 1s are separated by one digit, the 2s are separated by two digits, and the 3s are separated by three digits. (*Time:* 4 minutes)

2. What day of the week was yesterday if five days before the day after tomorrow was Wednesday? (*Time:* 3 minutes)

3. In the figure at the right, *ABCD* is a square whose sides each measure 2 units. Following the lines of the figure, the length of the shortest path from *A* to *C* is 4 units. How many *different* shortest paths are there from *A* to *C*? (*Time:* 5 minutes)

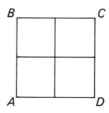

4. A dollar was changed for 16 coins consisting of just nickels and dimes. How many coins of each kind were in the change? (*Time:* 5 minutes)

5. What is the least number that gives a remainder of 1 when divided by 4, a remainder of 2 when divided by 5, and a remainder of 3 when divided by 6? (*Time:* 4 minutes)

Set 13

1. Each of the small boxes in the figure at the right is a square. What is the total number of different squares that can be traced using the lines of the figure? (*Time:* 4 minutes)

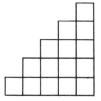

2. In the multiplication at the right, each letter repre-sents a different digit. If *A* is not zero, what are the values of *A*, *B*, *C*, and *D*? (*Time:* 5 minutes)

$$\begin{array}{r} A\ B\ C \\ \times\quad\ \ C \\ \hline D\ B\ C \end{array}$$

3. Consecutive numbers are whole numbers that follow in order, such as 7, 8, 9, 10, 11, and 12. Find three consecutive numbers such that the sum of the first and third is 118. (*Time:* 4 minutes)

4. Al, Bill, and Carl went shopping. When they compared the totals that each had spent they found that: Al and Bill together spent a total of $12; Bill and Carl together spent a total of $18; and Al and Carl together spent a total of $10. How much did each person spend? (*Time:* 6 minutes)

5. Fifteen pennies are separated into four piles so that each pile has a different number of pennies. What is the least possible number of pennies in the largest pile? (*Time:* 5 minutes)

Set 14

1. The perimeter of a certain rectangle measures 20 ft. If its length and width each measure a whole number of feet, how many different shapes are possible for this rectangle? (*Time:* 4 minutes)

2. In a math contest of 10 problems, 5 points were scored for each correct answer and 2 points were deducted from the score for each incorrect answer. If Steve worked all 10 problems and scored 29 points, how many correct answers did he have? (*Time:* 4 minutes)

3. If the counting numbers are arranged in four columns as shown at the right, under which letter will the number 101 appear? (*Time:* 4 minutes)

A	B	C	D
1	2	3	4
8	7	6	5
9	10	11	12
..	..	14	13

4. Three water pipes are used to fill a swimming pool. The first pipe alone takes 8 hours to fill the pool, the second pipe alone takes 12 hours to fill the pool, and the third pipe alone takes 24 hours to fill the pool. If all three pipes are opened at the same time, how long will it take all three together to fill the pool? (*Time:* 6 minutes)

5. It is possible to make the figure at the right a magic square by replacing the letters with numbers so that the sum of the four numbers in each row, column, and major diagonal is the same. What values of *A*, *B*, *C*, *D*, *E*, *F*, and *G* will make this a magic square?
(*Time:* 5 minutes)

A	B	7	12
C	4	9	D
E	5	16	3
8	11	F	G

Set 15

1. A certain train can hold 78 passengers. The train starts out empty and picks up 1 passenger at the first stop, 2 passengers at the second stop, 3 passengers at the third stop, and so on. After how many stops will the train be full? (*Time:* 5 minutes)

2. A wooden cube that measures four inches along each edge is painted red. The painted cube is then cut into one-inch cubes. How many of the one-inch cubes do not have red paint on any face? (*Time:* 5 minutes)

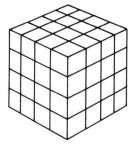

3. The number of two-dollar bills I need to pay for a purchase is nine more than the number of five-dollar bills I need to pay for the same purchase. What is the cost of the purchase? (*Time:* 5 minutes)

4. When 24 gallons of water are poured into a certain empty tank, the tank becomes $\frac{3}{4}$ full. How many gallons does the tank hold when full? (*Time:* 4 minutes)

5. The last digit of the product 3 × 3 is 9, the last digit of the product 3 × 3 × 3 is 7, and the last digit of the product 3 × 3 × 3 × 3 is 1. What is the last digit of the product when thirty-five 3s are multiplied? (*Time:* 6 minutes)

Set 16

1. The last Friday of a certain month is the 25th day of the month. What day of the week is the first day of the month?
(*Time:* 2 minutes)

2. Dale's age is the same as Ann's age with the digits reversed. The sum of their ages is 99, and Dale is 9 years older than Ann. How old is Dale? (*Time:* 4 minutes)

3. A group of 21 people went to the county fair either in a stagecoach or in buggies. Later the same stagecoach and buggies brought them back. On the trip to the fair, 9 people rode in the stagecoach and 3 people rode in each buggy. On the return trip, 4 people rode in each buggy. How many people rode in the stagecoach on the return trip? (*Time:* 4 minutes)

4. Below are three views of the same cube. What letter is on the face opposite *H*? *X*? *Y*? Give your answer in the same order.

(*Time:* 5 minutes)

5. Suppose that *D* is the sum of the odd numbers from 1 through 99 inclusive and that *N* is the sum of the even numbers from 2 through 98 inclusive. In other words, $D = 1 + 3 + 5 + \ldots + 99$ and $N = 2 + 4 + 6 + \ldots + 98$. Which is greater, *D* or *N*? How much greater? (*Time:* 5 minutes)

Set 17

1. I have exactly ten coins whose total value is $1. If three of the coins are quarters, what are the remaining coins and how many of each are there? (*Time:* 3 minutes)

2. One loaf of bread and six rolls cost $1.80. At the same prices, two loaves of bread and four rolls cost $2.40. How much does one loaf of bread cost? (*Time:* 4 minutes)

3. The small boxes in Figures A and B below are congruent squares. If the perimeter of Figure A is 48 centimeters, what is the perimeter of Figure B?

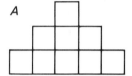

(*Time:* 5 minutes)

4. If a kindergarten teacher seats the class with 4 children on each bench, there will be 3 children who will not have a place. However, if 5 children are seated on each bench, there will be 2 empty places. What is the least number of children the class could have?
(*Time:* 5 minutes)

5. In the addition at the right, each letter represents a different digit. What are the values of A, B, and C? (*Time:* 5 minutes)

Set 18

1. The sum of the weights of two students is 138 pounds, and one is 34 pounds heavier than the other. How much does the heavier student weigh? (*Time:* 4 minutes)

2. When I open my mathematics book, there are two pages that face me. If the product of the two page numbers is 1806, what are the two page numbers? (*Time:* 5 minutes)

3. Eight one-inch cubes are put together to form the T-shaped figure shown at the right. The complete outside of the T-shaped figure is painted red, and the one-inch cubes are then separated. How many of the cubes have exactly four red faces? (*Time:* 4 minutes)

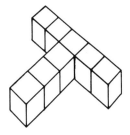

4. The members of an Olympiad team contributed a total of $1.69 for refreshments for their weekly practice session. Each member contributed the same amount and paid for her or his share with exactly five coins. How many nickels were contributed by all the members together? (*Time:* 5 minutes)

5. Consecutive numbers are counting numbers that follow in order, such as 7, 8, 9, and 10. The average of a set of 15 consecutive numbers is 15. What is the average of the first five numbers of this set? (*Time:* 5 minutes)

Set 19

1. A camera and case together cost $100. If the camera costs $90 more than the case, how much does the case cost? (*Time:* 2 minutes)

2. In the additions at the right, A, B, and C are different digits. If C is placed in the ones' column, the sum is 52. If C is placed in the tens' column, the sum is 97. What are the values of A, B, and C? (*Time:* 3 minutes)

$$\begin{array}{r} A\ B \\ +\quad C \\ \hline 5\ 2 \end{array} \qquad \begin{array}{r} A\ B \\ +C \\ \hline 9\ 7 \end{array}$$

3. Suppose K, L, and M represent the number of points assigned to the three target regions shown at the right. The sum of K and L is 11, the sum of L and M is 19, and the sum of K and M is 16. How many points are assigned to M? (*Time:* 5 minutes)

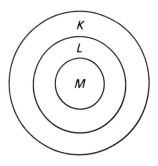

4. Janice went to a store, spent half of her money, and then spent $10 more. She went to a second store, spent half of her remaining money, and then spent $10 more. Then she had no money left. How much money did she have in the beginning when she went to the first store? (*Time:* 5 minutes)

5. The six-digit number $A4273B$ is divisible by 72 without a remainder. Find the values of A and B. (*Time:* 5 minutes)

Set 20

1. A train is traveling at the rate of 1 mile in 1 minute and 20 seconds. If the train continues at this rate, how far will it travel in one hour? (*Time:* 4 minutes)

2. Which number between 1 and 100 satisfies the following conditions? If it is divided by 3 or 5, the remainder is 1. If it is divided by 7, there is no remainder. (*Time:* 4 minutes)

3. Pretend that blocks of wood that are either 6 inches long or 7 inches long can be used as train cars and hooked together to make longer trains. Which of the following train-lengths cannot be made by hooking together either 6-inch train cars, 7-inch train cars, or a combination of both?

      29 inches, 30 inches, 31 inches, 32 inches, 33 inches

   (*Time:* 5 minutes)

4. A circular track is 1000 yards in circumference. Cyclist A races around the track at the rate of 700 yards per minute, cyclist B races at the rate of 800 yards per minute, and cyclist C races at the rate of 900 yards per minute. If the three cyclists start from the same position at the same time and cycle in the same direction, what is the least number of minutes it must take before all three are together again? (*Time:* 5 minutes)

5. Alice and Bob each want to buy the same kind of ruler, but Alice still needs 22¢ and Bob still needs 3¢. When they combine their money, they still do not have enough. What is the most the ruler could cost? (*Time:* 5 minutes)

Solutions to Resource Problems

Set 1 Page 253

Answers: 1. Thursday 2. 19 3. 325 4. 12¢ 5. 18 days

1. Every 7 days from now will be a Tuesday. Since 98 is a multiple of 7, the 98th day from now will also be a Tuesday. Then the 99th day from now will be a Wednesday, and the 100th day from now will be a Thursday.

2.

Amounts Using 3¢ Stamps	Amounts Using 5¢ Stamps	Amounts Using Combinations	
$1 \times 3 = 3$¢	$1 \times 5 = 5$¢	$3 + 5 = 8$¢	$9 + 5 = 14$¢
$2 \times 3 = 6$¢	$2 \times 5 = 10$¢	$3 + 10 = 13$¢	$9 + 10 = 19$¢
$3 \times 3 = 9$¢	$3 \times 5 = 15$¢	$3 + 15 = 18$¢	$9 + 15 = 24$¢
$4 \times 3 = 12$¢		$6 + 5 = 11$¢	$12 + 5 = 17$¢
		$6 + 10 = 16$¢	$12 + 10 = 22$¢
		$6 + 15 = 21$¢	$12 + 15 = 27$¢

A total of 19 different amounts of postage can be made.

3. The numbers can be paired so that there are 12 pairs of numbers whose sum is 26: $1 + 25, 2 + 24, 3 + 23, \ldots, 11 + 15, 12 + 14$. Following this pattern, there is only one number, 13, that cannot be paired with another number. Therefore, the sum of all the numbers is $12 \times 26 + 13 = 312 + 13 = 325$.

4. Combine the given information to obtain the fact that 5 pencils and 5 pens cost 78¢ $+ 72$¢ $= \$1.50$. Then 1 pencil and 1 pen cost $\frac{1}{5}$ of $\$1.50$, or 30¢, and 2 pencils and 2 pens cost 2×30¢ $= 60$¢. Since one piece of the given information is that 3 pencils and 2 pens cost 72¢, then one pencil must cost 72¢ $- 60$¢ $= 12$¢.

5. Each person in the work crew worked 24 days. Working alone, then, it would take one person $3 \times 24 = 72$ days to do the job. Therefore, it would take 4 persons $72 \div 4 = 18$ days to do the job.

Set 2 Page 253

Answers: 1. He made $10. 2. 17 nickels, 13 quarters
3. 144   4. 154   5. 200

1. Suppose that Jeremy began with a certain amount of money, such as $50. Then his transactions can be represented by the following string of additions and subtractions.

$$\$50 - \$10 + \$15 - \$20 + \$25 = \$60$$

He started with $50 and finished with $60. Therefore he made $60 - $50 = $10.

2. Make a table of possible combinations of nickels and quarters and their total value.

nickels	29	28	27	. . .	?
quarters	1	2	3	. . .	?
total value	$1.70	$1.90	$2.10	. . .	$4.10

In the table above, each time one nickel is "exchanged" for one quarter, the total value of the collection increases by $0.20. To increase the first total, $1.70, to $4.10, 12 of the 29 nickels must be "exchanged" for quarters, since this increases the total by 12 × $0.20 = $2.40. Therefore, there are 29 − 12 = 17 nickels and 1 + 12 = 13 quarters in this collection.

3. Since the dimensions of the sheet and the cards are such that it is possible to cut a whole number of cards from the sheet without any waste, consider the area. The area of a 2-in. by 3-in. card is 2 × 3 = 6 in.²; the area of the sheet is 24 × 36 = 864 in.². Then the number of cards that can be cut from the sheet is 864 ÷ 6 = 144.

4. Alice's first score is 6 less than the desired average, her second score is 2 less, and her third score is 1 less. Then the sum of her three scores is 6 + 2 + 1 = 9 less than the desired average. Therefore, she needs a fourth score that is 9 *greater* than the average, or 145 + 9 = 154.

5. Consider the page numbers place-by-place.

   Ones' place: The digit 1 appears in the ones' place once in every group of 10 consecutive counting numbers. Since the numbers from 1 to 500 contain 50 such groups, the digit 1 will appear in the ones' place 50 times.

Tens' place: The digit 1 appears in the tens' place 10 times in every group of 100 consecutive counting numbers. Since the numbers from 1 to 500 contain 5 such groups, the digit 1 will appear in the tens' place $5 \times 10 = 50$ times.

Hundreds' place: The digit 1 appears in the hundreds' place 100 times (100, 101, 102, . . . , 199).

The digit 1 appears in the page numbers a total of $50 + 50 + 100 = 200$ times.

Set 3 *Page 254*

Answers: 1. 60   2. 24 mi/h   3. 7   4. $\frac{5}{6}$ 5. 298

1. Find the least common multiple of 2, 3, 4, 5, and 6.

LCM = $2 \times 2 \times 3 \times 5 = 60$

2. Recall that the relationship among distance, rate, and time is distance = rate $\times$ time. So the motorist made the original trip in $60 \div 20 = 3$h and then made the return trip in $60 \div 30 = 2$h. The entire trip covered a distance of $60 + 60 = 120$ mi and took the motorist $3 + 2 = 5$h. Therefore, the motorist's *average* speed for the entire trip was $120 \div 5 = 24$ mi/h.

3. A number is divisible by 9 if the sum of its digits is divisible by 9. The sum of the known digits is $3 + 1 = 4$, so the sum of the unknown digits must be either 5 or 14. ($5 + 4 = 9$ and $14 + 4 = 18$; any greater multiple of 9 would require a value of A that contains more than one digit.) But $A + A = 5$ is impossible, since the same number must be substituted for each A and A must be a whole number. Therefore, $A + A$ must equal 14, and it follows that the value of A must be 7.

4. Each fraction in the given sum can be expressed as the difference of two consecutive unit fractions. Making the appropriate substitutions, note that all but the first and last fractions drop out.

$$\frac{1}{1 \times 2} + \frac{1}{2 \times 3} + \frac{1}{3 \times 4} + \frac{1}{4 \times 5} + \frac{1}{5 \times 6}$$

$$= \left(\frac{1}{1} - \frac{1}{2}\right) + \left(\frac{1}{2} - \frac{1}{3}\right) + \left(\frac{1}{3} - \frac{1}{4}\right) + \left(\frac{1}{4} - \frac{1}{5}\right) + \left(\frac{1}{5} - \frac{1}{6}\right)$$

$$= \frac{1}{1} - \frac{1}{6} = 1 - \frac{1}{6} = \frac{5}{6}$$

5. The given sequence of numbers follows a pattern of adding 3s. Then to reach the 100th number, 3 would be added to the first number, 1, a total of 99 times. Therefore, the 100th number of the sequence is $1 + 99 \times 3 = 1 + 297 = 298$.

Set 4 Pages 254-255

Answers: 1. $300   2. $A = 3$, $B = 8$ 3. 5
4. $A = 4$, $B = 12$ or $A = 12$, $B = 4$ 5. 11

1. The total number of the smaller blocks of cheese is $100 \div 1\frac{1}{4} = 80$. Then the selling price of all 80 smaller blocks is $80 \times \$3.75 = \$300$.

2. Since the product of AB and A is the first partial product, 114, A must be a one-digit factor of 114. Thus, A could be 1, 2, 3, or 6. But only $A = 3$ could result in the partial product 114. Since $A = 3$, the product of 3 and B must have 4 as its ones' digit, and B must be 8.

$$\begin{array}{r} 38 \\ \times\ 83 \\ \hline 114 \\ 304 \\ \hline 3154 \end{array}$$

3. According to the order of operations, first perform the operation indicated in the parentheses.

$$6 \, \# \, 8 = \frac{6 + 8}{2} = \frac{14}{2} = 7$$

Then $3 \, \# \, (6 \, \# \, 8) = 3 \, \# \, 7$.

$$3 \, \# \, 7 = \frac{3 + 7}{2} = \frac{10}{2} = 5$$

4. Using trial and error, test $A = 4$.

$$\frac{1}{3} = \frac{1}{4} + \frac{1}{B}$$

$$\frac{1}{3} - \frac{1}{4} = \frac{1}{4} + \frac{1}{B} - \frac{1}{4}$$

$$\frac{1}{12} = \frac{1}{B}, \text{ so } B = 12$$

It follows that a second solution is $A = 12$, $B = 4$.

5. Test various placements of the four segments. Note that, to obtain the greatest number of regions, the segments must be placed so that each one intersects each of the other three. The figure at the right shows one such placement of the segments. The greatest number of regions possible is 11.

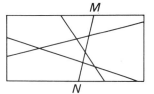

Set 5 Page 255

Answers: 1. 60   2. 10   3. $\frac{12}{29}$ 4. 15, 21, 35

5. 2 boxes of 12 marbles, 15 boxes of 5 marbles

1. Since 320 is the sum of the 5 numbers, the average of the numbers is $320 \div 5 = 64$. Then since the numbers are consecutive even numbers, 64 is the middle number of the group, and the entire group of 5 numbers is 60, 62, 64, 66, 68.

2. One square yard contains $3 \times 3 = 9$ square feet. Therefore, one square foot is $\frac{1}{9}$ of one square yard, and 600 square feet are $\frac{1}{9}$ of 600 square yards. Since Amy needs $1\frac{1}{2}$ h to mow 600 square yards, she will need $\frac{1}{9}$ of $1\frac{1}{2}$ h to mow 600 square feet. $\frac{1}{9}$ of $1\frac{1}{2}$ h is $\frac{1}{9} \times 1\frac{1}{2} = \frac{1}{6}$ h, which is equal to 10 min.

3. Work backwards from the last denominator.

$$\cfrac{1}{2 + \cfrac{1}{2 + \cfrac{1}{2 + \frac{1}{2}}}} = \cfrac{1}{2 + \cfrac{1}{2 + \cfrac{1}{\frac{5}{2}}}} = \cfrac{1}{2 + \cfrac{1}{2 + \frac{2}{5}}} = \cfrac{1}{2 + \cfrac{1}{\frac{12}{5}}} = \cfrac{1}{2 + \frac{5}{12}} = \cfrac{1}{\frac{29}{12}} = \frac{12}{29}$$

4. If a number divides 109 with a remainder of 4, then it is a factor of
   109 − 4 = 105. The prime factorization of 105 is 3 × 5 × 7, so the two-
   digit factors are 3 × 5, 3 × 7, and 5 × 7; or 15, 21, and 35.

5. The number of marbles packaged in the smaller boxes must be a
   multiple of 5, and the number of marbles packaged in the larger boxes
   must be a multiple of 12. Since all multiples of 5 have a ones' digit that
   is either 5 or 0, the ones' digit of the required multiple of 12 is either 4
   or 9. (99 − ▓5 = ▓4 and 99 − ▓0 = ▓9.) The only multiples of 12 to
   be considered, then, are 24 and 84.

   $\dfrac{2 \text{ boxes of } 12}{15 \text{ boxes of } 5}$ = 2 × 12 + 15 × 5 = 24 + 75 = 99

   $\dfrac{7 \text{ boxes of } 12}{3 \text{ boxes of } 5}$ = 7 × 12 + 3 × 5 = 84 + 15 = 99

   Note that the second possibility violates the condition that *more than*
   10 boxes were used, so there were 2 boxes of 12 and 15 boxes of 5.

Set 6 Page 256

Answers: 1. 99   2. 78   3. 12 L
          4. 5 pennies, 13 nickels, 3 dimes; or
             10 pennies, 4 nickels, 7 dimes
          5. 13

1. The greatest value of the expression will occur when the
   denominator is the least positive number possible and the numerator
   is the greatest number possible. The least possible positive
   denominator is $X − Y = 1$, and this will occur when Y and X are
   any consecutive pair of the counting numbers. However, the one
   pair that yields the greatest possible numerator $X + Y$ is 49 and 50.
   Since $X − Y$ must be a positive number, $X = 50$ and $Y = 49$.

   $$\frac{50 + 49}{50 − 49} = \frac{99}{1} = 99$$

2. The total number of chimes is 1 + 2 + 3 + . . . + 12. These
   numbers can be paired so that there are 6 pairs of numbers whose
   sum is 13, so the sum of all 12 numbers is 6 × 13 = 78.

3. Since the average capacity of the set of 5 containers is 13 L, the
   total capacity is 5 × 13 = 65 L. The sixth container increases the

total capacity to $65 + 7 = 72$ L. Then the average capacity of the set of 6 containers is $72 \div 6 = 12$ L.

4. To have a total value of exactly $1.00, the number of pennies that you select must be a multiple of 5. Since the total number of coins is 21, the only numbers of pennies to consider are 5, 10, 15, and 20. If there are 15 or 20 pennies, it is impossible to reach a total of $1.00. Therefore, there are only two remaining cases to consider.

Case 1: Select 5 pennies.
There are $21 - 5 = 16$ remaining coins to select, and their total value must be 95¢.

nickels	15	14	13	12	11	. . .
dimes	1	2	3	4	5	. . .
total value	85¢	90¢	95¢	100¢	105¢	. . .

If you select 5 pennies, you must also select 13 nickels and 3 dimes.

Case 2: Select 10 pennies.
There are $21 - 10 = 11$ remaining coins to select, and their total value must be 90¢.

nickels	10	9	8	7	6	5	4	3	. . .
dimes	1	2	3	4	5	6	7	8	. . .
total value	60¢	65¢	70¢	75¢	80¢	85¢	90¢	95¢	. . .

If you select 10 pennies, you must also select 4 nickels and 7 dimes.

5. A Venn diagram such as the one at the right may be helpful. Here circles F and S represent, respectively, those students who study French and Spanish. Region II represents those students who study both French and Spanish. Thus, regions I and III represent, respectively, those students who study only French and only Spanish, and region IV represents those students who study neither French nor Spanish. Using the given information, region I $= 8 - 3 = 5$ and region II $= 12 - 3 = 9$. Then regions I, II, and III $= 5 + 3 + 9 = 17$, and region IV $= 30 - 17 = 13$.

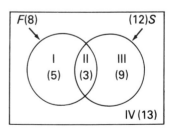

Set 7 Pages 256-257

Answers: 1. 6666   2. F   3. 9   4. 8   5. 96 cm

1.

354	807	1515
+ 453	+ 708	+ 5151
$X = 807$	$Y = 1515$	$Z = 6666$

2. In any given column, each entry yields the same remainder when divided by 7. $1000 \div 7 = 142$ R6. Therefore, 1000 will appear in the same column as the number 6, which is column F.

3. Make an organized list of all the possible combinations of two coins and the sums of their values.

Coins	Value	Coins	Value
penny, penny	2¢	nickel, nickel	10¢
penny, nickel	6¢	nickel, dime	15¢
penny, dime	11¢	nickel, quarter	30¢
penny, quarter	26¢	dime, dime	20¢
		dime, quarter	35¢

There are 9 different possible sums.

4. The number of individual daily shares purchased is $12 \times 10 = 120$. Therefore, if the size of the group of people is increased to 15, the number of days that the supplies will last is $120 \div 15 = 8$.

5. Since the figure is formed by 11 congruent squares, the area of each square is $176 \div 11 = 16$ cm². Therefore, the length of a side of each square must be $\sqrt{16} = 4$ cm. The perimeter of the given figure is formed by 24 of these sides, so the total perimeter is $24 \times 4 = 96$ cm.

Set 8 Pages 257-258

Answers: 1. 21   2. 12   3. 38   4. $36   5. 4

1. If you select 20 beads, the possibility exists that you have selected 4 beads of each of the 5 colors. If you now add just one more bead to the number you select, you are certain that you have selected at least 5 beads of one color. Thus you need to select 21 beads.

2. Think of the double of the number as six thirds $\left(\frac{6}{3}\right)$ of the number. Then according to the conditions of the problem, 20 must be $\frac{5}{3}$ of the number. Then 4 is $\frac{1}{3}$ of the number, and the number is 12.

3.

Size of Square	Number of Squares
1 × 1	21
2 × 2	12
3 × 3	5
Total	38

4. Work backwards from $4, the final amount. Since Danny lost $\frac{2}{3}$ of the money that was left after he spent some money, $4 must be $\frac{1}{3}$ of this money. So Danny had $12 left after he spent some money. Since Danny originally spent $\frac{2}{3}$ of the money that he had in the beginning, $12 must be $\frac{1}{3}$ of this money. Thus Danny had $36 in the beginning.

5. Each factor that has one terminal zero will contribute one terminal zero to the product; since 10 and 20 are factors, the product will have at least two terminal zeros. Also consider any factor pairs whose product contains a terminal zero; since $2 \times 5 = 10$ and $4 \times 15 = 60$, the product will have two additional terminal zeros, for a total of four terminal zeros.

Set 9 *Page 258*

Answers: 1. $A = 40$, $B = 30$, $C = 10$, $D = 20$, $E = 45$
                  2. 150   3. 5   4. 140 min, or 2 h 20 min
                  5. $A = 3$, $B = 8$

1. From the first column, note that the sum of each group of three numbers must be 90. Then A must be 40 and B must be 30, and the values of C, D, and E follow easily.

15	40	35
50	30	10
25	20	45

2. Since the given sequence of numbers follows a pattern of adding 3s, note that $449 = 2 + 149 \times 3$. Thus, to reach 449 in this sequence, 3 must be added to the first number, 2, 149 times. Therefore, 449 is the 150th number of the sequence.

3. Since the entire perimeter of the rectangle measures 22 in., the sum of a single length and width must be only half as much, or 11 in. Make a table of all the possible lengths, widths, and corresponding areas. There are 5 possible areas.

length (*l*)	10	9	8	7	6
width (*w*)	1	2	3	4	5
Area (*l* × *w*)	10	18	24	28	30

4. Driving to the shopping center at a speed of 30 mi/h, it takes Sam 2 min to drive each mile for a total of $2 \times 20 = 40$ min. Returning from the shopping center at a speed of 12 mi/h, it takes Sam 5 min to drive each mile for a total of $5 \times 20 = 100$ min. Thus the entire trip to and from the shopping center takes Sam $40 + 100 = 140$ min, or 2 h 20 min.

5. Note that $B \times 5 \blacksquare = 432$. So *B* must be 8, and the divisor is 54. Now observe that $A \times 54 = \blacksquare 6 \blacksquare$. The only possible value of *A* is 3.

$$
\begin{array}{r}
38 \\
54\overline{)2052} \\
162 \\
\hline
432 \\
432 \\
\hline
0
\end{array}
$$

Set 10   Page 259

Answers: 1. $H = 2, E = 3, A = 9$ 2. 26
3. $A = 3, B = 2$ 4. 22   5. 3

1. Since the sum has two digits, *H* is less than 3. *H* is not 1, since the sum of four *E*s cannot be odd, so $H = 2$. Since the sum of four *E*s has 2 as its ones' digit, *E* = 3 or 8. But *E* is not 8, since the sum would have three digits, so $E = 3$ and $A = 9$.

$$
\begin{array}{r}
23 \\
23 \\
23 \\
+ 23 \\
\hline
92
\end{array}
$$

2. List all the pairs of whole numbers whose product is 144.

144	72	48	36	24	18	16	12
1	2	3	4	6	8	9	12

The only pair whose difference is 10 is 18 and 8; $18 + 8 = 26$.

3. Rewrite the first two fractions as equivalent fractions with a common denominator.

$$\frac{A}{11} + \frac{B}{3} = \frac{31}{33} \qquad \frac{3A}{33} + \frac{11B}{33} = \frac{31}{33} \qquad 3A + 11B = 31$$

Using the information that A and B are whole numbers, test for values that satisfy the last equation; the only values are $A = 3$ and $B = 2$.

4. Since the prime factorization of $121 = 11 \times 11$, the only way to satisfy the conditions of the problem is with 11 members contributing 11¢ apiece. The only 3 coins that have a total value of 11¢ are 2 nickels and 1 penny. Therefore, the number of nickels was $11 \times 2 = 22$.

5. On the average, for every 8 tests that Nancy took, she passed 7 and failed 1. Thus, on the average, for every 8 tests she took, she received 7×25¢ $= \$1.75$ and paid 1×50¢ $= \$0.50$, for a total profit of $\$1.25$. Since $\$3.75 = 3 \times \$1.25$, she took $3 \times 8 = 24$ tests, passed $3 \times 7 = 21$, and failed $3 \times 1 = 3$.

Set 11   *Pages 259-260*

Answers: 1. IV, II, I, V, III   2. 15,762
3. Glen: tennis; Harry: soccer; Kim: baseball
4. 10   5. 7

1. Consider the statements of the problem in order as a series of simpler problems.

Statement	Order of Numerals
I before III but after IV	IV, I, III
II after IV but before I	IV, II, I, III
V after II but before III	IV, II, V, I, III or IV, II, I, V, III
V is *not* the third numeral	IV, II, I, V, III

2. Consider $4 \blacksquare \blacksquare \times 7 = \blacksquare \blacksquare 82$. Since the ones' digit of the first partial product is 2, the ones' digit of the first factor is 6. Then the tens' digit of the first factor is 2, and $426 \times \blacksquare = 12 \blacksquare \blacksquare$. Thus the missing tens' digit of the second factor is 3. Complete the multiplication to arrive at the product 15,762.

$$\begin{array}{r} 426 \\ \times\ 37 \\ \hline 2982 \\ 1278\ \\ \hline 15762 \end{array}$$

3. Since Glen does not like baseball or soccer, tennis must be his favorite sport. Since Harry does not like baseball, and tennis is Glen's favorite sport, then Harry's favorite sport is soccer. The remaining sport, baseball, must be Kim's favorite.

4. Let a, b, c, d, and e represent the five rays. Then (a, b) can represent the angle formed by rays a and b, (a, c) can represent the angle formed by rays a and c, and so on. All ten angles in the figure can be listed as follows.

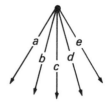

(a, b)	(a, c)	(a, d)	(a, e)	(b, c)
(b, d)	(b, e)	(c, d)	(c, e)	(d, e)

5. Let p, a, and r represent, respectively, the weights of one plum, one apple, and one pear. Then the given information can be translated into the following two equations.

(1) $13p = 2a + r$

Since $r = 4p + a$, substitute $4p + a$ for r in equation (1).

$$13p = 2a + 4p + a$$
$$13p = 3a + 4p$$
$$13p - 4p = 3a + 4p - 4p$$
$$9p = 3a$$
$$3p = a$$

(2) $4p + a = r$

Since $a = 3p$, substitute $3p$ for a in equation (2).

$$4p + 3p = r$$
$$7p = r$$

Since $7p = r$, 7 plums weigh as much as 1 pear.

Set 12   Page 260

Answers: 1. 312,132 or 231,213   2. Friday   3. 6
4. 4 dimes, 12 nickels   5. 57

1. Work backwards. Since the 3s are separated by three digits, then one of the 3s must be either the first digit or the last digit: 3 ▓ ▓ ▓ 3 ▓ or ▓ 3 ▓ ▓ ▓ 3. Since the 2s are separated by two digits, only two placements of the 2s are possible: 3 ▓ 2 ▓ 32 or 23 ▓ 2 ▓ 3. The 1s must occupy the remaining spaces: 312132 or 231213.

2. Draw a diagram such as the following. Yesterday was Friday.

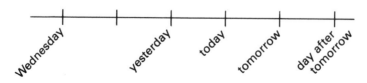

3.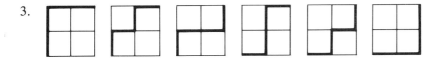

4. Make a table of the possible combinations of coins and their value.

nickels	1	2	3	4	. . .	?
dimes	15	14	13	12	. . .	?
total value	$1.55	$1.50	$1.45	$1.40	. . .	$1.00

In the table above, each time one dime is "exchanged" for one nickel, the total value of the coins decreases by $0.05. To decrease the first total, $1.55, to $1.00, 11 of the 15 dimes must be exchanged for nickels, since this decreases the total by 11 × $0.05 = $0.55. Therefore, there were 15 − 11 = 4 dimes and 1 + 11 = 12 nickels.

5. Let n represent the unknown number. Note that, when n is divided by 4, 5, or 6, the remainder in each case is 3 less than the divisor. Thus, if n is increased by 3, the new number, $n + 3$, is divisible by 4, 5, and 6 without remainder. Therefore, this new number must be the least common multiple of 4, 5, and 6, which is 60. Since 60 = $n + 3$, $n = 57$.

Set 13   Page 261

Answers: 1. 22   2. $A = 1$, $B = 2$, $C = 5$, $D = 6$ or
$A = 1$, $B = 7$, $C = 5$, $D = 8$ 3. 58, 59, 60
4. Al: $2; Bill: $10; Carl: $8   5. 6

1.

Size of Square	Number of Squares
1 × 1	15
2 × 2	6
3 × 3	1
Total	22

2. C must be either 1, 5, or 6, since these are the only digits that, when multiplied by themselves, have a product whose ones' digit is the same. But $1 \times ABC = ABC$, so C must be 5 or 6. Then A must

be 1, since the product has only three digits. If $C = 5$, $B = 2$ or 7. If $B = 2$, $D = 6$; if $B = 7$, $D = 8$. If $C = 6$, no solution is possible.

$$
\begin{array}{r} 125 \\ \times\ \ 5 \\ \hline 625 \end{array}
\qquad
\begin{array}{r} 175 \\ \times\ \ 5 \\ \hline 875 \end{array}
$$

3. Since the numbers are consecutive, the average of the first and third is equal to the second number. Therefore, the second number is equal to one half the sum of the first and third numbers. In this case then, the second number is equal to one half of 118, which is 59. The other numbers are 58 and 60.

4. Use a, b, and c to represent the amounts spent by Al, Bill, and Carl, respectively. Translate the given information into three equations, then add the equations.

$$
\begin{array}{r}
a + b \qquad = 12 \\
b + c = 18 \\
a \qquad + c = 10 \\
\hline
2a + 2b + 2c = 40
\end{array}
\qquad
\begin{array}{c}
\dfrac{2a + 2b + 2c}{2} = \dfrac{40}{2} \\[2mm]
a + b + c = 20
\end{array}
$$

Since $a + b = 12$, $c = 20 - 12 = 8$; since $b + c = 18$, $a = 20 - 18 = 2$; and since $a + c = 10$, $b = 20 - 10 = 10$.

5. List all possible ways that the 15 pennies can be distributed.

1, 2, 3, 9	1, 2, 4, 8	1, 2, 5, 7
1, 3, 4, 7	1, 3, 5, 6	2, 3, 4, 6

The possible numbers of pennies in the largest pile are 9, 8, 7, and 6. The least of these is 6.

Set 14   Pages 261–262

Answers: 1. 5   2. 7   3. D   4. 4 h   5. $A = 1$, $B = 14$, $C = 15$, $D = 6$, $E = 10$, $F = 2$, $G = 13$

1. Since the entire perimeter of the rectangle measures 20 ft, the sum of a single length and width must be only half as much, or 10 ft. Make a table of all the possible lengths and widths. There are 5.

length	9	8	7	6	5
width	1	2	3	4	5

2. Make a table of possible combinations of correct and incorrect answers and the corresponding total scores.

number correct	9	8	7	6	5	. . .
number incorrect	1	2	3	4	5	. . .
total score	43	36	29	22	15	. . .

Steve had 7 correct answers and 3 incorrect answers.

3. In any given column, each entry yields the same remainder as *one* of the first two entries when divided by 8. $101 \div 8 = 12$ R5. Thus 101 will appear in the same column as the number 5, which is column D.

4. In one hour, the first pipe alone will fill $\frac{1}{8}$ of the pool, the second pipe alone will fill $\frac{1}{12}$ of the pool, and the third pipe alone will fill $\frac{1}{24}$ of the pool. In one hour the three pipes together will fill $\frac{1}{8} + \frac{1}{12} + \frac{1}{24} = \frac{6}{24}$ or $\frac{1}{4}$ of the pool. Therefore, the three pipes will fill the pool in 4 hours.

5. Note that all the numbers along one major diagonal are given, and their sum is 34. Then B must be 14, E must be 10, and F must be 2. It follows that $A = 1$ and $G = 13$. Finally, $C = 15$ and $D = 6$.

1	14	7	12
15	4	9	6
10	5	16	3
8	11	2	13

Set 15 Pages 262–263

Answers: 1. 12   2. 8   3. $30   4. 32   5. 7

1. Starting at 1, add the consecutive counting numbers until a total of 78 is reached.

$1 + 2 = 3$
$1 + 2 + 3 = 6$
$1 + 2 + 3 + 4 = 10$

. . .

$1 + 2 + 3 + 4 + 5 + 6 + 7 + 8 + 9 + 10 + 11 + 12 = 78$

2. The four-inch cube contains $4 \times 4 \times 4 = 64$ one-inch cubes. Of these, 56 are visible and would be painted on one or more faces. The number of cubes with no paint on any face is $64 - 56 = 8$.

3. If the cost of the purchase was $10, the speaker would need 5 $2 bills or 2 $5 bills. So the number of $2 bills needed is three more than the number of $5 bills needed. It is given that the number of $2 bills needed is 9 more than the number of $5 bills needed. $9 = 3 \times 3$. So the purchase must cost $3 \times \$10 = \$30$.

4. If $\frac{3}{4}$ of the tank holds 24 gallons, then $\frac{1}{4}$ of the tank holds $24 \div 3 = 8$ gallons, and the full tank holds $4 \times 8 = 32$ gallons.

5. Solve a series of simpler problems.

   $3 = 3$ $3 \times 3 \times 3 \times 3 = 81$

   $3 \times 3 = 9$ $3 \times 3 \times 3 \times 3 \times 3 = 243$

   $3 \times 3 \times 3 = 27$ $3 \times 3 \times 3 \times 3 \times 3 \times 3 = 729$

   The ones' digits of the products are beginning to repeat, and they will continue to repeat in a cycle of four: 3, 9, 7, 1, 3, 9, 7, 1, . . . Every fourth product has 1 as its ones' digit, and so when *thirty-six* 3s are multiplied the ones' digit of the product will be 1. Therefore, when *thirty-five* 3s are multiplied, the ones' digit of the product will be the number previous to 1 in the cycle, which is 7.

Set 16 Page 263

   Answers: 1. Tuesday   2. 54   3. 5   4. *E*; *A*; *N* or *Z*
   5. *D* is 50 greater than *N*.

1. Three weeks or 21 days before Friday the 25th is Friday the 4th. Working backwards, then, the first day of the month is a Tuesday.

2. Make a table of all possibilities for Dale's age and Ann's age and the corresponding differences. Clearly, Dale must be 54.

Dale's age	81	72	63	54
Ann's age	18	27	36	45
difference	63	45	27	9

3. On the trip to the fair, the number of people who rode in buggies was $21 - 9 = 12$. Since 3 people rode in each buggy, the number of buggies was $12 \div 3 = 4$. On the return trip, 4 people rode in each of the 4 buggies for a total of $4 \times 4 = 16$ people. Thus the number of people who rode in the stagecoach on the return trip was $21 - 16 = 5$.

4. From the first and third views of the cube, note that the letters on the faces adjacent to H are A, Y, X, and N (or Z). The only letter that remains, E, must be *opposite* H. Similarly, from the second and third views of the cube, the letters on the faces adjacent to X are E, Y, H, and N (or Z). Then A must be opposite X. The remaining letters, Y and N (or Z), must be opposite each other.

5. Note that D is the sum of 50 numbers, while N is the sum of 49 numbers. Arrange the numbers as follows, then subtract.

$$D = 1 + 3 + 5 + 7 + \ldots + 99$$
$$\underline{N = 2 + 4 + 6 + \ldots + 98}$$
$$D - N = 1 + 1 + 1 + 1 + \ldots + 1$$

$D - N$ is the sum of 50 differences of 1, for a total of $50 \times 1 = 50$.

Set 17 Page 264

Answers: 1. 5 pennies, 2 dimes   2. 90¢
3. 60 cm   4. 23   5. $A = 9$, $B = 1$, $C = 8$

1. Since three of the coins are quarters, their value is $3 \times 25¢ = 75¢$, and the value of the remaining 7 coins must be 25¢. Of the seven coins, 5 must be pennies. Then the value of the remaining 2 coins is $25¢ - 5¢ = 20¢$, and the 2 coins must be dimes.

2. If 2 loaves and 4 rolls cost $2.40, then 1 loaf and 2 rolls cost $2.40 \div 2 = \$1.20$. Since 1 loaf and 6 rolls cost $1.80, 4 rolls cost $1.80 - \$1.20 = 60¢$. So 1 roll costs $60¢ \div 4 = 15¢$, 6 rolls cost $6 \times 15¢ = 90¢$, and 1 loaf costs $\$1.80 - 90¢ = 90¢$.

3. The perimeter of Figure A is formed by 16 sides of the squares. Since the squares are congruent, the measure of one side of a square is $48 \div 16 = 3$ cm. The perimeter of Figure B is formed by 20 sides of the squares, so the perimeter of Figure B is $20 \times 3 = 60$ cm.

4. The number of children in the class is 3 greater than a multiple of 4. Therefore, the number could be 7, 11, 15, 19, 23, 27, 31, 35, 39, . . .

The number of children in the class is 2 less than a multiple of 5. Therefore, the number could be 3, 8, 13, 18, 23, 28, 33, 38, 43, . . .

Examining the two lists, the least number common to both is 23.

5. Since the ones' digit of the sum is C, $A + B =$ 10, and there is a 1 carried to the tens' column of the addition. Since the tens' digit of the sum is A, $B + C + 1 = 10$, or $B + C = 9$. Since B is the hundreds' digit of the sum, it is possible that B is either 1 or 2. If $B = 2$, $A = 8$ and $C = 7$, but the sum is $88 + 22 + 77 = 187$, and B would have to be 1, a contradiction. If $B = 1$, $A = 9$ and $C = 8$, and the sum is $99 + 11 + 88 = 198$.

$$
\begin{array}{r}
99 \\
11 \\
+\ 88 \\
\hline
198
\end{array}
$$

Set 18 Pages 264–265

Answers: 1. 86 lb   2. 42, 43   3. 4   4. 26   5. 10

1. The average of the two weights is $138 \div 2 = 69$ lb. Then the lighter student weighs 17 lb less than the average, or $69 - 17 = 52$ lb; and the heavier student weighs 17 lb more, or $69 + 17 = 86$ lb.

2. Begin by finding two perfect-square numbers that bound the product, such as $40^2 = 1600$ and $50^2 = 2500$. Then the two page numbers are between 40 and 50. The ones' digit of the product is 6. Since the page numbers are consecutive, their ones' digits must be either 2 and 3 or 7 and 8. But pages 47 and 48 are not facing, so the page numbers must be 42 and 43; and, indeed, $42 \times 43 = 1806$.

3. The only cubes that have exactly four red faces are those four marked with an X in the figure at the right. All other cubes have either 3 or 5 red faces.

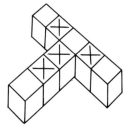

4. Since the prime factorization of 169 is 13×13, the only way to satisfy the conditions of the problem is with 13 members contributing 13¢ apiece. The only five coins that have a total value of 13¢ are 3 pennies and 2 nickels. Therefore, the number of nickels contributed is $13 \times 2 = 26$.

5. The average of the set of consecutive numbers, 15, is also the middle number. Thus the set of fifteen consecutive numbers consists of 15, seven numbers preceding 15, and seven numbers following 15:

8, 9, 10, 11, 12, 13, 14, 15, 16, 17, 18, 19, 20, 21, 22. The sum of the first five of these numbers is $8 + 9 + 10 + 11 + 12 = 50$. The average of these five numbers is $50 \div 5 = 10$.

Set 19 *Pages 265–266*

Answers: 1. $5   2. $A = 4, B = 7, C = 5$ 3. 12
              4. $60   5. $A = 5, B = 6$

1. Use m to represent the value of the camera in dollars and s to represent the value of the case in dollars. Translate the given information into two equations and add them.

$$m + s = 100$$
$$\underline{m - s = 90}$$
$$2m = 190 \qquad m = 95$$

The camera costs $95, so the case costs $100 - $95 = $5.

2. Note from the second addition that $B = 7$. Substituting this into the first addition, it then follows that $C = 5$ and $A = 4$.

3. Translate the given information into three equations and add them.

$$\begin{aligned} K + L &= 11 \\ L + M &= 19 \\ \underline{K + M} &= 16 \\ 2K + 2L + 2M &= 46 \end{aligned} \qquad \begin{aligned} \frac{2K + 2L + 2M}{2} &= \frac{46}{2} \\ K + L + M &= 23 \end{aligned}$$

Since $K + L = 11$, $M = 23 - 11 = 12$.

4. Work backwards. Janice had $10 before her last purchase in the second store. This is half of the money she had when she entered the second store, so she had $20 when she entered. In the first store she had $10 more than this, or $30, before she made her final purchase. But $30 is half of the money she had when she entered the first store, so she had $60 when she entered.

5. If a number is divisible by 72, it must be divisible by both 8 and 9. A number is divisible by 8 if the number formed by its last three digits is divisible by 8; if $73B$ is divisible by 8, B must be 6, and the number is now $A42736$. A number is divisible by 9 if the sum of its digits is divisible by 9; since $4 + 2 + 7 + 3 + 6 = 22$, A must be 5.

Set 20 Page 266

Answers: 1. 45 mi   2. 91   3. 29 in.   4. 10   5. 24¢

1. Since 1 min 20 s $= 1\frac{1}{3}$ min, the train travels 1 mi every $1\frac{1}{3}$ min.
   Since 1 h $=$ 60 min, in 1 h the train travels $60 \div 1\frac{1}{3} = 45$ mi.

2. If the remainder is 1 when the number is divided by 3 or 5, then the remainder is 1 when the number is divided by 15. Therefore, the number must be 1 greater than a multiple of 15, and the possibilities are 16, 31, 46, 61, 76, and 91. Of these, 91 is the only number that is divisible by 7 without remainder.

3. To make the required lengths, the total number of 6-in. cars cannot be more than 5 (6 × 6 in. = 36 in.), and the total number of 7-in. cars cannot be more than 4 (5 × 7 in. = 35 in.). Make a table of some possible combinations of 6- and 7-in. cars.

number of 6-in. cars	5	4	3	2	1
number of 7-in. cars	0	1	2	3	4
total length in inches	30	31	32	33	34

There is no combination that yields a 29-in. length.

4. In 10 min, *A* will have traveled 7000 yd, *B* will have traveled 8000 yd, and *C* will have traveled 9000 yd. But, since the track is circular and 1000 yd in circumference, each will be back at the starting point. This is the first time they are together since they started the race.

5. The ruler must cost at least 22¢, since that is the amount Alice still needs. Make a table of possible costs.

Cost of Ruler	Alice	Bob	Alice and Bob
22¢	0¢	19¢	19¢
23¢	1¢	20¢	21¢
24¢	2¢	21¢	23¢
25¢	3¢	22¢	25¢
26¢	4¢	23¢	27¢

If the ruler costs 25¢ or more, Alice and Bob together will have enough to purchase it. Therefore, the most the ruler could cost is 24¢.

Appendixes

Appendix 1
Answers to Problems Discussed in Part A

Coin Problems, page 8

● There are 3 + 2 + 1 = 6 coins in the collection.

● The value of the coins is 3 × 5 + 2 × 10 + 1 × 25 = 60¢, or $0.60.

● The value of the nickels is 3 × 5 = 15¢; the value of the dimes is 2 × 10 = 20¢; the value of the quarter is 25¢. The quarter has the greatest value, and the set of nickels the least value.

● There are 12 different amounts: 5¢, 10¢, 15¢, 20¢, 25¢, 30¢, 35¢, 40¢, 45¢, 50¢, 55¢, 60¢.

● There are 23 combinations. Let N represent a nickel, D a dime, and Q a quarter. Then the 23 combinations are:

> N, D, Q, NN, ND, NQ, DD, DQ, NNN, NND, NNQ, NDD, NDQ, DDQ, NNND, NNNQ, NNDD, NNDQ, NDDQ, NNNDD, NNNDQ, NNDDQ, NNNDDQ.

● *In addition to the set of coins listed, there are 12 other combinations of nickels, dimes, and quarters that have a total value of 60¢. Let N represent one nickel, D one dime, and Q one quarter. The the following sets of nickels, dimes, and quarters also have a total value of 60¢.*

12N	10N, 1D	6N, 3D	2N, 5D	5N, 1D, 1Q	2N, 2Q
6D	8N, 2D	4N, 4D	7N, 1Q	1N, 3D, 1Q	1D, 2Q

Cube Problems, page 12

● Six 1-cm cubes have red paint on 1 face.

● Twelve 1-cm cubes have red paint on 2 faces.

● Eight 1-cm cubes have red paint on 3 faces.

● No 1-cm cubes have red paint on 4 or more faces.

● If the original cube measured 4 cm along each edge, there would be eight 1-cm cubes with no red paint on any face.

● If the original cube measured 5 cm along each edge, there would be 27 1-cm cubes with no red paint on any face.

● If the original cube measures n cm along each edge, the number of 1-cm cubes with no face painted red is $(n - 2)^3$.

Appendix 2
Formulas for Arithmetic and Geometric Series

The following formulas for the sums of arithmetic and geometric series may serve as a convenient reference in solving some of the problems presented in this book and in creating your own problems. A derivation of each formula is also given as an aid in understanding why it works.

Arithmetic Series

The sum of an arithmetic series in which a represents the first term, d represents the constant difference between terms, l represents the last term, and n represents the number of terms can be calculated using the following formula.

$$S = \frac{n}{2}(a + l)$$

Derivation Let a represent the first term and l the last term of an arithmetic series of n terms with constant difference d. The sum of the series, S, may be written by starting with a and adding d repeatedly until the last term, l, is obtained. Another way to write the sum is to start with l and to subtract d repeatedly.

$$S = a + (a + d) + (a + 2d) + \ldots + (l - 2d) + (l - d) + l$$
$$S = l + (l - d) + (l - 2d) + \ldots + (a + 2d) + (a + d) + a$$

Next, add the corresponding members of the two equations above.

$$2S = (a + l) + (a + l) + (a + l) + \ldots + (a + l) + (a + l) + (a + l)$$

where $(a + l)$ occurs n times.

Thus, $2S = n(a + l)$, and $S = \frac{n}{2}(a + l)$.

Geometric Series

The sum of a geometric series in which a represents the first term, r represents the constant quotient between terms, and n represents the number of terms can be calculated using the following formula.

$$S = \frac{a - ar^n}{1 - r}$$

Derivation   Let a be the first term of a geometric series with constant quotient r. The sum, S, of the first n terms can be written as

$$S = a + ar + ar^2 + \ldots + ar^{n-2} + ar^{n-1}.$$

Multiply each member of the equation by r.

$$rS = ar + ar^2 + ar^3 + \ldots + ar^{n-1} + ar^n$$

Next, subtract the corresponding members of the above equations.

$$S - rS = a - ar^n$$

Finally, solve for S.

$$S(1 - r) = a - ar^n$$
$$S = \frac{a - ar^n}{1 - r}$$

Appendix 3
Further Discussion of the Divisibility Tests for 3, 9, and 11

The discussion that follows presents an explanation of the reason that the divisibility tests for 3 and 9 work for a three-digit number and that the divisibility test for 11 works for a four-digit number. Note that the same methods could be extended to explain why the tests work for greater numbers.

Divisibility Test for 3

A number is divisible by 3 if the sum of its digits is divisible by 3.
If a, b, and c represent, respectively, the hundreds', tens', and ones' digits of a three-digit number n, then the number can be expressed as $100a + 10b + c$. Assume that $a + b + c$ is divisible by 3.

$$
\begin{aligned}
n &= 100a + 10b + c \\
&= (99a + a) + (9b + b) + c \\
&= (99a + 9b) + (a + b + c) \\
&= 3(33a + 3b) + (a + b + c)
\end{aligned}
$$

The expression $3(33a + 3b)$ represents a number that is divisible by 3. The expression $a + b + c$ was assumed to be divisible by 3. Therefore, by the divisibility principle for sums, the sum of these expressions is divisible by 3. Since the sum of these expressions is equal to the three-digit number n, n is also divisible by 3.

Divisibility Test for 9

A number is divisible by 9 if the sum of its digits is divisible by 9.

If a, b, and c represent, respectively, the hundreds', tens', and ones' digits of a three-digit number n, then the number can be expressed as $100a + 10b + c$. Assume that $a + b + c$ is divisible by 9.

$$
\begin{aligned}
n &= \quad 100a \quad + \quad 10b \quad + c \\
&= (99a + a) \quad + (9b + b) + c \\
&= (99a + 9b) + \quad (a + b + c) \\
&= 9(11a + b) + \quad (a + b + c)
\end{aligned}
$$

The expression $9(11a + b)$ represents a number that is divisible by 9. The expression $a + b + c$ was assumed to be divisible by 9. Therefore, by the divisibility principle for sums, the sum of these expressions is divisible by 9. Since the sum of these expressions is equal to the three-digit number n, n is also divisible by 9.

Divisibility Test for 11

A number is divisible by 11 if the difference between the sum of its odd-place digits and the sum of its even-place digits is divisible by 11.

If a, b, c and d represent, respectively, the thousands', hundreds', tens', and ones' digits of a four-digit number n, then the number can be expressed as $1000a + 100b + 10c + d$. If the sum of the odd-place digits is greater than or equal to the sum of the even-place digits, assume that $(b + d) - (a + c)$ is divisible by 11.

$$
\begin{aligned}
n &= \quad 1000a \quad + \quad 100b \quad + \quad 10c \quad + d \\
&= (1001a - a) + (99b + b) + (11c - c) + d \\
&= 1001a + 99b + 11c - a + b - c + d \\
&= (1001a + 99b + 11c) + (b + d) - (a + c) \\
&= 11(91a + 9b + c) + [(b + d) - (a + c)]
\end{aligned}
$$

The expression $11(91a + 9b + c)$ represents a number that is divisible by 11. The expression $(b + d) - (a + c)$ was assumed to be divisible by 11. Therefore, by the divisibility principle for sums, the sum of these expressions is divisible by 11. Since the sum of these expressions is equal to the four-digit number n, n is divisible by 11.

If $(b + d) - (a + c)$ is a negative multiple of 11, then the four-digit number n is divisible by 11 according to the divisibility principle for differences.

Appendix 4
Geometric Formulas

The following list of commonly-used geometric formulas may serve as a useful reference in solving some of the problems presented in this book and in creating your own problems.

Perimeter

Triangle	$P = a + b + c$
Rectangle	$P = 2l + 2w$
Square	$P = 4s$
Circle	$C = 2\pi r$ or $C = \pi d$

Area

Triangle	$A = \frac{1}{2}bh$
Rectangle	$A = lw$
Square	$A = s^2$
Parallelogram	$A = bh$
Trapezoid	$A = \frac{1}{2}h(b_1 + b_2)$
Regular Polygon	$A = \frac{1}{2}ap$
Circle	$A = \pi r^2$

Volume

Rectangular Solid	$V = lwh$
Cube	$V = s^3$
Cylinder	$V = \pi r^2 h$
Cone	$V = \frac{1}{3}\pi r^2 h$
Sphere	$V = \frac{4}{3}\pi r^3$
Pyramid	$V = \frac{1}{3}Bh$

Total Surface Area

Rectangular Solid	$S = 2(lw + lh + wh)$
Cube	$S = 6s^2$
Cylinder	$S = 2\pi rh + 2\pi r^2$
Cone	$S = \pi r^2 + \pi rs$
Sphere	$S = 4\pi r^2$

Index